MACDONALD TRENDS AND DEVELOPMENTS
IN ENGINEERING SERIES

General Editor: Sir Willis Jackson, F.R.S.
Professor of Electrical Engineering,
Imperial College of Science and Technology

NEW APPLICATIONS OF
MODERN MAGNETS

NEW APPLICATIONS OF
MODERN MAGNETS

G. R. POLGREEN
B.Sc.(Eng.), M.I.E.E.

MACDONALD : LONDON

First published in 1966 by
Macdonald & Co. (Publishers) Ltd.
Gulf House, 2 Portman Street, London, W.1

Made and printed in the Republic of Ireland
by Hely Thom Limited, Dublin

CONTENTS

PREFACE   7

PART 1. MAGNETIC MATERIALS

1. THE IMPORTANCE OF NEW MATERIALS   13

2. ELECTRO-MAGNETISM   33

3. HISTORICAL SURVEY   67

4. THEORETICAL BACKGROUND   95

5. POWDERS & MICROPOWDERS   112

6. FERRITES   138

PART 2. NEW APPLICATIONS

7. MODERN MAGNETS IN PRACTICE   165

8. NEW DESIGNS   194

9. ROTATING MACHINES   225

10. MAGNETIC SUSPENSION & LINEAR PROPULSION   257

11. FUTURE PROSPECTS   292

    GLOSSARY   319

    APPENDIX   323

    INDEX   325

PREFACE

THIS book deals principally with the future of applied permanent magnetism. Some years ago I was asked to write a textbook on recent developments in magnetic materials from the engineering standpoint but, when this was partly done, the excellent volumes appearing in the references at the end of Chapter 1 were published. In view of the remarkable progress in commercial permanent magnets during recent decades, with promise of considerably more to follow, these were much overdue. Indeed, they seem to be the first authoritative books on this important subject for over three and a half centuries! It was therefore arranged that I should rewrite my manuscript within the extended scope of its present title, including the essence of my development work on new kinds of magnetic material and their future from the application aspect.

It soon became clear that the scope of this work would ultimately extend far beyond the present range of magnetic materials as high quality electrical components, into such broad fields as mechanical and automotive engineering and new kinds of track transportation. Moreover, the whole subject could become, like nuclear energy, of direct interest to a wide section of the technically-minded public to whom modern kinds of transportation are part of the way of life— and, unfortunately too often, of death. To most of these people magnetism would generally be a subject briefly encountered at school, and long forgotten. This book is therefore presented in a way intended to interest those whose knowledge may be limited to the practical aspects of everyday electrical circuits in home, office, factory and farm; in order to associate these with magnetism, remember Professor Bragg's apt definition: 'magnetism is electricity looked at sideways.'

The book is in two approximately equal parts, 'Magnetic Materials' and 'New Applications', with the opening chapter containing a summary of the whole subject in non-technical terms. The following chapters deal respectively with the technical, historical and theoretical aspects of applied magnetism, mainly by means of charts, diagrams and Tables (with the minimum of mathematics and Greek symbols). This varied knowledge is essential for a proper understanding of the significance of the new materials then described in the remainder of Part I, an understanding that is vital to the whole of Part II, the main objective. However, the reader should find that the matter becomes more readily assimilated as he approaches the later chapters, containing what is doubtless his main interest.

Perhaps the most surprising discovery in this relatively unexplored application territory has been that the designs, calculations and circuits become progressively simpler as the real quality of the permanent magnet materials improves, and this is confirmed in the final chapter by summarizing all the conclusions in a single Table. A forecast is then made that the elementary electrical machines specified therein will ultimately dominate the all-important demands for short power transmission links, in linear form for track systems as well as in rotary machines for road vehicles, and could well provide the solution of the principal traffic problems that at present plague modern congested communities.

In order to explain the background to this book it is necessary to add a personal note. My technical education in mechanical and electrical power engineering was expected to lead to traction as a career, but circumstances decided a different direction. My work started with research in magnetic materials (a schoolday interest) but advanced steadily away from power to higher frequencies. It soon reached the odd (by present standards) level of 800 c/s for telephone transmission components, on to sound and music reproduction, up to carrier and then radio frequencies into radio, radar, electronics and the various HF's. To meet the stringent quality demands it had become necessary early in this programme to leave clinical electrical conditions for strange and untidy substances, particularly iron oxide, the basis for an endless variety of mixtures, compounds and metallic powders. Looking back over three decades, it is remarkable to consider the significance that these now have in modern technology, but the following chapters will indicate that this can be only a beginning.

With the rapid increase in the manufacture and application of these materials up the frequency ladder, finer and finer grades of magnetic powder were in constant demand. But at the top the technical atmosphere changed completely, and unaccountably at first, from high frequency to high coercivity as the powders became micropowders or reverted to the original mixed oxides form, usually in a spectacular display. When the latter material appeared in sintered form as ceramics they were found, surprisingly, to lead right back to medium-power engineering.

With this extensive first-hand experience of the revolution caused by unusual magnetic materials throughout light electrical engineering, it came as a shock to find that electric traction, at least in its most important form of the d.c. motor, was virtually unchanged. Indeed, my textbooks on this subject purchased second-hand as a student and dating to early in the century, appear to be valid even today; their lifetime has seen the demise of such technically promising achievements as electric cars, petrol-electric buses, trams and trolley buses, with electric railways being placed very much on the defensive. These factors must be related, and this book sets out an explanation. It may be expected, from the above brief biographical note, that this will be in terms of magnetic materials, especially those relating to permanent magnetism.

The main answer in this account lies in the prospect of applying, on any required scale, permanent magnets to power engineering. The practical turning point in this quest came at the middle of this century, at a time of severe shortages of strategic metals for conventional alloy magnets, when it first became widely known that permanent magnets need not for ever be expensive and relatively weak components. Outstanding scientific work done under severe wartime conditions had shown that the best kind of magnet could actually be made from the most common metal, iron; moreover, it could be in two alternative forms, as very fine powder (micropowder) or as mixed oxides (ferrite). While the first of these has so far not come up to expectations, the second is greatly exceeding them, from economic as well as technical standpoints. My experience, possibly unique, has covered both kinds from their infancy, in both material and applications development.

But this mid-century is a turning point in an equally significant manner. At that time a new system of magnetic units was internationally adopted, based on the only logical foundation, the electric circuit and its units. This has made it possible for the first time to explain the whole subject of magnetic materials to those with a general technical knowledge, rather than to limit it to specialists. These new units are employed exclusively here and I have taken a few other steps to simplify the nomenclature and symbols. The appendix contains conversion tables from the old system and a glossary of the important technical terms. I have reluctantly added conversions into English units from the metric measurements which should dominate this whole engineering subject, not only the electrical and magnetic parts of it. But mechanical and hydraulic analogies are introduced wherever possible, because explanations are still difficult in spite of the great recent progress.

This subject has become so wide in recent months that it has been essential to prune some of the chapters and to limit the volume of references to those of the past few years, preferably using the modern system of units. In these circumstances I must apologize for omissions in this respect.

My sincere thanks are extended to the many helpers throughout my career in one of the largest electrical manufacturing companies, to the many magnetic materials specialists here and abroad who have supplied me with valuable literature and to members of educational establishments and other electrical engineers who have encouraged me to write this book. Much of what follows may take years to confirm and the task of foretelling the future is always hazardous. To this must be added the high chance of error in so broad a field as that covered by the proposed applications. The responsibility for all this is mine alone and, if it produces even some of the predicted results, the risks and hazards will be well justified.

Wendover.   GEOFFREY POLGREEN

Part 1

MAGNETIC MATERIALS

1

THE IMPORTANCE OF NEW MATERIALS

1.1 Scope

Permanent magnets are key components in telephone receivers and loudspeakers, electricity meters and instruments, tape recorders and computers, radar and much scientific apparatus. The early development of electrical engineering depended mainly upon the magnet and, in the magneto, it was prominent in all early internal combustion engines. In the natural form, magnetite or lodestone, the magnet is as old as history; in the needle of the mariner's compass it was one of Francis Bacon's famous three inventions, with printing and gunpowder, which he claimed had heralded Europe's climb out of the Dark Ages many hundreds of years ago.

In past and present the great importance of magnets is thus clearly established, though they have been little publicised and less understood. During the last two decades, however, progress in both the science and the technology of magnet materials has been so remarkable that this situation has been completely changed. In place of the unpredictable hit-and-miss advance of the past, development can now be planned and results forecast with a considerable degree of accuracy. Consequently, various new and unfamiliar kinds of magnet material are now appearing on an expanding commercial scale which show promise of making an even greater impact on the future.

Several millions of permanent magnets are now being made each week throughout the world. These are supplied mainly to the light industries—electronics, automation and telecommunications—which can attribute their rapid advance in large measure to magnetic materials. However, the average weight of all these magnets is only about 20 grams, or less than an ounce, so the specialized industry that makes them remains small by modern standards. Their many merits could be theoretically applied with equivalent success on a much more massive scale, but the vast power engineering market remains virtually untapped.

The reasons for this limitation are economic as well as technical. The better grades of conventional metal magnets are made from costly and complex alloys and would be progressively demagnetized under the severe mechanical and magnetic conditions in power-handling machines and equipment. But the new materials, chiefly ceramics, that are now becoming available in relatively large pieces at low cost on a considerable tonnage scale, can serve as strong and stable magnets which are really permanent and will meet the practical requirements of power engineering. This applies principally to medium-sized units that can be mass-produced on the biggest scale. These new materials and their applications provide the main objective and scope of this book.

The great improvements in permanent magnet strength during the past half-century are seldom appreciated: between the two world wars there was a five-fold increase, and a further five-fold advance has been achieved in the past two decades. During this latter period it was shown that iron, the most common and plentiful of materials, could be produced in a highly subdivided form that would theoretically yield another five-fold improvement in strength. It is most significant to this general subject that all the pioneer inventions and developments of the nineteenth century that led to the great electrical industry were carried out with permanent magnets possessing less than one-hundredth of their possible strength, but the invention of the self-excited electrical machine just 100 years ago appears to have removed *permanent magnet* from the power engineer's vocabulary.

Although there is still room for improving the many a.c. motors associated with the nationwide fixed power networks, the most needed use for these new materials appears to be in d.c. machines for mobile power. Later chapters are mainly devoted to their expected great contribution towards the ultimate electrical propulsion, braking and control of both road and rail vehicles, conventional and unorthodox. There are many other important fields of application for these modern magnets, but those included under the broad heading of transportation show signs of making a major contribution towards the solution of some of the most baffling practical problems of modern congested communities.

The main purpose of this book is to describe these new magnet materials as an introduction to a survey of their possible applications in this important branch of power engineering. However, this task is harder than it may at first appear because it necessitates an up-to-date knowledge of magnetism, which, owing to the heritage of its ancient history, is probably the most misunderstood and difficult subject in the whole range of modern technology. Hitherto it has been the preserve of a dedicated band of specialists with an unusually complex jargon and a set of units which were often altered and had different meanings in other countries; moreover, the manufacturers produced an endless list of alloys of ever-increasing complexity to which they gave a bewildering variety of trade names. Indeed, it has been said that their activities were more art than science.

Fortunately this obscure era appears to have ended with the arrival of the new materials and the modern theories that gave them birth. From the middle of this century a new system of units based on the well-known and widely understood electrical circuit, with which magnetism should always be intimately associated, has been internationally accepted and standardized. It is the author's aim that this book can be read and understood by anyone who is familiar with the electrical circuits to be found in the modern home, or typical place of work.

The new magnet materials are as simple as their metal predecessors were complex and this should apply to machines made from them, appearing more like mechanical products than the traditional electrical variety with their costly and vulnerable insulated coils. Their improved performance and better efficiency level will be matched by smaller and more rugged designs with simpler ventilation problems and lower noise level; but above all they give every indication of being far cheaper to manufacture in vast quantities, often a deciding factor in modern engineering conditions.

In the first half of this book the technical and historic background of electro-magnetism, i.e. conventional magnetism treated in the modern manner as a form of stored electrical energy, is used as an introduction to the various magnet materials which are the basis of this work. It is also essential to include a brief survey of the latest theories of magnetism, but this is not so difficult to grasp in an age when all our lives are literally dependent upon the control and understanding of atomic energy. The latter half deals with present and probable future applications of the new materials. Sufficient has been published on this subject already that this is based mainly on confirmed experimental work rather than on deductions from the technical merits of novel substances. But the properties of the latter are so radically different from those of all conventional materials that mere substitution of them in traditional designs is unsatisfactory, though it may yield useful technical and economic benefits.

One common conclusion shared by all who have worked in this field is that the immense latent merits of these novel materials can be attained only by designing machines which use them around their unusual magnetic and physical properties and limitations. A further point is that conventional methods of quality assessment and figures of merit greatly underestimate their possibilities and these must be brought up-to-date. In other words, this whole subject needs a new approach in order to cope with this new situation and this is a prime objective of this book.

In addition to the improvement of known machines and methods, these new materials permit for the first time the practical realization of past technical dreams such as magnetic suspension, which may extend from the smallest instrument shaft up to a complete railway system rather like a tracked air-ferry for cars as well as passengers. In this category may be included kilocycle electric power at low cost, which has great scope for improved lighting, cleaning and special machining purposes.

1.2 The Function of Magnets

A magnet is a device that maintains a magnetic field. A good permanent magnet retains the field, imparted by an intense pulse of electric current usually at the manufacturing stage, for an indefinite period of years at constant strength. A good electromagnet maintains the field only so long as the applied current flows through its winding and loses it completely when switched off. Both these two kinds of magnet are included within the scope of this book, with special attention to their relative technical and economic merits. This comparison has received negligible attention in the past because each kind of magnet has usually been treated as a specialised component in isolation from the other.

The electromagnet consists of a core of magnetic material, generally soft iron when supplied by direct current, surrounded by an insulated copper wire winding, or coil. The iron core enables the strength of the magnetic field generated by the current to be increased in the region of 1000 times compared with that inside the coil if the core is removed, i.e. an air-core coil. If a hard steel core of similar size is now inserted into the coil, the magnetic field for the same current will not be so strong as before with the soft iron but much of it will be retained—perhaps for years—after the current is switched off. The hard steel core has become a weak permanent magnet, and its field was imparted during the first few seconds of current flow, all further electric power being dissipated as heat.

This magnetized core can be removed from the coil and used to perform a variety of useful functions in isolated or mobile positions where the use of an electromagnet with its essential power source would be inconvenient or impracticable. The best examples are the early large-scale uses of hard steel magnets—electrical instruments and meters, magnetos and telephone earpieces. By contrast, electromagnets have always used soft iron or mild steel in order to avoid the retention of any magnetic flux or field, so these two opposite magnetic qualities became directly related to their corresponding physical properties and were known respectively as magnetically 'hard' or 'soft'. Although the new kinds of magnetic material that have been developed during the past 25 years defy this classification, these terms are still used. The modern term for this magnetic hardness is 'coercivity' which is the most important property of a magnetic material; today the coercivity of the best magnets is over a million times higher than that of the best 'soft' or low-loss material in commercial use, whereas early this century, when the electrical industry was limited to steels for magnetic uses, this ratio was only around a hundred.

The other property of prime importance in magnetic materials is their ability to carry a high flux density, analogous to conductivity in the electrical circuit; both depend on the physical properties of the metal employed, but all magnetic substances have an upper limit or saturation point beyond which they will retain or carry no more flux. If the current in the electromagnet coil is increased well above this saturation level, the flux will continue to increase slowly because the air inside it does not saturate. Indeed, air-core coils give as much as ten or a hundred times the highest flux density in iron by passing very heavy current through a small coil, but this presents a severe cooling problem and is extremely costly in power and equipment.

Iron and its various steel alloys have the highest saturation values of commercial materials but, as noted above, they are relatively poor by modern standards in high-coercivity materials. The great improvements in the latter, however, tend to be at the expense of saturation; the latest ferrite ceramic magnets, for example, give over 20 times higher coercivity but about one-third the saturation of typical hard steel. Since highest flux density is essential for most practical purposes, methods must generally be applied to concentrate the flux in low-saturation materials and this is done by fixing soft iron polepieces; this practice has become almost universal for high-strength magnets and it is desirable to treat them as magnetic assemblies rather than components in their principal applications.

The supreme merit of the electromagnet is the ease with which its flux can be controlled from zero up to saturation by varying the applied current over any required distance. It is the heart of electric bells, relays and contactors, and electrical machines, so it may well be regarded as the most important device in the history of electrical engineering. As a method of control it is still outstanding, but as a means of maintaining a steady magnetic field it is a power-wasting liability if a permanent magnet could be used in its place, and the latest high-coercivity magnets make this possible over a wide area of applications.

The ultimate answer is a combination of both kinds of magnet, the permanent magnet providing the basic flux and the electromagnet, in the form of a simple coil added to the magnet-polepiece assembly, being used only for controlling or modulating this field in the best manner for the purposes required. This is described in Part II as the *ideal magnet* and is the basis of a number of novel designs in later chapters.

1.3 New Materials

The hard-steel magnet era lasted until about 40 years ago. Although magnetically weak and lacking stability, the product had the merits of low cost and good mechanical strength with machinability; the high saturation made the use of polepieces generally unnecessary.

The alloy-magnet era has achieved a ten-fold increase in coercivity, but at an increase in material cost that at times appeared to advance proportionally. This disadvantage was, however, largely minimized for the main class of consumer in light engineering by progressive reductions in size for equivalent service, but the product became more brittle and almost unmachinable. The saturation fell somewhat and polepieces became essential in most applications.

The new moulded-magnet era employs powder-metallurgy, ceramic and plastic techniques to produce magnets in a much wider and more useful range of products than hitherto—bricks, discs, rings, rigid mouldings, flexible sheet and thin tape or coated drums. Their basic raw material is iron oxide, one of the cheapest and most plentiful substances in the world which, together with these production methods, gives scope for the manufacture of vast repetition quantities at lower costs than seemed possible earlier, when magnets were always regarded as an inherently expensive commodity. Except for magnetic recording uses, all tend to have higher coercivity than had previously been known but much lower saturation densities.

The new materials consist of two groups, different from both technical and scientific standpoints, known respectively as ferrite and micropowder magnets. The first of these, a ceramic like porcelain, is already being manufactured by leading industrial countries in several grades on a considerable tonnage scale at price levels competitive with electromagnet coils that it could replace. Micropowder magnets have so far been manufactured only on a limited scale and their processing costs are still unresolved, though their raw material can be cheap iron or more expensive alloy. But their attraction lies in the promise of attaining the further tenfold increase in magnetic strength indicated earlier, on account of their inherent superiority over any kind of ferrite in saturation level, while theoretically reaching similar coercivities; so far they are only half way in the latter property.

Although other compositions are possible, the many available grades of ferrite magnet being produced today consist of one material, barium ferrite ($Ba\ Fe_{12}\ O_{19}$) in sintered or powder form, the latter being used as filler for well-known plastics in order to improve the mechanical strength, dimensional tolerances and finish, but at the expense of magnetic strength. The latest sintered grades have magnetic performance on a weight basis about equivalent to the best metal magnets, but exhibit the following outstanding advantages:—

1. Permanence of magnetic properties under severest practical operating conditions (very high coercivity).
2. The physical properties of electrical insulators (electrical resistivity over 10^{10} times higher than that of metal magnets).
3. Potentially the abundance and cheapness of steel, being made from the same basic raw material by other established processes.

The first of these means that this kind of magnet can be built into the operating zones of electrical machines and equipment which handle power without risk of demagnetization; the second enables massive blocks of this insulator material to be magnetized by very short pulses of heavy current that consume negligible power; the third indicates that at last it is possible to consider the use of permanent magnets in power engineering on any desired scale as an economic proposition. Any one of these three advantages represents a technological milestone; together they hold out the promise of an engineering revolution that this book attempts to predict and describe.

1.4 Comparison of Magnetic Materials

Today the number of different kinds of magnetic material in commercial use is so great that it is necessary to place in perspective those of immediate interest here for power conditions. In Table 1.1 they are presented in brief outline with only essential properties indicated in relative terms. All magnetic materials are grouped under three headings—metal, powder (micropowder), ferrite—of which the first includes all conventional types, while the others comprise the range of new moulded materials described in this book, together with their possible applications. The latter substances have been developed during the past 25 years.

The group sub-heading names in the Table are given as either *high energy* or *low energy* because all the powder materials are physically soft while all the ferrites are glass-hard, and these energy-based names are simpler and more exact than the high and low coercivities to which reference is generally made in this context. The alternative of low-loss (or high permeability) relates to the most important alternating current requirement of low magnetic hysteresis (described later) coupled with the highest possible electrical resistance to minimize eddy currents in a magnetic material; this must also carry as much flux as possible (high saturation) for all power applications. The great majority of magnetic materials, exceeding a million tons per annum throughout the world, are in this category and most consist of silicon steels of various grades.

If alternating currents of appreciably higher frequency than present power values (50 c/s principally) are required, and these can give many advantages for such purposes as mobile power, it is necessary to make the silicon steel sheet so thin that it becomes inefficient and very expensive. The most promising alternative is coarse iron or iron-alloy powder converted into flake or needle-shaped particles and compressed with a plastic binder into mouldings. This is described later in connection with the development of high frequency alternators of a very simple kind based upon ferrite permanent magnets.

Low-loss ferrites were developed and made some years before the permanent magnet grades appeared and so are generally better known. They achieved great importance in the expanding telecommunications and electronics industries owing to their high electrical resistance. This is in the semi-conductor region (see fig. 2.2 later) and millions of times higher than that of all metal magnetic materials, which had consequently to be made in the plastic-bonded powder form for most higher frequency uses. Ferrites, in sharp contrast, can be used in the much more elementary sintered form, in large size if necessary, without causing appreciable eddy current loss. Unfortunately, their saturation is very low, an inherent limitation applying also to the permanent magnet grades, so they are generally unsuitable for use as pole pieces needed to concentrate the magnetic flux of most high-coercivity magnet materials. Similarly, the wide variety of nickel-iron alloys (often known as permalloys) which have found a number of uses in the lighter industries, also have the disadvantages of low saturation with relatively high cost, so they also are not often used for power applications.

The coatings of magnetic tapes and drums, used for recording sound and television, computers and instrumentation data, consist of permanent magnet grades of iron oxide and are therefore in the ferrite category. Although strictly within the scope of this work as modern magnets, their specialized application has been covered by a great number of textbooks and technical articles in recent years as a result of the remarkable extension of their uses. Both their coercivity and saturation value are only about one-tenth those of the commercial grades of permanent magnet ferrites, so their power-handling ability is much too small for practical use in the applications to be considered later. Nevertheless, they are of great technical interest as plastic-bonded magnet powder and will be referred to in Chapter 6 as a class of ferrites.

Of all these kinds of magnetic material, those of particular interest here are thus the highest coercivity substances available at low cost and with resistance approaching the insulator level. Since these will have low flux density, they must be used with pole pieces of soft iron for direct current uses, silicon steel sheets for lower frequency power and some kind of iron-powder core material for higher frequencies.

For the past four decades, with the expansion of research in permanent magnet materials, it became general to assess the quality of such material by a figure of merit known as the *energy product* with the symbol $(BH)_{max}$. Recently the unit in practice in the old (c.g.s.) system has been the mega-gauss-oersted, abbreviated to Mgo (but here the new unit *joules/metre*^{3} is used exclusively). Unfortunately, when used alone it generally had little reference to the facts from the user standpoint. It gave equal weight to coercivity, the most important property, and flux-carrying ability (related to remanence) which could be improved by the use of polepieces; these

GROUP	METAL		POWDER		FERRITE	
CATEGORY *	HIGH ENERGY	LOW ENERGY	HIGH ENERGY	LOW ENERGY	HIGH ENERGY	LOW ENERGY
MATERIAL	HARD STEELS & CAST ALLOYS	SHEET STEELS SOFT IRON (d.c.)	IRON MICRO-POWDER pressed or bonded	IRON POWDER plastic-bonded	BARIUM FERRITE	MANGANESE-ZINC, NICKEL-ZINC etc.
PHYSICAL HARDNESS	HARD	SOFT	SOFT	SOFT	VERY HARD	VERY HARD
DENSITY	HIGH (7 to 8)	HIGH (7 to 8)	LOW (3 to 5)	MEDIUM (5 to 7)	LOW (3 to 5)	LOW (4 to 5)
MAGNETIC COERCIVITY	MEDIUM to HIGH	LOW	MEDIUM to HIGH	LOW	VERY HIGH	VERY LOW
SATURATION	MEDIUM to HIGH	VERY HIGH	MEDIUM to HIGH	HIGH	LOW	LOW
ELECTRICAL RESISTIVITY †	VERY LOW	VERY LOW	LOW to HIGH	LOW to HIGH	VERY HIGH	HIGH
PRODUCTION METHODS	Cast alloys ground to size, others readily machined.		Moulded, generally at high pressure. Iron-alloy powders & micropowders are also important.		Material is sintered mixed oxides. Product moulded and sintered, or ground to powder and plastic-moulded.	
NOTES	* HIGH ENERGY: generally known as Permanent Magnet or magnetically "Hard" (sometimes High Coercivity). LOW ENERGY: generally known as Low-loss, High Permeability or magnetically "Soft" (Low coercivity). Note that coercivity is only one factor (with remanence) in energy value, though dominant. † Classification by resistivity categories is given in Fig. 2.2 and Appendix Table 2.					

TABLE 1.1. COMPARISON OF MAGNETIC MATERIAL GROUPS

are generally needed for a variety of other reasons also. But the chief criticism of this traditional energy product assessment is that its validity is applicable primarily for static applications of low power level, giving a distorted measure for the dynamic power uses of the kind covered in this book. As a result, the great potentialities of the new high-coercivity materials were at first overlooked because their flux density was unusually low.

It is therefore not possible at this stage to give a clearcut picture of the relative quality of the new permanent magnets with the conventional, and it must suffice to state that, in their best grades, they are roughly equal in magnetic strength. A separate dynamic energy product is defined and used in Chapter 6, but a figure of merit based on coercivity alone has much to recommend it. However, whatever arguments are used in this matter, the ultimate criterion is the performance obtained in practice, with polepieces in place and with the inevitable leakage; results so obtained represent the real interests of the user of magnetic materials.

These doubts and difficulties have been given in some detail to explain why the many new possibilities given later have not been forecast earlier, an event that usually applies in other directions at the laboratory stage. But in spite of the great recent advances in applied magnetism, it is still some way from becoming an exact science, like electric circuits for example, and workers in this field must therefore continue as far as is practicable with the traditional trial-and-error approach to make sure of claims to practical progress.

1.5 Modern Magnets in Practice

Recent progress in permanent magnets has been so rapid that it is necessary to correct various misconceptions, inherited from the past, widely held among engineers. The most prevalent is that permanent magnets must inevitably be inefficient substitutes for electromagnets and that their flux is expendable; this has even led to the view that the use of magnets in place of the field windings for electric motors and generators must in some way violate the Law of Conservation of Energy.

The facts are that, in terms of magnetic strength, the electromagnet of typical commercial equipment is much as it was when invented 140 years ago whereas the permanent magnet has been improved a hundred-fold. During the hard-steel era, while electrical engineering became established in its present pattern, the electromagnet was many times better, but the invention of alloy-magnets closed the gap between them. About 20 years ago the introduction of crystal orientation along a preferred axis almost trebled the magnetic strength of certain alloys and a high percentage of all metal magnets are now of this kind; these have placed the permanent magnet well ahead of its power-wasting competitor of conventional design.

The expendable flux view arose from the elaborate precautions needed in handling low-coercivity magnets and their prolonged ageing for achieving the stability required for measuring instruments and meters. These precautions became less stringent in recent years as the magnetic strength multiplied; but no metal magnet has yet reached the point that it really deserves the prefix 'permanent' under intense vibration or the strongest practical demagnetizing fields in power-handling machines. The latest ferrite magnets, with about three times higher coercivity, have arrived at this desirable goal; under practical conditions the only method of demagnetizing them is to heat them to above their Curie point (temperature at which a magnetic material loses its magnetic field), which is 450°C. for barium ferrite.

Other novel features contribute to the unprecedented stability of this ceramic material. It can be made with an almost linear demagnet-ization curve (described later), which means that it remains magnetic-ally stable with polepieces removed or without the keeper usually regarded as essential for metal magnets. Also, since permanence of physical structure is essential for stability, the non-corrosive nature of all ceramics is of greatest importance and this is well illustrated by the pottery of the earliest human communities which is discovered virtually unchanged after thousands of years.

The remarkable ability of the earliest grades of barium ferrite magnet to retain their magnetic flux under adverse conditions is well shown by attempting to neutralize it in the opposing field of a power-ful electromagnet. As soon as the latter field is removed, the perman-ent magnet will revert to its original strength although its flux has been temporarily reduced to zero or even partly reversed. To do this, the current density of the electromagnet has to be so intense that the coil will burn out unless special cooling is applied.

The electrical resistance of ferrite is so high, in the insulator region, that the material can be almost instantaneously magnetized by a current pulse from a condenser discharge. Though the peak magnetiz-ing force has to be much greater than any needed for conventional magnets, on account of the higher coercivity level, the time is so short that the power used is almost negligible. So a portable mains-operated gear can be used, and a ton of ferrite can be fully magnetized with as little as one kilowatt-hour by this means. If, during the operating life of typical electrical equipment, the magnetic flux that this quantity of ferrite can maintain indefinitely had to be produced with electromagnets, about a million times more power would be consumed, nearly all being dissipated as heat.

It is perhaps difficult to understand how such a relatively strong field, produced so quickly and cheaply, can last indefinitely under normal terrestrial conditions but natural magnetite (lodestone) with much lower coercivity is thought to have retained its field for millions of years in spite of orientation changes relative to the Earth's field during this period. A modern example is seen in the tape recorder, for which the useful life of the record is limited, not by loss of magnetism, but by the physical disintegration of the tape coating brought about by the severe mechanical handling it receives.

These examples indicate that there should now be every reason for these modern magnets to be used for the provision of the basic magnetic flux in electrical machines, without appreciable change during their working life.

1.6 Magnets in Electric Circuits

Apart from the transformer cores in a.c. circuits, magnetic materials are required mainly in terminal equipment as transducers, means for converting electrical into other forms of energy, such as sound or motion. For this study the most typical is the electric motor (or generator, since these are generally reversible), which operates by the interaction of two magnetic fields, one produced in the armature by the supply current and the other by the field windings or excitation. In present machines the latter is mostly also generated by the supply current in the familiar series or shunt windings, but either a separate local supply or permanent magnets could be employed.

In simpler terms this is the interaction of the fields of either two electromagnets or alternatively of one electromagnet and a permanent magnet, the second combination having all the advantages already mentioned. The basic flux or field is analogous to the fluid in a hydraulic machine; if provided by the permanent magnet it is sealed-in during manufacture and is always available to do useful work at no extra cost; if supplied by field windings it must be pumped all the way from the power station, at great trouble and expense, every time it is used. The armature winding or its equivalent is the essential part of the circuit, by which the operating power in a motor is converted into magnetic flux under optimum conditions. This takes place in a low-loss core where it can react with this magnetic 'fluid', however this may have been produced.

Thus, the use of permanent magnets for the excitation of motors and generators will improve their efficiency, by a considerable step in the sizes of interest here, and correspondingly reduce the heat dissipated in them; these in turn give further advantages, such as reduced size and noise.

Another important group of power transducers is the actuator, which converts electrical energy into limited motion, either rotary or linear. A good example of the latter kind is the simple contactor for remote switching; its mechanism consists merely of an electromagnet with a movable core which remains partly out of the coil in the 'off' position. Passage of control current through the coil attracts the core to the central position and this movement closes the switch by a mechanical link. The control current is essential only to produce the mechanical movement; the holding of the switch in the 'on' position could be carried out far better with a permanent magnet which would remain cold and be unaffected by power supply failure or fluctuation.

A smaller, cheaper and more reliable system would be obtained by using a high-coercivity magnet controlled by a short pulse of direct current of such magnitude that it temporarily neutralized the field of the magnet in one direction and greatly strengthened it in the other direction. A mechanical spring, or in some cases gravity, would open the switch while the magnet was momentarily fluxless. This principle is old, having been used for many years in polarized relays; but earlier magnets had to be spaced apart from the operating coil to avoid demagnetization, causing complication and limiting efficiency. Only ceramic magnets can be used with a coil surrounding the magnet in the form of the ideal magnet described earlier.

This proposal of combined electromagnet and permanent magnet can be very simple in practice. Ferrites are readily available in fairly thin discs magnetized along the axis so that the large circular faces are respectively North and South poles; these faces are ground parallel and flat for polepieces which are usually turned from sheet-iron and are known as poleplates. These can be cemented to the ferrite with epoxy resin to make a very strong assembly that can be rotated, if required, at high speeds without risk of failure or of disintegration if suitably reinforced. If the poleplates project slightly outwards from the ferrite periphery and have a regular set of slots cut in them, this can be used with a corresponding set of fixed inductors and coil in a surrounding stator to make a simple inductor alternator to produce power at kilocycle frequencies.

Large and relatively thin ferrite ring magnets can be used for the excitation of low voltage d.c. machines of the Faraday double-disc kind; by fixing a number of series-connected units on one shaft, a practical voltage level can be attained at the size and speed ranges associated with this work. This type of machine does not need a commutator and the losses are limited to brush frictional drag and voltage drop, which can be minimized by use of latest materials and methods; so there are good prospects of smaller, less expensive and more efficient d.c. machines being developed from these new magnets. Currents are in the 1000 ampere region so the transmission distances must be very short, but these conditions apply to most road vehicles.

This subject of simpler d.c. motors and generators is closely allied to possible improvements in clutches and brakes. Motors with permanent magnet excitation used to propel a vehicle from a traction battery, will automatically start to become generators if run very fast down a hill, and current will be returned to the battery with corresponding braking action. If associated with a variable resistor, this dynamic braking can become the best and safest method of controlling a vehicle, as well as avoiding wear and overheating; the possibilities of regenerative braking mean reduced running costs but also extend the range of a given battery per charge.

Braking by permanent magnets has been universally employed in electricity meters since their earliest development and requires no adjustment, maintenance or replacement; this is a marked contrast to present methods of stopping vehicles which, especially in the case of railways, are reminiscent of ancient chariots. In silent, predictable dynamic braking it is not possible to skid or lock the wheels.

These merits of electrical traction braking have been known since the latter part of the last century, but they are complicated and expensive to apply when wound fields are used, especially the usual series winding; moreover, the need for switching introduces some degree of risk. With permanent magnet excitation, on the other hand, the flux is always present at maximum strength and no switching is needed so the operation is automatic and completely safe.

Development work, described in a later chapter, is being carried out on these low-voltage propulsion-braking machines and the losses in the slipring-brushgear system needed to convey the heavy direct current to and from the rotor are being put to good use. Switching and control are obtained by brush movement, and limited friction braking required to slow and stop the vehicle (when the speed-dependent dynamic braking becomes ineffective) is provided by brush friction with power source off.

This machine is small enough to be installed, together with its associated step-down plastic gearing, within the hub of the wheel it is required to propel or retard, with the aim of replacing present friction brakes. Since good conversion efficiency is expected, with braking energy absorbed externally, the cooling problems should be less than at present. By these means, every wheel of a vehicle could be powered and braked by a single control, giving optimum use of regenerative, resistive and frictional methods automatically as well as the known merits of stepless, high starting torque d.c. propulsion; if necessary, each wheel could be individually controlled. Apart from the evident economic and technical advantages of these proposals, they could introduce a new degree of safety to the present hazards of the motorcar age.

1.7 Magnetic Suspension

The last paragraph outlined improvements in known machines and devices that may be expected from the new kinds of magnet, but the achievement of ideas and inventions that have hitherto been impracticable may well be of equal importance. The outstanding example is magnetic suspension for static or dynamic conditions, ranging in magnitude from small instruments up to complete transportation systems, such as railways operating up to aircraft speeds or moving platforms and roadways.

In all these cases, the objective is the elimination of frictional drag, with its resulting wear and need for maintenance and replacements. The method is to neutralize the force of gravity by the mutual repulsion of two sets of magnets with adjacent surfaces of similar polarity, one set on the ground and the other fixed underneath the object to be suspended.

Although many attempts were made in the past to apply this principle to sensitive measuring instruments, they were never successful until the arrival of latest high-coercivity materials. Today a considerable proportion of all new electricity meters are made with vertical rotor shafts suspended by two pairs of disc magnets at top and bottom or sometimes only one pair.

Over half a century ago, before the possibilities of aircraft became known, patents were issued for high speed railways using magnetic suspension by electromagnets. Though only one scheme appears to have reached the working model stage, they were doomed from the start by the vast amount of power and associated equipment needed to provide the suspension only, apart from propulsion, and the risks incurred in the event of power failure or even fluctuations. Similar power-dissipation suspension systems, but using airjets or aircushions generated by engine-driven turbines, are being developed at present but these also have these inherent hazards and in addition produce noise and fumes when suspended at rest as well as in transit. The only known method of maintaining suspension indefinitely without dissipation of power, and therefore without risk, is by the use of permanent magnets.

During the past seven years since barium ferrite magnets became commercially available, much work has been carried out by the author on the development of 'magnetic railways' using bricks of this material, and this is reported in detail later in the appropriate chapter. Many novel problems such as dynamic stability, cornering and gradients were solved with a variety of working models on a small scale, and the development has reached the stage of constructing a one-sixth scale man-carrying model of a proposed overhead railway system for maintaining between main city centres, the equivalent of a continuous air-ferry service for passengers, cars and express freight.

One remarkable feature of magnetic suspension is its great weight-carrying ability, being in the higher speed version over ten times better than present aircraft and railways in terms of the operating weight to the load carried, when the simple kind of automatic linear motors that can be incorporated in the suspension system are employed. Thus, a light supporting structure can be used to carry the overhead track with long spans and limited use of land. The estimated weight of the track, consisting mainly of angle-iron girders and ferrite bricks, is around one-fifth that of conventional railways and each fusilage-type vehicle has a full weight of about 10 tons, with half as payload. With the automatic spaced propulsion that linear motors can give, the dynamic loading of each track support could be as little as one percent of the equivalent in present road and rail bridges. With the possibilities of operating a double-track continuously at six times present average speeds, a greater volume of priority traffic could be moved for hundreds of miles over a light and easily installed overhead structure than is possible by any known system of transport.

The ferrite bricks form the highest cost of this project, but there appear to be good prospects of making them from byproducts from new steel processes in the required tonnage with costs ultimately coming down to the steel level. In these circumstances this magnetic railway could become cheaper than the alternatives, as well as being more silent, comfortable and reliable, and very much faster. It is also, incidentally, a further example on a grand scale of the permanent magnet's superiority over the electromagnet for maintaining magnetic fields.

1.8 Conclusions

The contents of this book have been summarized in this first chapter in non-technical terms (except for coercivity and magnetic saturation), so that conclusions can be reached at an early stage on the outstanding importance of the new magnet materials now available. The details of the novel designs that have been evolved around their unique properties cannot be adequately explained, however, without studying the scientific and technical background, given in the following chapters in a manner suitable for those with general technical knowledge. To back up a point made earlier, that these machines are more mechanical than electrical by present standards, the basic flux concept can be explained by analogy to a new kind of weightless hydraulic fluid.

Although the main applications outlined above may appear in the light of novel and untried ideas, they mostly originated in the last century but hitherto lacked the materials and technology needed for fulfilment. The most significant of these is cheap high-coercivity ferrite, which may well prove to be the missing link in the evolution of a common mechanical-electrical engineering practice; and yet, paradoxically, this new material is a reversion to the pre-metal era of the remote past. For the first permanent magnet, the lodestone of the ancient Chinese and Greeks, was a natural form of iron ferrite, and the new sophisticated grades are made by ceramic and brick-making methods which are basically the first production processes in history.

With this material the resulting engineering developments could well lead towards universal electric power transmission links for short distances of a few yards or metres as well as for the present many miles or kilometres, for mobile power by direct current as well as for present fixed power by alternating current. At the end of last century this indeed appeared to be the future prospect for d.c. power, when there were more electric cars than the now ubiquitous petrol-driven kind, when towns of any importance had electric tramways, to be followed by petrol-electric buses and trolley buses; but all these technically advanced transport systems, even by modern standards, went to the scrapyard. Significantly, today's d.c. motor (functionally misnamed because it converts the main current to a.c. in the rotor) is virtually unchanged, with the same bulky and costly commutator. But the new magnet materials make it possible for the first time to develop true d.c. motors—small and light high speed machines with good efficiency—to match the best prime-mover performance compactly and economically.

Two such machines as a generator-motor combination could then provide this much-needed short electric transmission link, which in vehicles and similar conditions would replace intermediate gear-trains and friction-operated devices in the same way that forests of belts and shafting were superseded in factories by silent a.c. power. The heavy current at low voltage, by which they must operate is the kind of d.c. power produced by direct generation methods, such as fuel cells. So, while such an electric drive could be applied to present vehicles as an improvement on mechanical or hydraulic transmissions, it might ultimately lead to a vehicle in which the only moving parts are the wheels, containing the hub-motor propulsion/braking system. For track transportation, the other essential kind, magnetic suspension can virtually eliminate wheels for the support of vehicles. With the use of the track permanent magnet rows for excitation as well as for suspension, propulsion could be arranged simply by use of the linear version of the above new kind of d.c. motor. This would achieve the ultimate in propulsion mechanisms: only one moving part—the vehicle itself.

1.9 References

In recent years progress in magnetic materials and their applications has been so rapid that these references are limited to books published during the past five years. A detailed amplification of section 1.4, with emphasis on low-loss materials, is contained in the first reference. The second, written by 14 authorities on all aspects of permanent magnetism in this country, is the most complete publication yet issued on this subject; it contains latest theories as well as manufacturing methods and numerous applications. The third book is by leading manufacturers in America, who have also done pioneer work on high-energy micropowder magnets. Written specially for the general public, the fourth reference has considerable significance in this present work. Finally, a massive three-volume treatise 'Magnetism' which has been published in recent months, covers all aspects of this now extensive subject, principally from the scientific standpoint.

1. Bardell P. R. *Magnetic Materials in the Electrical Industry*, 2nd Edition, Macdonald, London, 1960.

2. Hadfield D. (Ed.) *Permanent Magnets & Magnetism*, 14 Authors, Iliffe, London, 1962.

3. Parker R. J. & Studders R. J. *Permanent Magnets & their Application*, Wiley, U.S.A., 1962.

4. Lee E. W. *Magnetism*, Pelican Original, London, 1963.

5. Rado & Suhl (Eds.) *Magnetism*, 3 Volumes, Academic Press, New York & London, 1963/4.

2

ELECTRO-MAGNETISM

Applied magnetism can be best explained by emphasising the close relationship with its inseparable partner, electricity. For this reason the unusual hyphen has been inserted after the prefix in this chapter heading, and the following account of practical magnetism in modern units is preceded by a brief summary of the status of electric power today.

2.1 Electricity

Although the definition may appear unfamiliar, electricity is a medium for transmitting energy. The publicity associated with competition usually brackets electric power with coal and oil as another fuel, but the unique and universal nature of its service to mankind is far more significant. An electricity supply network pools the energy from remote sources of wind and water power with the main stream from various fossil fuels and nuclear reactions, and transmits it over any required distance as a continuous service. It meets *all* needs— not only the traditional heating and lighting demands—but provides highly convenient mechanical power, special process services, entertainment and telecommunication channels. In place of the innumerable small fuel-burning local heaters and prime-movers, which create inevitable air pollution and other serious hazards in congested industrial conditions, the necessary reactions in energy conversion can be carried out remotely on the largest scale to give greatest efficiency and best suppression of noxious byproducts. Electricity has therefore the attributes of a universal power medium, and this appears to be well on the path of achievement for fixed installations.

But, in spite of the great promise at the turn of this century, electricity has been steadily losing its position as a medium for mobile power. This is now dominated by the many grades of a single fuel, oil, and the reasons are purely practical—lightness, cost and convenience. Electrical methods of vehicle propulsion have always been known to be the best from theoretical, control and amenity aspects which have become of the utmost importance in modern congested

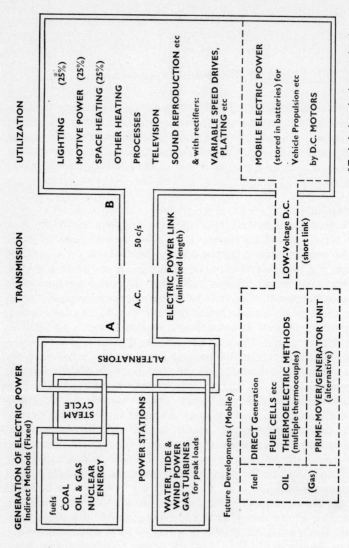

Fig. 2.1 Electricity as Power Transmission Medium.

communities. But they have remained technically static while mechanical alternatives have made remarkable strides. This book attempts to provide the answer in terms of magnetic materials.

The vital part played by electricity as this main link in the energy chain is shown diagrammatically in fig. 2.1. Most power generated today has to pass through two other links: steam and an electro-magnetic generator or alternator, which involve the loss of over half the fuel's energy content, but methods of direct generation are now being developed. These extract the energy in a single step, usually in a static device, and the fuel cell shows signs of ultimately yielding greatest overall efficiency. The principle of the diagram applies to the smallest as well as the largest installations, so that the distance between A and B can technically be yards or metres as well as hundreds of miles or kilometres, or in practical terms, for mobile as well as fixed uses.

Electrical engineering can be divided into two categories, heavy and light, though the translated German equivalents of strong and weak current are more appropriate, with differing methods of assessing the transmission link AB. The power engineer's criterion is efficiency, ratio of output to input, but accuracy is most important in light current work since reliable thermionic and semiconductor amplifiers became available. The problem then usually consists of the remote control of a local power source, to give results that may vary in complication from an on-off signal to a television or computer channel of megacycle bandwidth. Light electrical engineering is now becoming generally known as electronics, in place of earlier telecommunication associations, so that power applications can be more appropriately included in conventional engineering, regardless of scale or length of transmission link.

There already exist several kinds of small links in which electro-magnets are used for the remote control of such well-known mechanical devices as friction-operated brakes and clutches, but these use electricity solely for its remote control advantage. The power is transmitted purely by conventional solid and visual methods whereas it could be greatly improved if both operation and control were unified in a single medium—the basic magnetic flux provided by permanent magnets. But it will be clear from the above considerations that these magnets will be required to carry out a much different task from that so well performed by countless numbers installed in most modern electronic equipment and instruments, in terms of efficiency and operating conditions.

Direct and alternating current both became available on an engineering scale during the final decade of the last century and there was much controversy about their practical merits, but they are now regarded as colleagues rather than competitors. There is now another alternative for some purposes, higher frequency a.c., so that it is desirable to summarize their respective fields of use :—

Direct Current (d.c.) is best for electric traction and for other variable speed drives with wide range at high torque, and is asynchronous, i.e. free of the speed-dependent limitations that are inherent with a.c. supply. It is generated in dynamos or rectified from a.c. mains power, can readily be stored in various kinds of battery and has numerous process uses, such as electroplating. The main disadvantage is that it cannot be directly transformed in voltage.

Alternating Current (a.c.) with frequency standardised at 50 cycles/second (60 c/s in America) has become the universal supply medium for nation-wide fixed power networks, due to ease and economy of voltage transmission to any required level. It is excellent for cheap motors running at fixed speeds, clocks and other timing devices, but only limited speed control is possible. There is no direct way of storing a.c. power, its greatest disadvantage.

Higher Frequency Power (h.f.a.c.) at sonic frequencies (e.g. 400, 800 or 2400 c/s) or ultrasonic (15000 to 25000 c/s for appreciable power). The highest of these frequencies gives greater efficiency and economy for fluorescent lighting and is desirable for new electroluminescent lighting. There are important new uses in ultrasonic cleaning and processing, as well as for novel methods of drilling and machining hard substances such as glass and ceramics. Any frequency increase over the 50 c/s level gives corresponding reduction in size of all transformers, chokes and transducers for equivalent power-handling but losses increase steeply and designs are more expensive. Present commercial methods of producing h.f.a.c. on a multi-kilowatt basis are too expensive for widespread use.

It will be seen that the defects of one system are balanced by the merits of the others, so that together they tend to meet all major demands if they can be converted easily and cheaply to the best system at the point of final utilization. In the past this was a considerable obstacle involving rotating machines but recent developments in metal rectifiers, silicon rectifiers and power transistors have greatly improved the situation. There have also been important advances in storage batteries which, in association with small static charging units, greatly improve the prospects of d.c. mobile power.

There are various frequency changer units for giving high frequency from either d.c. or a.c. and small enough to be used with individual fluorescent lighting schemes for vehicle illumination but the far greater fixed a.c. lighting could be much improved if cheap conversion on a considerable scale could be achieved. This is one of the objectives of a new kind of inductor alternator based on the unique properties of ferrite magnets and described later.

2.2 Electrical Units

In order to define and describe the measurement of electric and magnetic quantities, it is first desirable to visualize their characteristics and this was done by the pioneers early in the last century when dynamic electricity was discovered. Some were most appropriate, like the flow of current, but those relating to magnetism, such as unit poles, created severe obstacles for future generations; yet even today it is hard to find useful analogies, and a physicist or metallurgist will tend to have a different outlook on these phenomena from that of an engineer. In this study it will be assumed that electromagnetism is a superior kind of fluid that can transmit more power through a given area of pipe (conductor) than any visual alternative. Its dual nature can be compared with water flowing through an open channel surrounded by water vapour, of low or high density according to the conditions at every point along the line of flow, which can be intensified and controlled to meet practical purposes. This analogy is inadequate insofar as water is almost incompressible whereas the density of electric current can be varied over an almost unlimited range.

Modern theory has amplified the current flow idea in a rather unexpected way. The world today accepts as a fact that electromagnetic waves travel through space with the speed of light; it is being verified daily by the instantaneous transmission of speech and pictures by modern telecommunications methods used by every radio and television organisation. But when electromagnetism is used to transmit power along a metallic conductor, this far more dense substance slows down the rate, and increases the intensity enormously. The current flows by means of free electrons, and each ampere represents about six trillion (10^{18}) of them flowing at a speed of only around six millimetres per minute, so this is a more viscous 'liquid' than most users of it expected. This explanation makes it much easier to understand how alternating currents are transmitted along conductors up to very high voltages and frequencies, and can carry such a great volume of information as well as so much power. It defines an insulator as a material with negligible free electrons.

The hydraulic analogy, if its limitations are taken into account, can be helpful in the operational as well as the application sense. A fluid needs motive force or potential to make it flow and has to overcome resistance when confined to a pipe, measured by the potential drop over any specified length divided by the flow. The delivered power is proportional to the product of potential and flow, and it is possible to transmit a given amount either with a large flow at low potential, like a river, or a small high-pressure flow as in the case of a hosepipe. The first alternative needs much space and a large channel that may be difficult to control, while the high pressure system is compact and easy to handle but requires expensive and more complex equipment. The economic and engineering problems of reaching the best compromise between these alternative methods of transmitting energy are very similar in principle for a given set of conditions, whether the medium be liquid, gas or electromagnetism. The latter has the outstanding merits of being weightless and is easily confined to its channel with small leakage risks, so that the transmission distance is almost unlimited; but its ability to transmit greater power through a given channel area will apply for short as well as long links. Thus, the similarities between the various competing engineering methods in this general field are considerably greater than the differences, especially in regard to methods of measurement and assessment.

The following well-known relationships between the principal electrical quantities, and their units, also serve to indicate the symbols and abbreviations now in general use:

Power = **Electromotive Force** × **Current** $P = E \times I$
watts W   volts V   amperes A

Resistance $= \dfrac{\text{E.M.F.}}{\text{Current}}$ in ohms $R = \dfrac{E}{I}$

The watt is much too small for most engineering purposes, being the power needed to light a tiny lamp, so units of 1000 watts—kilowatts (kW)—are generally used (1 kW=1.34 horsepower). Power stations and their associated 'grid' transmission network have now grown so enormous in power-producing capacity that the kilowatt is too small if inconveniently large figures are to be avoided. So units of a million watts (1000 kW), megawatts (MW), have been generally adopted in recent times; latest alternators for this application are being made in the 100 to 1000 MW range. In contrast, the medium-power machines which comprise the principal subject matter of this book lie mainly in the 1 to 100 kW range of power.

All these electrical units have been universally employed for so many years throughout the world that they are household words in every country, and have the same meaning and value regardless of language or other system of measurement, whether metric or traditional. This unique advantage could readily be conferred upon other related quantities, such as the output of prime-movers (a highly significant point in later chapters), and this applies with special emphasis to the new magnetic units of the M.K.S.A. system which were internationally adopted in 1950 but are still not widely enough used.

Materials used for electrical purposes,—insulators, conductors and semiconductors—are classified by their *resistivity*, the resistance in ohms between the opposite faces of a centimetre cube of the substance and expressed in ohm.centimetre units (ohm.cm.). These values are tabulated in fig. 2.2 with the relevant figures in the Appendix (Table 2); it will be seen that this covers such a wide ratio, 10^{20}, that a logarithmic scale must be used and insulators are sometimes measured in megohm.cm units, with conductors in microhm.cm units. The positions of all the magnetic and conducting materials described later are given with appropriate information.

If in the above power relationship the product (resistance × current) is substituted for e.m.f., it becomes:

$$\textbf{Power} = (\textbf{Current})^2 \times \textbf{Resistance} = \textbf{I}^2 \textbf{ R watts}$$

Electric power lost in a circuit, for example, as a result of its resistance will appear as heat and will increase as the square of the current. This imposes a severe limitation on the current-carrying ability of every kind of electrical conductor, the actual limit being decided by the means for dissipating the heat. This most important factor to all designs involving electric power is the *allowable current density*. It decides the performance of an electromagnet in comparison with a

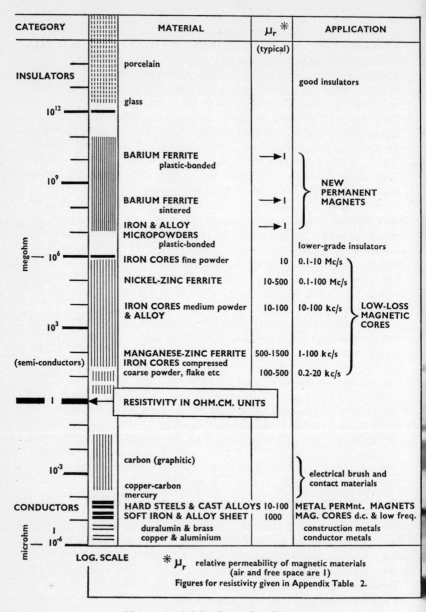

CATEGORY		MATERIAL	μ_r *	APPLICATION
			(typical)	
INSULATORS		porcelain		good insulators
10^{12}		glass		
10^9		BARIUM FERRITE plastic-bonded	→1	NEW PERMANENT MAGNETS
		BARIUM FERRITE sintered	→1	
		IRON & ALLOY MICROPOWDERS plastic-bonded	→1	
megohm — 10^6				lower-grade insulators
		IRON CORES fine powder	10	0.1-10 Mc/s
		NICKEL-ZINC FERRITE	10-500	0.1-100 Mc/s
10^3		IRON CORES medium powder & ALLOY	10-100	10-100 kc/s	LOW-LOSS MAGNETIC CORES
(semi-conductors)		MANGANESE-ZINC FERRITE	500-1500	1-100 kc/s
		IRON CORES compressed coarse powder, flake etc	100-500	0.2-20 kc/s
1		**RESISTIVITY IN OHM.CM. UNITS** ←		
10^{-3}		carbon (graphitic)		electrical brush and contact materials
		copper-carbon mercury		
CONDUCTORS		HARD STEELS & CAST ALLOYS	10-100	METAL PERMnt. MAGNETS
		SOFT IRON & ALLOY SHEET	1000	MAG. CORES d.c. & low freq.
microhm 1 10^{-6}		duralumin & brass		construction metals
		copper & aluminium		conductor metals

LOG. SCALE

* μ_r relative permeability of magnetic materials
(air and free space are 1)
Figures for resistivity given in Appendix Table 2.

Fig. 2.2 Resistivity Categories of Materials.

possible permanent magnet alternative, so is prominent in Part II of this book. A good example of the use of high current density is the fusewire used to protect domestic electric circuits: it operates (melts) at about 50 times the current density of the cables and wires that have to conduct the current without appreciable rise in temperature.

In this brief preliminary survey of electric power circuits it is also necessary to note the significance of voltage level to application. From the purely technical aspect it should be closely related to the length of the circuit. This is readily arranged in an a.c. power supply network by the use of suitable transformers for each transmission link, up to 400 kV in the latest 'grid' transmission lines, and reduced by steps to the standard domestic single phase supply of $240 \pm 6\%$. This degree of control accuracy is imposed principally by lighting requirements which represent about one-quarter of the total load, but is highly desirable for space heaters and innumerable small electric motors that take similar shares; indeed it is impossible to contemplate the existence of nationwide power supply fixed networks without such rigid control.

But if electricity is to be used with equal effectiveness for the transmission of mobile power, as indicated in the lower part of Fig. 2.1, by the very short links that apply to vehicles—the dominant example —such voltages and the machines designed for them are quite unjustified. Much of Part II is devoted to the need to develop special low-voltage machines, and suitable but unfamiliar forms of electric power (low-voltage direct currents of up to thousands of amperes or high frequency alternating currents) for these conditions without the restrictions imposed by the traditional fixed supply requirements. These could then use both new magnets and new direct generation methods in the best way.

2.3 The Electric Circuit

The simplest kind of electric circuit is shown in Fig. 2.3 and consists of a battery connected to an electromagnet, with switch and ammeter to control and measure the current according to the number of cells joined in series. The core of the electromagnet is a bar of soft iron bent into a U-shape so that the field is concentrated mainly between its ends, and its flux can then be varied over a wide range by placing a flat iron piece, known as the keeper or armature, across them. In this way there is formed a clearly defined magnetic circuit linked to the electric circuit by means of the coil of the electromagnet, and this elementary arrangement can be used to explain the relationship between them, as well as the basic magnetic properties of the core material. Also, the soft iron can be replaced by hard steel of similar size in order to show the formation of a permanent magnet, or the cores can be omitted to leave an air-core coil, as already outlined in Chapter 1.2.

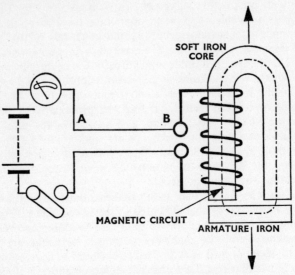

Fig. 2.3 Electric Circuit for Electromagnet.

At first the essential nature of the electric circuit alone should be noted. It has three discrete stages—generation (battery), transmission line of desired length, and apparatus for utilizing the power—as in the diagram of fig. 2.1, but on a small scale. The arrangement can be used to attract the armature from an off position, with air-gaps separating it from the core, when current is switched on, in order to operate a signal or move a control lever from a remote position. The transmission distance can be progressively increased by adding cells to the battery so that the current level in the coil is maintained; in other words the voltage is raised to compensate for the extra resistance of the line of any required length between A and B.

In the form of the electric telegraph, this was the first major application of electricity on a commercial scale and led on to the endless variety of electrical engineering activities that exist today.

This is therefore an appropriate means for examining the relationship between the two inseparable partners in this prolific marriage—electricity and magnetism—on a practical scale. The simplest explanation based upon latest knowledge will be employed, leaving the complex historical approach to the next chapter.

A preliminary examination of the magnetic effects associated with this simple circuit can be made with the iron cores removed. It is necessary to have some elementary means for detecting the presence and direction of magnetism, such as a small compass needle with a shallow transparent box containing fine iron filings or iron powder to give a visual aid. These show that the magnetic effect in air, known as the *magnetic field* is strongest along the centre and ends of the coil and spreads out uniformly through a considerable volume of the surrounding space. The traditional way of regarding this field is a large number of 'lines of force' like closed elastic bands crowded together inside the coil but being free to spread to a much lower density in the outside space, but the modern view is that it is an energy density which is better expressed by a small number. This is applied to the new units for magnetic flux described later.

The most important conclusions are that a magnetic field has a direction (shown by the compass) related to the direction of the current that causes it, and an intensity dependent upon the position of the point considered in relation to the conductor and the value of the current. A straight wire has a relatively weak field with concentric lines of force but these can be concentrated by bending the wire into a circle or loop, and the degree of concentration can be greatly increased by the use of many turns in the form of the familiar coil, also known as a *solenoid*. It must always be borne in mind that every current-carrying conductor automatically creates its surrounding magnetic field but this is generally too weak to detect in practice unless the current is of the order of hundreds of amperes or more. The coil is a simple and handy device for concentrating the field where it is wanted with a relatively small current generally supplied from a great distance.

If the soft iron core is now brought near to the end of the air-core coil while current is flowing, it will be pulled inside with appreciable force owing to the intensification of the magnetic flux brought about by the iron core. This will reach a position of equilibrium when the highest flux density that the circumstances permit has been reached, which can be expressed in another way by saying that the mean magnetic path will be of minimum length. It is important to note that the magnetic flux density has increased only within the space occupied by the iron and magnetic circuit associated with it, but this increase can be over 1000 times if the ends of the U-shaped core are closed by the armature and the current through the coil is limited to avoid the approach to the magnetic saturation point of iron. Under these conditions the whole magnetic effect of this arrangement is concentrated, from the practical standpoint, within the iron circuit and this will apply if the armature is withdrawn slightly to insert a non-magnetic sheet between it and the two poles to represent the air-gap conditions of an electrical machine or device.

In this form there is a clearly defined *magnetic circuit* as well as an electric circuit and they are coupled together by means of the coil, the load of the electric circuit. There are many similarities between these two kinds of circuit, described in detail later, but at this stage it must be noted that the airgaps represent the magnetic load; by their means it is possible to transfer the energy trapped inside the electrical circuit to some kind of mechanical structure moving in air within the restricted space of the air-gaps. For reasonable efficiency the magnetic length of air-gap has to be a fraction of 1% of the total magnetic circuit length, so that the iron can play its vital part to greatest effect.

This represents a generalized picture of the conversion of electrical into mechanical energy and it will be seen that this is done by a combination of electricity and magnetism, which are two manifestations of a single phenomenon, *electromagnetism*. Dynamic electricity inevitably and simultaneously produces magnetism. A battery has electro-motive force (e.m.f.) always available at its terminals but the appearance and magnitude of the resulting current will depend upon the existence of a conducting circuit. As soon as current flows, a *magneto-motive force* (m.m.f.) is created around the electric circuit and the resulting flux will be dependent upon the circuit geometry and presence of iron or other ferro-magnetic materials. Since air is not a magnetic insulator and m.m.f. is spread unevenly around the circuit, it is more difficult to evaluate magnetic quantities than electrical.

Although this study of practical magnetism has these inherent complexities, they have been exaggerated in the past by being isolated from their prime source, the electric circuit. The remedy is to convert to electric circuit equivalents at every possible opportunity while making due allowance for their basic differences. In this way the two forms of this medium can be automatically regarded as the internal and external effects relative to the conductor, and the fact that each can exist apart from the other will become incidental. Thus, a battery without a circuit is stored electricity and a permanent magnet is stored magnetism, which today on a practical scale is also stored electricity. But the latter is static and not recoverable except as an agent for energy conversion purposes; so in this form it should not be expendable.

The outstanding conclusion up to this stage in the study of this subject is that magnetic fields are generated by the flow of electric currents and so the only logical way of measuring their motive force is by the unit of current, the ampere. Since the usual method of concentrating the magnetic field is by the use of multi-turn coils, it has been general for many years to measure this magneto-motive force in units of *ampere-turns* (symbol AT) and, though some now prefer to restrict this to amperes alone, the earlier version gives it a more clear association with the magnetic function. Unlike the e.m.f. of an electric circuit which is conveniently concentrated at the terminals of a generator or battery, the m.m.f. is spread along an appreciable length of the circuit and the unit of magnetizing force must be related to the unit of length, the metre. Thus, this most important magnetic unit is expressed by:—

Magnetizing Force = m.m.f./metre in ampere-turns/metre(AT/m)

In the past this unit appeared in another form with the name of an early pioneer, so it appeared to be divorced from the electric circuit, but in the new form there is no possible doubt as to the cause of the magnetic flux which may have been produced for some practical purpose by either permanent magnets or electromagnets.

2.4 Magnetic Circuits and Units

While the principal magnetic unit, magnetizing force, is defined in the familiar terms and units of the electric circuit, there must inevitably be new and lesser-known units confined to the magnetic circuit, such as flux and flux density. Though many attempts were made throughout this century to bring uniformity and clarity to this important subject, international agreement was reached only by 1950 in what is known as the M.K.S.A. system of units based on the use of the metre, kilogram, second and ampere. The latter provides the link with the universally accepted set of practical electrical units and has the new unit of force, the newton (a force of one kilogram equals 9.81 newtons), and the joule as the unit of energy (1 watt equals 1 joule/second). Within this framework a new unit for magnetic flux was agreed that is directly related to the volt of the electric circuit, the e.m.f. generated in a conductor moving through a uniform magnetic field, by dividing the old flux unit (maxwell or 'line') by 10^8. This new unit is called the 'weber' after the German pioneer of absolute electric and magnetic units, and the new flux density unit is therefore expressed in webers/square metre, abbreviated to Wb/m^2.

Many practical advantages, as well as the logical derivation, arise from use of these new magnetic units in the assessment of magnetic materials. Magnetizing force can be directly related to electric circuit conditions in comparing permanent magnet material with corresponding electromagnets, and one Wb/m^2 represents a typical air-gap flux density level without having to visualize innumerable mythical lines of force. The numerical relationship between these units and those they replace is:—

Magnetizing Force (H) $1 \text{ AT/m} = 4\pi \times 10^{-3}$ oersted

Flux Density   (B) $1 \text{ Wb/m}^2 = 10^4$ gauss

Other changes are necessary. The permeability of free space μ_0, formerly assumed unity, is $4\pi \times 10^{-7}$ and the permeability of a magnetic material (B/H) must be converted to 'relative permeability' ($B/\mu_0 H$) to give the traditional numerical value. This is the magnetic equivalent of electrical conductivity, the reciprocal of resistivity, and magnetic reluctance (cf. resistance) has to include the above figure for the permeability of free space as well as relative permeability.

A comparison between the various properties, similarities and differences, of electric and magnetic circuits, together with their main units, symbols and abbreviations, is given in Table 2.2. The chief conclusion to be drawn from this is that the similarities, especially in the close parallel of the circuit quantities, are of much greater consequence than the differences, though the latter must be kept continually in view if the full benefits of regarding electro-magnetism as a single entity are to be achieved. The accuracy of the comparison is dependent upon the extent to which a particular magnetic circuit can be regarded as 'closed', or in other words the extent to which leakage flux can be neglected. A transformer core, for example, is a closed magnetic circuit although the presence of joints and lack of symmetry will represent some degree of reluctance, but it can be designed with considerable accuracy and this applies to large machinery also. Small electrical machines and devices, however (in which it is difficult to avoid the use of air-gaps that

COMPARISON	ELECTRIC CIRCUIT		MAGNETIC CIRCUIT	
	QUANTITY	UNIT	QUANTITY	UNIT
SIMILARITIES	ELECTROMOTIVE FORCE (E.M.F.)	VOLT (V)	MAGNETOMOTIVE FORCE (M.M.F.)	AMPERE-TURN (AT)
	CURRENT	AMPERE (A)	MAGNETIZING FORCE (H)	AMPERE-TURN/METRE (AT/m)
	CURRENT DENSITY	AMPERE/SQ.MILLI-METRE (A/mm²)	MAGNETIC FLUX	WEBER (Wb)
			FLUX DENSITY (B)	WEBER/SQ.METRE (Wb/m²)
RELATIONSHIP	$\text{CURRENT} = \dfrac{\text{E.M.F.}}{\text{RESISTANCE}}$ $\text{RESISTANCE} = \dfrac{L}{A} \times \rho$ where ρ is resistivity L & A are length and area of conductor ($1/\rho$ is conductivity) CURRENT FLOW IN CIRCUIT CREATES M.M.F.		$\text{MAGNETIC FLUX} = \dfrac{\text{M.M.F.}}{\text{RELUCTANCE}}$ $\text{RELUCTANCE} = \dfrac{L}{A} \times \dfrac{1}{\mu_0 \mu_r}$ where μ_0 is permeability of space ($4\pi \times 10^{-7}$) μ_r is relative permeability of material L & A are length and area of magnetic circuit RELATIVE MOVEMENT OF FLUX & CONDUCTOR CREATES E.M.F.	
DIFFERENCES	CURRENT RESTRICTED TO CONDUCTOR CURRENT DENSITY LIMITED BY HEATING CURRENT CREATES RESISTANCE LOSSES CONTINUOUSLY AS HEAT		MAGNETIC FIELD OCCUPIES SURROUNDING AIR AS WELL AS CIRCUIT FLUX DENSITY LIMITED BY MAGNETIC SATURATION CURRENT CREATES FLUX AT ONCE: FURTHER POWER WASTED AS HEAT	

TABLE 2.1. COMPARISON BETWEEN ELECTRIC & MAGNETIC CIRCUITS

cause high leakage) cannot easily be treated as discrete magnetic circuits that are in any way equivalent to the simple electric circuits associated with them.

Magnetic saturation is another factor in this comparison which acts in quite a different manner from the ability of a conductor to carry current. If the current density in a wire or cable is too high, it becomes hot and usually signals the fact by burning its insulation and producing smoke, smell and even flames if sufficiently overloaded. On the other hand a magnetic circuit that is overloaded by applying excess m.m.f. will saturate without giving an indication, and the leakage flux will be increased with a corresponding deterioration of efficiency. If an indication does appear, it will probably be delayed and become apparent through the electric circuit, which again shows that magnetism cannot be treated in an isolated manner.

In any case the non-linear relationship between magnetizing force and the resulting flux density in all magnetic materials, coupled with the fact the strong fields used in power-handling machines and equipment are usually confined to narrow and inaccessible air-gaps, makes

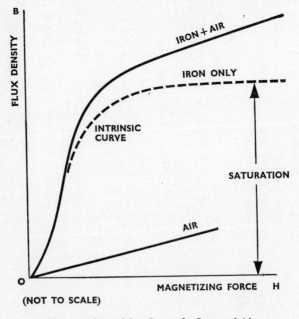

Fig. 2.4 Magnetizing Curves for Iron and Air.

it desirable to gain as much magnetic information as possible by way of the electric circuit.

Magnetic materials are tested by the makers on ring-shaped specimens with negligible leakage by use of special-purpose test gear that gives good accuracy, but it is difficult to translate this from their published performance data into practical designs of small and medium size. Hence it is necessary in application development to check any calculations involving magnetic circuits with practical tests on models which can usually be readily constructed, and essential magnetic tests can fortunately be carried out with simple and inexpensive apparatus.

Magnetizing force is readily measured by reading the current flowing through the coil when the number of turns is known. Flux density can be read directly from a portable fluxmeter with thin probes for inserting into narrow airgaps, and indirectly by the force of attraction if there is a movable armature or keeper or the magnetic equivalent. All that is then needed is a spring balance, preferably calibrated in kilograms, to measure the pull needed to break the magnetic circuit, and different thicknesses of non-magnetic metal such as brass can be used as artificial airgaps to give a range of scale readings. The force of attraction varies as the (flux density)^2 times the pole area in square metres. Details are given in Chapter 7 and Fig. 7.7 but these points indicate that elementary tests are adequate for measuring the relatively strong fields considered here.

2.5 Magnetizing and Demagnetizing Curves

The elementary electromagnetic circuit of Fig. 2.3 can be used to study and measure the magnetic properties of the materials in the coil—iron, steel and air. The multi-cell battery enables equal increments of current and magnetizing force to be applied and flux density is measured at the centre of the coil end, giving the following contrasting results:—

(a) at lower current levels iron multiplies the flux density inside the air-core coil many hundreds of times.

(b) flux density increases linearly with magnetizing force in the case of air, but for iron at first it rises steeply and then tails off steadily as saturation is approached.

A comparison of this contrasting behaviour is best seen in their magnetizing curves (Fig. 2.4) from which may be derived the dotted *intrinsic magnetizing* curve by plotting values of $(B—\mu_0H)$ against H.

4

This gives that part of the flux provided by the iron alone and the point where this curve becomes horizontal is the saturation flux density. This value is of great importance for all power applications, in which the greatest possible concentration of flux is required. These curves are not drawn to scale because the permeability of solid iron is much greater than that of the air in the coil (which has linear response) so that its curve would be nearly horizontal. But the latest permanent magnetic materials have a permeability approaching that of air or of free space, so their intrinsic curves are of utmost importance.

Sets of such magnetizing curves (sometimes called B H curves) are provided for electrical designers by the makers of the various grades of sheet steel or iron alloys used for this purpose, so that best working conditions for each application can be assessed. Typical curves for a silicon steel in comparison with mild steel and cast iron are shown in Fig. 2.5 in relation to the saturation value for iron (2.15 Wb/m^2). The curves show that carbon has the effect of deteriorating the magnetic quality: the tenfold increase in carbon from mild steel to cast iron

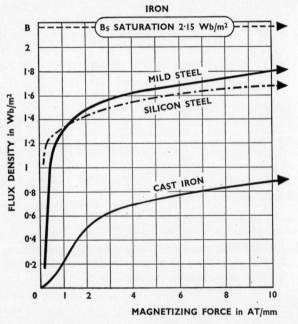

Fig. 2.5 Magnetizing Curves for Mild Steel, Silicon Steel and Cast Iron.

reduces the permeability at low magnetizing forces to nearly one-tenth of that in the purer grade. Early permanent magnets were made from a hard steel with 1% carbon which would be about four times the mild steel figure and have an intermediate position in between the two curves. Ferromagnetic metals tend to be very sensitive in their magnetic quality to small amounts of certain impurities, chiefly carbon, sulphur, oxygen and nitrogen.

Silicon acts as a deoxidizing agent and greatly improves the magnetic properties of iron and its alloys up to 6%, but it causes brittleness which makes the rolling process to produce sheet very difficult. Hence there are a number of lower silicon-steel alloys supplied on the market in sheet form to meet the diversity of mechanical and economic demands. The silicon has the further advantage of increasing the resistivity of iron, which reduces the eddy current loss under alternating flux conditions in a.c. power supply machines and equipment with magnetic cores. It will be seen from these magnetizing curves, however, that these merits of silicon steel are obtained at the expense of some reduction in the values of flux density at the higher H values in comparison with mild steel. If a magnetic circuit is needed for uni-directional flux, it is therefore better, as well as cheaper, to use solid mild steel and this applies especially in the case of air-gap circuits, where the higher initial permeability of the silicon alloys would not be utilized.

The curve also indicates how great a level of magnetizing force would be needed to reach saturation point, so that this is not even approached in practical circumstances. As the magnetizing force is raised to points well above the upper bend in the curve it takes a tenfold increase in power to yield only about 10% improvement in flux density and this is not economical even when the ultimate machine is operating on a figure of merit based on B^2, which occurs in various applications. The actual working point needs to be considered for each kind of use and calls for a careful balance of economic and technical factors.

Magnetizing curves of the kind shown represent the simple working conditions of a d.c. circuit and it is necessary to consider the effect of demagnetizing forces and alternating currents. In the circuit of Fig. 2.3 this means that the current, after saturation has been reached, is progressively reduced by the same equal steps back to zero and the flux density readings continued as before. It will be found that there is a small value in the mild steel core, and a considerable proportion in the hard steel, of remanent flux at zero current known as *remanence*: under these conditions the hard steel has become a permanent magnet because this remanent flux can last a considerable time, though it would tend to diminish rapidly in the mild steel.

If the polarity of the battery is now reversed so that the current steps are then increased in the reverse direction, a point will be reached at which the remanent flux has been reduced to zero and this particular value of magnetizing force (H) is the *coercivity* of the material, which mainly indicates its magnetic quality and sphere of usefulness. By continuing the current increase in this reverse direction up to the negative saturation point, back to the zero current and on to the original saturation position, a complete cycle of alternating current has been applied in slow steps and a closed B H loop can be plotted from the results. By repeating this cycle of current variation several times, the same symmetrical curve will be repeated and this is named from the Greek 'hysteresis loop' to indicate that the flux lags behind the magnetizing force producing it. Hysteresis is also a well-known property in a mechanical sense for such materials as rubber, and in relation to magnetism it provides the main properties and characteristics of the great variety of magnetic materials now available. The symbol for coercivity is H_c.

The area of the hysteresis loop gives the energy loss in the material, but this is more appropriately termed *energy product* for permanent magnets. It is now measured in units of joules/cubic metre (J/m^3), replacing mega-gauss-oersted (Mgo) of the earlier c.g.s. system. The performance of magnet material has also been displayed hitherto in the form of demagnetizing curves comprising that portion of the hysteresis loop in the second quadrant where negative magnetizing force is applied in order to reduce the flux density to zero. The coercivity value so far considered does this on a temporary basis while the demagnetizing force is maintained and, while this would almost demagnetize all metal magnets permanently, it has little effect upon most ferrite magnet grades. For them to be permanently demagnetized it is necessary to apply still greater negative magnetizing force which is named the 'intrinsic coercivity' of the particular material, and this value is of great significance to all practical applications described in this book (symbol H_{ci}).

A typical demagnetizing curve for a permanent magnet is shown in Fig. 2.6 in relation to its hysteresis loop, in order to indicate the most important performance figures and their symbols. The three main properties are coercivity H_c, remanence B_r and energy product

$(BH)_{max}$; the point at which the latter operates is found by the intersection of the curve by the $B_r H_c$ rectangle diagonal, as shown. The corresponding working values of flux density B_d and of magnetizing force H_d are those used in all design calculations which should be based upon a balance between the reluctance of the magnet and that

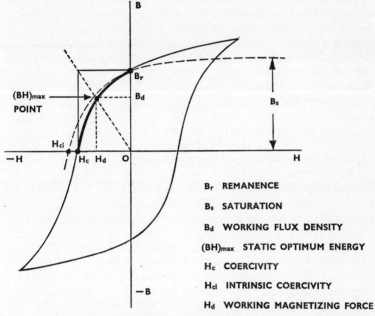

B_r	REMANENCE
B_s	SATURATION
B_d	WORKING FLUX DENSITY
$(BH)_{max}$	STATIC OPTIMUM ENERGY
H_c	COERCIVITY
H_{ci}	INTRINSIC COERCIVITY
H_d	WORKING MAGNETIZING FORCE

Fig. 2.6 Permanent Magnet Demagnetizing Curve with Symbols

of the air-gap in all cases where the latter is fixed, i.e. static conditions. When it is variable over a wide reluctance ratio, dynamic conditions, it is desirable to use a demagnetizing curve of different shape, discussed later, and to give attention to the intrinsic coercivity H_{ci} and the magnitude of the H_{ci}/H_c ratio.

2.6 Material Performance

The various properties of magnetic materials can be related to the two fundamental properties, coercivity and saturation, in association with the shape of the hysteresis loop. Material tests to obtain these figures must be carried out with sufficient magnetizing force to reach saturation point with an adequate margin, otherwise the results will be too low and the material wrongly assessed. For example, early magnetizers are useless for ferrites and manufacturers generally give B_S values for each type listed, for the use of those who magnetize their products after assembly.

High saturation is desirable for all magnetic materials that operate at high flux density, whether of magnet or low-loss grades, but the range of B_S values for solid materials is only about 7/1 from iron to ferrite, though their powders bonded with non-magnetic metals or plastics will reduce B_S considerably. However, this subdivision may increase the coercivity enormously from anything between 100 and 100 000 times, and the discovery of this fact followed by its practical proof has been a major event of the past 25 years. Thus coercivity is dependent upon physical structure, whether created by the heat-treatment of suitable alloys or by synthetic powder-metallurgy processes, and the practical problem is to achieve the maximum value for permanent magnets and the minimum for low-loss materials.

For further explanation at this juncture it is necessary to anticipate briefly the account of the magnetic domain theory described in the following chapters. Now fully confirmed, this states that all magnetic material if sufficiently subdivided will increase in coercivity up to a critical particle size dependent upon the physical properties of the material. Below this critical dimension the coercivity falls off rapidly for still finer powder until a non-magnetic stage is reached. Expressed in other terms, all magnetic materials consist of tiny groups of mobile magnets normally arranged in small closed circuits so that there are no external manifestations, but the latter can be brought about by application of magnetizing force.

The domain size of barium ferrite is about one micron, or one thousandth of a millimetre, which is in the region of the finest particles' diameter used in modern powder metallurgy processes. But the domain size of iron is around a hundred times finer and the resulting micropowder is so corrosive that it spontaneously ignites on coming into contact with air. This pyrophoric effect can be overcome in practice and is eliminated when the material is compressed into solid blocks, so mechanically sound magnets can be made by this method, although the process is at present somewhat complex and hence costly on a limited production scale. This brief mention of a subject described in detail later indicates the importance of subdivision in explaining the connection between coercivity and saturation; it may be brought about by use of special alloys and heat treatments, as in the case of nearly all the conventional magnets, or produced synthetically by powder techniques in the form of ferrite and micropowder magnets.

In order to show the subdivision effect on the shape of hysteresis loops and magnetizing curves, it is necessary to note the following in regard to Figs. 2.4 and 2.5:—

(a) air having no hysteresis, this curve and loop for air is a straight line with no saturation, and

(b) the curve and loop for iron powder would be progressively flattened as the proportion of air to iron is increased.

The effect of the air is so great that the relative permeability of loose iron powder comes as low as 2 or 3, though the solid metal value μ_r is over 1000. In practice the structure must be rigid and this is achieved by use of binders and compression together, so that any required range of magnetic material density can be chosen by varying these two process factors as well as the powder properties.

The extremes comprise micropowders with such low density that the coercivity is very great but the saturation is too low for practical use, and the same material pressed without binder to such a value that the density approaches that of the solid metal and the magnetic properties become those of a low-loss material. In between there is a wide area of useful magnet materials with optimum $(BH)_{max}$ value occurring at a physical density about two-thirds that of the solid metal. In this manner all the different kinds of alloy magnets that have so far been manufactured can be simulated magnetically by the most common magnetic element, iron, in fine powder form.

This brief examination of magnetic materials in subdivided form leads to important economic and engineering conclusions. A good magnet of this kind will be one-third non-magnetic material, which can consist of a variety of plastic or metal substances introduced to give desirable mechanical properties of tenacity, rigidity or flexibility; special finishes can be used and manufacturing advantages gained. Lower purity raw materials than those needed for high permeability magnetic cores can be used to reduce the manufacturing costs, but in general the use of mild steel poleplates in magnetic circuits containing airgaps makes the quality and uniformity of permanent-magnet materials much less critical than those of low-loss circuits.

2.7 Demagnetizing Conditions

Most practical applications of these modern magnets described in later chapters depend upon their satisfactory performance under extremely strong demagnetizing conditions. Though there has now been accumulated in recent years by practical tests a wealth of results proving their worth under such circumstances, it is also desirable to have confirmatory test data relating to the materials themselves. These can best be provided by deriving the intrinsic demagnetizing curves from the published performance figures of the permanent magnet materials; this is done by plotting values of $(B - \mu_0 H)$ as shown by the dotted curves in Fig. 2.7 for typical oriented alnico and high-coercivity barium ferrite.

The object is to compare the performance of the two materials under dynamic operating conditions, such as in a magnetic circuit with a cyclically varying airgap between a small minimum to a large maximum length. In Fig. 2.3 this would mean that the armature would almost touch the poles of the U-shaped core and then be taken some distance away from them with a repeated motion. The

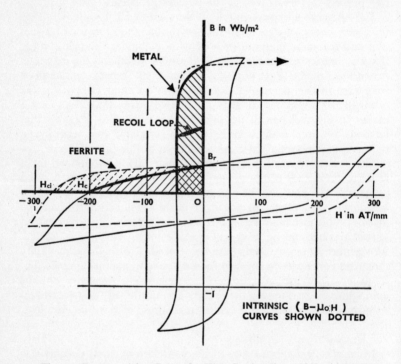

Fig. 2.7 Demagnetizing Curves for High-Grade Alloy and Ferrite Magnets.

curves usually provided by the magnet makers for their material performance are shown by heavy lines in Fig. 2.7, and these have been extended to display the whole hysteresis loops. It was stated earlier that the energy contained by, or loss due to, a hysteresis loop is measured by its area, which in these two examples is roughly the same.

In the second quadrant, however, the curve for the metal magnet is nearly rectangular while that for the ferrite magnet is almost linear. It appears from this limited information that the metal magnet has a considerably greater amount of available power, indicated by the difference in the areas shaded by solid lines. This is indeed the kind of difference shown by the traditional form of energy product $(BH)_{max}$. It is therefore necessary to see in what form the hidden energy of the ferrite magnet can be made available.

The intrinsic demagnetizing curves provide the answer, shown by the broken line area. If both magnet materials are subjected to demagnetizing force equivalent to their coercivity values, the metal will be practically demagnetized while the ferrite will be hardly altered in magnetic strength, because the intrinsic coercivity H_{ci} is so much higher than H_c. The two points are practically coincident for the alnico magnet, so there is no energy in reserve to withstand such severe demagnetizing conditions.

When subjected to the circumstances outlined above, the metal magnet operates on the small minor hysteresis loop, or *recoil loop*, indicated on the middle of its shaded area. The flux variation caused by the reluctance change is only that due to this recoil loop, a small fraction of the remanence value; hence this kind of material is used very inefficiently for this purpose. On the other hand, the recoil loop of the ferrite is almost coincident with the main curve because it is nearly linear and the greater part of the remanence flux is available for this dynamic application.

This may be summed up by stating that a lower coercivity material with high remanence can give the greatest available flux under static conditions, which mean small or negligible demagnetizing forces. For dynamic conditions it is desirable to have a limited amount of energy in the second quadrant with a considerable reserve in the third, and it has thus become necessary to show the whole demagnetizing conditions in the performance curves, i.e. the whole of the second and third quadrants. Alternatively the intrinsic coercivity value must be stated as well as H_c and a new method of assessing the energy product for dynamic conditions be adopted. These points are followed up in greater detail later, mainly in Chapter 6, but they have only become apparent in the few years since the high-coercivity ferrites became widely used.

Now that permanent magnets are becoming available with the ability to maintain their flux indefinitely, the problem in the design of power-handling machines and equipment using them changes to the control of their flux. The intrinsic coercivity levels under consideration represent magnetizing forces involving current densities of unprecedented magnitude, which necessitate the development of new kinds of insulated conductor operating at appreciably higher temperatures than present kinds and wound into special coil designs that can dissipate the heat. This subject is pursued in Chapter 7 which describes how the performance of electromagnets can be brought up to match that of these new permanent magnet materials.

2.8 Performance Figures

The limited design accuracy of magnetic circuits, especially those of smaller size with air-gaps, does not justify much of the detailed performance curves and figures for the great variety of materials now on the market. An attempt is therefore made here to rationalize this part of the subject and to choose units from the M.K.S.A. system that can also serve as simple figures of merit. It is clear from the above investigation into demagnetizing conditions that magnets must be judged according to use, with an energy product for dynamic conditions as well as the present $(BH)_{max}$ which is valid only for static magnetic circuits. For a linear demagnetizing curve this dynamic energy product is proportional to remanence times coercivity (B_rH_c) but for other shapes, which may vary up to near-rectangular, it will be coercivity times that proportion of remanence made available by the optimum recoil line. This is covered in detail in Chapter 6 but for present purposes the conventional figure of merit will be maintained, expressed in units of joules per cubic metre (J/m^3) in the new system. This fits in conveniently with magnetizing force in terms of the linear dimension (AT/m) and flux density in the corresponding area (Wb/m^2) to give a volumetric energy product in the $(BH)_{max}$ form with modern units in place of mega-gauss-oersted. In practice it is desirable to omit as many noughts as possible so that the properties of permanent magnet materials are best shown as coercivities in ampere-turns per *milli*metre (AT/mm) and energy products in *kilo*joules per cubic metre (kJ/m^3). With the convenience of a flux density unit that is within the limited range of 0.1 to 2 Wb/m^2 it is

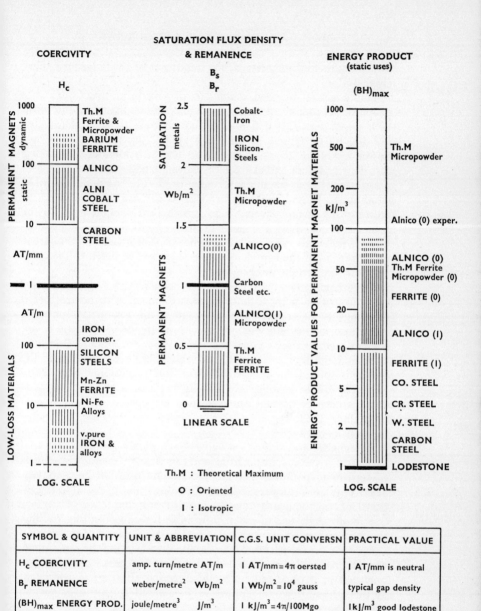

Fig. 2.8 Magnetic Properties of Principal Materials.

now possible to summarize all the important values in a single chart (Fig. 2.8).

This chart is intended mainly to display in compact form the properties of today's range of permanent magnet materials and those of low-loss materials that may be associated with them. The latter are difficult to express in similar terms because the coercivity and power losses are generally related to one of a number of working flux density values and at frequencies where eddy-currents may predominate, whereas permanent magnet results are based on saturation conditions. The ultimate theoretical values are also included to indicate the great development possibilities that remain to be achieved in coercivity and hence in energy products, chiefly in micropowder materials. The limited number of substances in the chart is an indication of the simplicity of the subject if confined to the commercially important applications.

All ferromagnetic materials can be included in a single coercivity chart drawn on a logarithmic scale, as shown, with powers of 10 coverings a 10^7 range. The new unit with millimetre measure, 1 AT/mm, comes conveniently in the centre of the neutral zone; present metal magnets cover the 10 to 100 range suitable for static uses, and the ferrites from 100 to about 300 are indicated in the dynamic application sphere, with possible extension up to nearly 1000. The low-loss group have roughly one-thousandth of the magnet values so can be best measured in the basic unit of AT/m. The cost of attaining the lower values shown is much too great for the kind of use considered here.

Remanence and saturation values have such a limited range that they are covered in a linear scale, and this clearly shows the limitation of ferrites in contrast to their outstanding position in coercivity. Their ultimate saturation is about one-third that of metal in micropowder form and nearly one-fifth in solid form, but this disadvantage is minimized by use of metal poleplates for concentrating the flux to the value needed for practical uses. The introduction of orientation processes over the past two decades greatly increased the remanence, more than doubled in some cases, for those magnets which could be operated in a preferred magnetic direction. Further development in this property would appear to be limited to improvements in orientation methods.

Energy product values, summarized in the third section of the chart and based on the conventional $(BH)_{max}$ units, now cover such a wide range that a log-scale is needed, though the ratio used for magnets only is 500/1. By use of kilojoules/m^3 the unit is about the value for good lodestone, the earliest magnet, so this scale indicates a figure of merit of improvement in magnet strength. The 10 level was reached 30 years ago with aluminium-nickel-cobalt-iron alloys (generally described here as 'alnico') in *isotropic* form, i.e. before orientation processes had been introduced. Within the past few years the 100 mark has been attained under experimental conditions with a selected alloy of this group giving optimum orientation, but the best commercial materials are in the region of half this value. From the above discussion of demagnetizing conditions, it will be clear that this chart is confined to static uses and the materials will appear in a different order when the appropriate new method of assessment for dynamic applications is dealt with in a later chapter.

It will be seen from the whole chart, and by appropriate use of the new system of units, that a series of figures of merit can be employed to express the quality of a magnetic material for any required application in a magnetic circuit. Flux density of 1 is average, 1.5 is good and 0.5 is poor. Coercivity of 50 to 100 is good for most static uses with high remanence, but 200 and over is desirable for dynamic purposes. Any material with energy product of around 10 and higher is of commercial value today according to its price. It is desirable to visualize coercivity in terms of current rather than the physical structure that causes it, and here the use of AT/millimetre is valuable because a conductor or coil a metre wide is remote from the facts. An insulated round wire one millimetre in diameter is about the familiar 20 S.W.G. size used in laboratories and workshops; with the normal current density of 2 A/mm^2 specified for wound coils of conventional type, this gives a current capacity of about 1 ampere. Hence this unit of coercivity or of magnetizing force represents one turn of this wire carrying one ampere and a low grade magnet will give the effect of 10 layers of these turns, or of one turn carrying 10 times its normal current and becoming overheated. This gives some idea of the value of a magnet with H_C of 100 AT/mm in terms of its equivalent electromagnet, which would have to operate un-cooled close to its melting point.

2.9 Shape of Magnetic Circuits

The usual objective in the design of a magnetic circuit is the provision of a field of highest flux density, within the limitations imposed by economics and space, across an airgap of the required length. The volume of this working magnetic field will have to be related to the size and energy-product value of the permanent magnet material that will be used to maintain it, or to the volume and permissible working value of current density for an electromagnet alternative, but this analysis will at present be limited to permanent magnets. The symbols to be used are L and A for lengths and areas of the magnetic circuit, with suffix g for gap, p for poleplates (or polepieces) and m for magnet. The working values of magnetizing force and flux density which apply to the conditions of use, normally obtained from the maker's curves or catalogue, are usually denoted by H_d and B_d respectively. All units should be in the M.K.S.A. system with dimensions in metres; some manufacturers still use the old units and provide conversion factors, but these are also given in the appendix to this book. (Table A.1)

For a first approximation it will be assumed that leakage flux can be neglected, by making the airgap length L_g very small compared with L_m so that nearly all the flux passes through the gap. In the usual static conditions which apply to most permanent magnet applications (with fixed airgap length), the optimum performance is obtained when the reluctance of the magnet is made to equal that of the gap; it corresponds to the matching of the load resistance or impedance of an electrical circuit with that of the generator or input. But the magnet reluctance is the ratio of its m.m.f. to its flux:

m.m.f. of magnet $= H_d L_m$

flux of magnet $= B_d A_m$

$$\text{reluctance of magnet} = \frac{H_d L_m}{B_d A_m}$$

$$\text{reluctance of airgap} = \frac{L_g}{A_g \mu_0} \quad \text{where } \mu_0 \text{ is } 4\pi.\,10^{-7}$$

$$\text{Hence } \frac{H_d L_m}{B_d A_m} = \frac{L_g.\,10^7}{A_g.\,4\pi}$$

so the required ratio of magnet dimensions is $\dfrac{L_m}{A_m} = \dfrac{L_g\,B_d\,10^7}{A_g\,H_d\,4\pi}$

The required flux is specified and the length of the permanent magnet can be obtained from the above m.m.f. and flux relations.

In the past, it was necessary with small low-coercivity magnet materials to use a much longer and thicker magnet than these figures would indicate in order to provide the inevitable large amount of leakage flux. But most of the designs described later are based on high-coercivity ferrites with large magnet area and short magnetic circuit, and these conditions give low leakage even when the flux is concentrated in poleplates to up to ten times the B_d value. Under these conditions it is not necessary to introduce leakage factors for approximate calculations, so these are not given in detail here; however, if ferrite magnets are substituted in traditional designs, the leakage will be so high that they will be used very inefficiently.

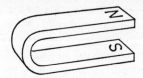

STAGE 1.   LOW COERCIVITY   (TO 40 AT/mm)

STAGE 2.   MEDIUM COERCIVITY   (40 – 100)

   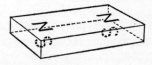

STAGE 3.   HIGH COERCIVITY   (OVER 100)

Fig. 2.9 Evolution of Magnet Shapes.

At this stage it is appropriate to look at the major alterations in magnet shape (Fig. 2.9) which have taken place with the great advances in magnet performance during recent decades. The original hard steels had adequate remanence (1 Wb/m²) but such low coercivity (4 AT/mm) that an artificially long magnetic path had to be provided to give sufficient m.m.f. at the working point (airgaps).

This was the reason for the familiar horseshoe design in all early commercial products based on permanent magnets—magnetos, telephone receivers, moving coil measuring instruments, integrating meter brakes—and this mainly decided their form and bulk.

The progressive multiplication of coercivity value of metal magnets throughout this century steadily reduced the magnetic path length for equivalent performance down to the shallow U-shape and cubic or rectangular blocks, with immense advantages to the designs of the above products as the demand for miniaturization extended throughout the industries concerned. During the 1930s the greatest single market for magnets, loudspeakers, could be expanded with such small and relatively efficient magnetic circuits, but much of this is being taken over by ferrite magnets of the final shape shown, flat rings with large A_m and small L_m. Details are given in Chapter 7, but the equivalent in rectangular form can be built up with flat rectangular blocks or bricks to any desired size. These two basic shapes, which can be made at low cost in large quantities and are most suitable for the latest oriented grades of ferrite, are used for all subsequent designs for the medium-power applications comprising the main subject matter of this book.

These latest shapes have various practical advantages: with bricks it is possible to build up large magnets by increasing either the magnetic area for greater flux or by increasing the magnetic length to provide more m.m.f. or by using both together in order to maintain a magnetic field of greater volume. Those grades of material with almost linear demagnetizing curve are so stable that they can be magnetized in the factory and transported or stored in this form without special precautions except against mechanical fracture, which applies equally to other ceramics and building bricks. Since mild steel plate is usually needed to concentrate the flux, this can also serve as a means for greatly increasing the overall strength of a large magnet assembly which will be held together with the powerful attractive forces of the magnetic flux. Hence, to the economic merits of cheap raw materials and manufacturing process can be added those of construction and assembly, so that it is now a practical proposition to build permanent magnets of any desired size.

A similar position is developing in regard to rotating magnets. Relatively large flat ferrite rings and discs weighing several pounds or kilograms are now being produced in the powerful oriented grades with axial direction of magnetization. A number of these can be assembled on one shaft with circular poleplates that can also serve as mounting and reinforcing discs, so that the assembly can operate at considerably higher speeds than are possible with any kind of conventional rotor with complex and vulnerable windings. Instead of heat being generated where it is most difficult to dissipate, the rotating permanent magnet unit will provide constant flux indefinitely without temperature rise, and could indeed be employed also to cool the stator circuit.

Power station generators, among the most efficient machines in use today, consist of rotating electromagnets in which less than 1% of the power output is used for their excitation owing to their great size. As the size of electrical machines is reduced, this proportion steadily increases so that small units of a few kilowatts capacity absorb in losses nearly as much power as they hand on in useful form and this applies especially to the d.c. motor which is an essential part of electric traction projects for small vehicles. This has been the main obstacle to progress in what could prove a vast market and the part that new magnets could play is already becoming apparent. Ferrite magnets are being used as substitutes for the fixed wound fields in small d.c. machines with resulting improvement in efficiency of 10 to 15% although, as already noted, this is not the best way to use this new material. The magnetic circuit is of incorrect shape and proportions while it is difficult and uneconomic to produce ferrite in this circular segment form. This calls for a new kind of design based on both magnetic and mechanical properties of the magnetic materials with highest coercivity and is described fully in Chapter 8.

Although most of the later chapters deal with practical uses of ferrite magnets, this is because they are commercially available in high-coercivity grades with good mechanical properties. But this account of the present and future possibilities of magnetic materials has indicated the wide area of research and development that exists in mechanical as well as magnetic strengths, thanks to the inherent subdivided structure by which the highest coercivity and stability levels are attained. It is possible that a combination of the merits of both micropowders and ferrites can be produced with good saturation level as well as high coercivity and resistivity, coupled with great mechanical strength and tenacity. This would have a profound effect upon the design of small high-efficiency electrical machines and equipment.

2.10 References

Many textbooks cover the ground of this chapter but the following are written exclusively with use of the new M.K.S.A. system of units:—

1. Morley A. & Hughes E. *Principles of Electricity*, 8th Edn., Longmans, 1958.

2. Molloy & Say (Editors). *Electrical Engineers' Reference Book*, 9th Edn., Newnes, 1959.

3. Say M. G. (Ed). *Magnetic Alloys & Ferrites*, 6 Authors. Newnes, London, 1954.

HISTORICAL SURVEY

Starting from the earliest records of lodestone used for navigation, this survey describes the history of the permanent magnet, the development of dynamic electricity which led to the electromagnet, and the inventions arising from it. These expanded into what is now electrical engineering, which created a demand for special magnetic materials that have been developed during the present century. This account ends at 1950 when the first new moulded magnets were being introduced, at a time when the reasons for magnetic performance were being clarified and when the M.K.S.A. units were internationally adopted. A brief summary of metallic magnetic materials is thus included in this chapter, with special reference to permanent magnets.

3.1 Outline

The long history of practical magnetism and its association with electricity may be divided into five eras, conveniently terminated in centuries or half-centuries. The first two, up to 1800, comprise most of recorded history when the two subjects were regarded as independent of each other with no practical value, with the outstanding exception of the mariner's compass. The latter's success inspired amateur experimenters to explore the mysteries of static magnetism and electricity which in time was extended from static charges to continuous current produced by chemical action in a battery. In a short time this led to the discovery that magnetism is produced by flow of electricity, and to the invention of the electromagnet which enabled current to be converted into mechanical power. Then methods for converting mechanical energy into electricity on any scale were devised and this created a demand for special magnetic materials much later.

The sequence of these five eras may be summarized:—

I. Up to 1600. Naturally magnetized lodestone starts the development of the mariner's compass which leads to world exploration.

II. 1600 to 1800. The effect of these discoveries promotes wide-spread interest and experiment in static magnetism and electro-statics.

III. 1800 to 1850. Dynamic electricity, first made by Volta's Pile, leads to practical electromagnetism, the means for converting mechanical into electrical energy and the reverse, by various forms of electromagnet.

IV. 1850 to 1900. Applications of electromagnets to machines lead to electric power supply and electric traction, for which the electrical engineering industry is formed.

V. 1900 to 1950. Fixed power networks become universal but electric traction (mobile power) is relatively a failure. Magnetic material developments reveal immense possibilities in permanent magnets.

The history of each of these eras is now summarized, with the fourth being described in separate sections for electric machines and electric traction, owing to their importance to this general subject. The whole chapter is given in the form of a chronological chart (Fig. 3.1) with a linear scale, necessarily suppressed for the first two periods. The degree of activity is indicated by shading the scale, in order to show how strongly this fluctuates, with scientific discoveries leading to inventions that start great industries. The size of the latter then acts as a deterrent to the introduction of fundamental improvements, but strongly encourages developments in its essential materials and production methods. This is enhanced by major world events and the effect of the two world wars on the initiation of magnetic developments, for example, is most striking. Events caused the electrical industry to take over this kind of work in some cases from the steel industry and the direction of progress was altered into quite different technologies, such as ceramics and powder metallurgy.

The great importance of history when studying the applications of novel and unfamiliar substances to traditional and established designs is illustrated here in many directions. Recent developments in liquid metals have led to to the first commercial application of the Faraday Disc machine and others, described later, are being designed with ferrite magnets. New semi-conductors have led to thermoelectric generators, and recent work on fuel cells is also a revival of discoveries made over a century ago and which have hitherto remained dormant as power converters. In mechanical engineering the gas turbine is an example of a long-established principle that had to wait for appropriate materials in the form of high temperature alloys, a very exacting metallurgical requirement. Few technical subjects have been so much retarded by their history as magnetism and the lessons to be learned from this aspect are all the more important in the study of future progress of its applications.

3.2 Magnets in Early Navigation

References to magnetism go back to the earliest records of Chinese and Greek philosophers and scribes who were curious and expressed wonder at the ability of natural magnetite, found in their countries in the magnetized state, to attract pieces of iron with a force that could not be detected by any of the senses. But necessity seems to have been the spur even at this early period, for this magnetized rock was known as 'lodestone' which is clearly associated with the lodestar, the chief form of navigation since prehistoric times. The Chinese are said to have used the lodestone in this way for crossing the vast land mass adjoining their country as early as the 9th century B.C. and later to have adapted it to the steering of 'south-seeking chariots'. This primitive form of compass appears to have consisted of a lump of lodestone floated on wood in a vessel of water as a result of accidental discovery; it could be readily carried and set up for use and operated by anyone without requiring skill.

The lodestone seems to have inspired poets and religious leaders, for it is mentioned in Homer and by Solomon and later by St. Augustine, but the most significant early record was made by Thales (of Miletus in Greece about 600 B.C.) who is now regarded as the first philosopher in history. The classical name for lodestone, 'magnes', was the origin of our magnet and associated words; it came from Magnesia, the district of Thessaly in Asia Minor where appreciable amounts of magnetite were found, magnetized by some terrestrial force such as lightning in the distant past. The Greeks recorded the power of this lodestone of attracting iron pieces but could not explain why they sometimes follow it and at other times fly away from it.

Metallic iron had first been produced in that country by the Hittites some centuries earlier by the high temperature reduction of an iron oxide such as magnetite, so its association with a naturally magnetized piece of lodestone could well have been observed at a very early date, but without the means for recording the fact until the arrival of Greek civilization. The next great step towards the construction of a more universal design of compass, however, was not recorded until many centuries later in the year A.D. 121 when a Chinese dictionary describes a way for magnetizing iron by methodically stroking it with a lodestone.

By this time much skill had been accumulated throughout the known parts of the world in the handling and shaping of iron, with its great and growing importance for tools and weapons, so that magnets made from it could be produced in any required size and shape. This contrasted strongly with the difficulty of shaping and handling irregular lumps of rock-like substance with its random inclusions and uneven structure, but with an appropriate pole formation this lodestone could readily be employed to magnetize thin bars or needles of iron. The mechanical working required to make them in these shapes would impart the necessary degree of hardness for the metal to retain enough magnetism for reasonable service and life as an independent permanent magnet. By the third century A.D. the suspended compass needle was in limited use for navigation at sea, though most ships at that time relied upon routes within sight of land.

During the following centuries the primitive compass became known to travellers in many parts of the world but the first detailed account of it was given by Peter Peregrinus, a French crusader of wide interests, in 1269. He described a floating compass and also a recent improvement of his day, a pivoted type with 360° scale marked with the N S E W points. He used a compass for plotting the position of the poles in nearly spherical lodestone, which represented a great advance in the study of magnetism, indicating the existence and direction of the lines of force but without attempting to explain the reason for them. By this time the compass had reached the stage of a reliable instrument that could be used in the worst conditions at sea, so that it was now possible for sailors and explorers to travel over the whole surface of the globe with its aid.

The compass was an essential factor in the celebrated voyage of Columbus to America which crossed the region of the Atlantic ocean where there are appreciable differences in polestar bearings and magnetic north, causing consternation to his mariners. But he appears to have been aware of this and was able to avoid the dislocation that would otherwise have happened. This is a measure of the confidence that must then have been general among seafaring men of that time in the mariner's compass, though there was no explanation of the magnetic force which operated it. This was thought to be 'effluvia'

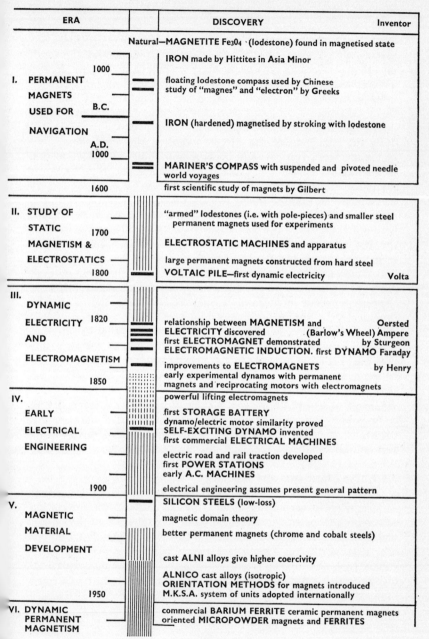

ERA		DISCOVERY	Inventor
		Natural—MAGNETITE Fe$_3$O$_4$ · (lodestone) found in magnetised state	
I. PERMANENT MAGNETS USED FOR NAVIGATION — 1000 B.C. A.D. 1000 1600		IRON made by Hittites in Asia Minor	
		floating lodestone compass used by Chinese study of "magnes" and "electron" by Greeks	
		IRON (hardened) magnetised by stroking with lodestone	
		MARINER'S COMPASS with suspended and pivoted needle world voyages	
		first scientific study of magnets by Gilbert	
II. STUDY OF STATIC MAGNETISM & ELECTROSTATICS 1700 1800		"armed" lodestones (i.e. with pole-pieces) and smaller steel permanent magnets used for experiments	
		ELECTROSTATIC MACHINES and apparatus	
		large permanent magnets constructed from hard steel	
		VOLTAIC PILE—first dynamic electricity	Volta
III. DYNAMIC ELECTRICITY AND ELECTROMAGNETISM 1820 1850		relationship between MAGNETISM and ELECTRICITY discovered	Oersted
		(Barlow's Wheel)	Ampere
		first ELECTROMAGNET demonstrated	by Sturgeon
		ELECTROMAGNETIC INDUCTION. first DYNAMO	Faraday
		improvements to ELECTROMAGNETS	by Henry
		early experimental dynamos with permanent magnets and reciprocating motors with electromagnets	
IV. EARLY ELECTRICAL ENGINEERING 1900		powerful lifting electromagnets	
		first STORAGE BATTERY	
		dynamo/electric motor similarity proved	
		SELF-EXCITING DYNAMO invented	
		first commercial ELECTRICAL MACHINES	
		electric road and rail traction developed	
		first POWER STATIONS	
		early A.C. MACHINES	
		electrical engineering assumes present general pattern	
V. MAGNETIC MATERIAL DEVELOPMENT 1950		SILICON STEELS (low-loss)	
		magnetic domain theory	
		better permanent magnets (chrome and cobalt steels)	
		cast ALNI alloys give higher coercivity	
		ALNICO cast alloys (isotropic)	
		ORIENTATION METHODS for magnets introduced	
		M.K.S.A. system of units adopted internationally	
VI. DYNAMIC PERMANENT MAGNETISM		commercial BARIUM FERRITE ceramic permanent magnets oriented MICROPOWDER magnets and FERRITES	

Fig. 3.1 Historical Development of Electromagnetism in relation to Magnetic Materials.

surrounding the magnetized needle which led to many superstitions such as the banning of garlic and onions from the food of the ship's navigators. The long voyages in open sea culminated in the circum-navigation of the world by Magellan and Drake. This led to a detailed investigation into all aspects of terrestrial magnetism, which showed the importance of the measurement of the dip, or inclination, of the needle at different parts of the globe.

By the beginning of the sixteenth century the great importance of the mariner's compass had become well known to a wide section of the public and was well expressed by Francis Bacon in the words quoted at the beginning of Chapter 1. In 1567 a compass factory was opened in London docks, which made a general type with dip compensated by small weights fixed to the needle and a special type with horizontal shaft for the measurement of dip. This appears to be the first industrial or commercial activity associated with electricity or magnetism and is a further indication of the practical importance that these subjects were starting to assume. It is therefore natural, in an age when the mind as well as the person was breaking free from the restrictions of past centuries, that educated men should start to investigate the obscure and invisible forces which had a profound effect on their daily lives. This was clearly a subject that lent itself to practical experiment and an open mind, and it is thus not surprising that the next great advance in the knowledge of this subject should be made by a physician during the renowned first Elizabethan era in the neighbourhood of London.

Gilbert of Colchester refuted all the superstitions associated with compasses by a series of practical tests and laid down all the essentials for the practical understanding of magnetism, which were to remain substantially unaltered for the following two centuries.

3.2 Static Magnetism and Electricity

Gilbert's famous book *De Magnete* was published in the year 1600 and so forms an appropriate bridge between the navigation era and the independent experiment era. Though most of the subject matter related to practical magnetism based on accumulated experience associated with compasses, the book also dealt with electrostatics. In spite of the fact that both subjects were similar, representing 'action at a distance' by invisible forces that could be detected only by their results, they were not otherwise considered to be in any way connected or associated together. The ancient Greeks noted that amber, when suitably rubbed, attracted light objects such as small pieces of paper, which was similar to the effect of lodestone on iron filings, and our word 'electric' is derived from their word for amber. They did not obtain the equivalent of attraction and repulsion, however, and Gilbert is thought to be the first who discovered that glass and sulphur also could be electrified by rubbing, but with different kinds of charge.

Many eminent men of his time immediately recognised the great importance of Gilbert's book, though it took several years for some of his conclusions to be generally accepted, such as the fact that the Earth is a gigantic magnet in whose field all other freely-suspended magnets will orientate. The power of the magnet was concentrated at the poles and, since like poles repel and unlike poles attract, the north pole of the compass must really be the north-seeking pole. The power of attraction in magnetism was limited to iron and was not brought about by rubbing, whereas electric charges attracted a variety of substances and did not have this unique kind of pole formation. It is thus possible to understand that at this historical period before modern scientific methods had been developed, the differences between magnetism and electricity were more prominent than their similarities. The founder of the new scientific approach was Galileo, a contemporary of Gilbert who published his main work some years later and who seems to have formed a high opinion of the value of Gilbert's book. Although both men are justly famous for their discoveries, their introduction of experimental method into the hostile climate of tradition and superstition is probably of even greater ultimate value.

One of Gilbert's important inventions was the 'arming' of lodestones by fitting them with soft iron caps at the poles to improve their effectiveness in lifting weights. By this method (Fig. 3.2 a) he was able to increase their lifting power by as much as five times, from 4 to 20 ounces, and this is the forerunner of the use of pole pieces for concentrating the magnetic flux, since the attractive force depends on the square of the flux density. He also noted, however, that the use of these armed or capped lodestones does not improve their power of attraction at a distance. He took great interest in the quality of steel or iron used for his experiments, their main use for weapons or tools and their metallurgical history. The magnets he made, described as being as thick as a goosequill and 8 to 12 inches long, were magnetized by lodestone using his 'single touch' method; the pole being placed on the middle of the needle and slowly drawn to the end, accompanied by gentle rubbing. Gilbert also discovered that steel can be magnetized in the Earth's field by forging or wire-drawing operations carried out with correct orientation.

Most of the experimental work carried out on magnetism during the following two centuries was limited to the improvement of the

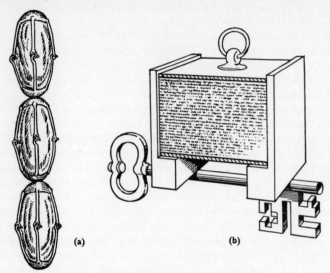

(a)   (b)

Fig. 3.2 First Magnets with Pole Pieces.
(a) Gilbert's "Armed" Lodestones 1600.
(b) Dalencé's Shaped Lodestone. 1687.

lifting power of magnets and to the effectiveness of magnetizing methods. But two developments are of special interest in view of the recent applications of ferrite magnets. In 1687 Dalencé described a method for shaping lodestone into rectangular blocks and fitting flat iron poleplates at the ends (Fig. 3.2 b) which was a great improvement on Gilbert's method in terms of lifting power. In the middle of the following century one of the leading authorities on magnets, Gowin Knight, produced the first moulded magnet on record from bonded iron oxide. He oxidized iron filings in water and made a paste of the oxide with linseed oil, placed the paste in a heated mould so that it formed a strong compact which could then be magnetized by use of the most powerful magnet then available. The limitation of the latter would have meant that this novel kind of oxide material could not be used to full advantage in those days.

During these 17th and 18th centuries most of the work was directed to the practical improvement of steel magnets by such methods as compound construction. Savary in 1730 used bundles of 1 mm. wire about 80 mm. long fitted with soft iron pole pieces, assembled into large compound magnets nearly half a metre long. Although magnetized from lodestone, these were found to have acquired greater strength than their source of magnetism and this posed a problem which has only been fully answered in recent times. But some of the other unusual features of magnetism had been studied and partially explained in earlier times; for example, Boyle in 1675 had observed that heat can destroy magnetism in iron without change in the metal, so he deduced that the magnetic effect was derived from its internal disposition or constitution.

Magnets were now being made of considerable size and the most important is the Christie horseshoe magnet (used much later at the Royal Society by Faraday in his famous experiment with the rotating copper disc). This was first made by Gowin Knight in the middle of the 18th Century in the form of a 'magnetic magazine' and was assembled from 240 rectangular steel bars each $15 \times 1 \times \frac{1}{2}$ inches. In its original form these were built into two equal parts about 5 feet long, each mounted upon a trolley, and each bar was magnetized by some variant of Gilbert's single or multiple 'touch' methods by use of lodestone or else a hard steel intermediate magnet. By this time there was a considerable demand from wealthy experimenters for magnets and Knight had built up an appreciable European market for what was an expensive commodity.

The figure of merit for these early magnets was simple and effective, the ratio of lifted load to the weight of the magnet. Knight's products weighed about a pound and lifted around 12 times their own weight, but for smaller magnets this ratio could be up to 28. The invention of the electromagnet in 1825 led to much better and faster methods of magnetization but improvements in the construction of permanent magnets continued for a further 50 years or more. In 1875 Janin made a U-shaped magnet, built up from steel strips and shaped pole pieces, that weighed 50 kilograms and lifted half a ton (500 Kgs). But by that time their practical importance had dwindled owing to the superiority of the electrically-operated alternatives which also provided simple and effective control from near or far.

While practical magnetism had made its slow progress during this experimental era, many interesting developments were taking place in applied electrostatics. About half a century after Gilbert, von Guericke made the first electrical machine consisting of a large ball of sulphur which could be rotated on a horizontal axis. This could produce large charges with sparks and enabled him to discover electrical repulsion, and his work was followed up by early Fellows of the Royal Society. Improved machines of this kind gave the first indications of the practical value of electricity in the form of early discharge tubes, and the difference between insulators and conductors soon became apparent. In 1720 Grey showed that electricity could be transmitted over appreciable distances by means of an insulated conductor and a few years later the first electrical instrument, the gold-leaf electroscope, was invented, based on the mutual repulsion of the parts of an electrified conductor. This was analogous to the mutual repulsion of parallel bars of a compound magnet and gave an indication of the similarity between static electricity and magnetism.

At this stage the famous American scientist, Benjamin Franklin, proved the meaning of positive and negative electricity by showing that when glass is rubbed with silk there is transference of electricity from glass to silk. Priestley and Coulomb then proved that the force between charges varies inversely as the square of the distance between them. This is the same relationship as the gravitational force between massive bodies which is only in the positive sense, without the equivalent of electric repulsion. In 1750 Mitchell discovered an inverse square law for the force between magnetic poles, but acting with repulsion as well as attraction; so the similarity with electro-statics had become very marked, and this was confirmed by the mathematical theories of Poisson. Franklin's work on the lightning conductor had brought what had been widely regarded as a super-natural force under a degree of human control, and a small scale version could be produced by electrical machines with associated Leyden Jars. So there were many pointers towards some kind of unification of these varied natural phenomena.

The next step was the accidental production of intermittent electricity from the chemical action of metals and weak acids by Galvani. This was actively pursued by Volta who produced the first source of continuous current in his Voltaic Pile at the end of the 18th century.

3.3 Dynamic Electricity and Electromagnetism
Though it took the first two decades of the 19th century to produce a reliable source of continuous current from electro-

chemical methods, the principles were relatively simple and could be set up by many investigators who became interested in these important developments. Although there was now an impressive array of facts and methods for exploring the similarity and connection between magnetism and electricity, it took the Danish professor Oersted about a dozen years to 1820 to achieve a positive proof. Current from a voltaic pile passed along a conductor held over and parallel to a compass needle caused the needle to be deflected, and a reversal of the current resulted in a reversal of the deflection. This showed that the current flow produced a magnetic field with a directional association between them. The publication of this experiment immediately set off an unprecedented volume of discovery and invention culminating

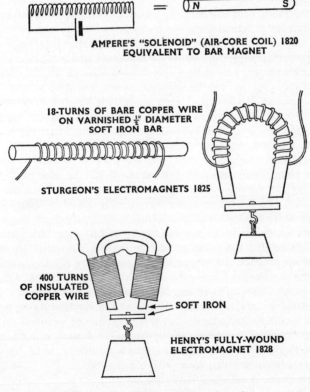

AMPERE'S "SOLENOID" (AIR-CORE COIL) 1820
EQUIVALENT TO BAR MAGNET

18-TURNS OF BARE COPPER WIRE
ON VARNISHED ½" DIAMETER
SOFT IRON BAR

STURGEON'S ELECTROMAGNETS 1825

400 TURNS
OF INSULATED
COPPER WIRE

SOFT IRON

HENRY'S FULLY-WOUND
ELECTROMAGNET 1828

Fig. 3.3 First Electromagnets 1820-28.

with Faraday's historic work on electromagnetic induction in 1831, but the first result was the practical proof by Ampere that a long thin coil of wire acts like a bar magnet when carrying a current of electricity (Fig. 3.3). This was the foundation of electromagnetism and all future practical developments start from this point.

Ampere did experiments to prove that two parallel wires will attract each other if carrying current in opposing directions and repel if the current through them flows in the same direction, and explained the results in terms of the magnetic fields they create. Schweigger showed that the effectiveness of Oersted's experiment could be multiplied a hundred-fold if a coil of 100 turns is wound round the compass needle and this led to the first sensitive current measuring instrument, called the *galvanometer*. Schweigger's 'multiplier' was of wide importance in showing for the first time how the comparatively weak magnetic field surrounding a current-carrying wire can be concentrated for practical purposes by means of multi-turn coils which were later to become the hallmark of electrical engineering.

The most significant invention for the future was that of the electromagnet by Sturgeon in 1825, which showed how the lifting power of a current-carrying coil can be enormously magnified by winding it on a soft iron bar. His first tests were made with $\frac{1}{2}$ inch bar wound with 18 turns of stout uncovered copper wire, the bar being first varnished to provide insulation. A horseshoe shaped core lifted the greatest weight; this electromagnet weighed only 7 ounces and yet it lifted 20 times its own weight, at once equalling the best permanent magnets of the time. Here was the first example of the electro-chemical energy of the voltaic cell being converted into the mechanical work associated with the lifting of a load, with the use of relatively simple equipment (Fig. 3.3).

However, the most important aspect of this experiment was not fully appreciated for some years. Unlike the constant flux of the permanent magnet, the magnetic field created by the electromagnet could be controlled from zero up to the maximum that the iron would carry. Also, with limited additions, it was possible to arrange the control at any convenient point, ultimately leading to remote control and remote indication, the forerunner of automation. But the first practical uses were the electric bell and many other kinds of electric signalling and telegraphs which could be built up on a considerable commercial scale with the limited current provided by the early primary cells and batteries.

The first results of Sturgeon's work were naturally directed to the historic lifting magnet applications in which the significance was immediately apparent, and most of the improvements in this direction were due to the American physicist, Joseph Henry. Using batteries with nearly half a square foot of plate area in half a pint of dilute sulphuric acid, he produced lifting powers of 60 up to 2000 pounds with a ratio of nearly 40:1. The English physicist, J. P. Joule, in 1836 at the age of 18 started to investigate electromagnets, with the idea of making electric motors supersede the steam engine, on the false assumption that their strength could be increased indefinitely, but he raised their lifting power ratio to over 100 and found that the work produced by a pound of expensive battery zinc was equivalent to that given by a pound of cheap coal in a Watt engine. This was the start of his renowned work on the mechanical equivalent of heat, and led to the Law of Conservation of Energy which was to prove of such outstanding importance to all forms of engineering.

In these numerous experiments on electromagnets supplied with current from the various kinds of cell becoming available, it took some time to base the electrical design of the coil on the properties of the associated battery. What is now known as a high resistance coil was termed an 'intensity magnet' and a low resistance coil was a 'quantity magnet' for which it was found that a heavy wire must be used. Practical experience soon showed that there was a limit to the number of turns that could be used, the effectiveness of multi-layer windings becoming less as their diameter increased. (The familiar system of electrical units—amperes, volts, ohms etc.—was not adopted until 1881 when industrial uses had become common, and it was one of the reasons for their rapid progress.) On the other hand the significance of magnetic leakage flux in electromagnets, and also in permanent magnets, was not fully understood for nearly a century.

Though this extensive work on electromagnets and their direct applications gave experimenters a useful insight into the value of electromagnetism, the full importance was not appreciated until after the publication in 1831 of Faraday's three famous experiments relating to electromagnetic induction. Faraday was one of many gifted men who were immediately impressed with the great scientific and technical possibilities opened up by the discoveries of Oersted and Ampere but much of his early work was directed towards the means for producing continuous current. About ten years later he became more interested in the use of the current, especially in electromagnets, and this led to rapid results. In view of the practical basis of this historic survey, Faraday's three experiments are summarized under the headings of the important branches of electrical engineering which later grew from this work:—

(*a*) *Transformer*. A soft iron ring 6 inches in diameter was wound with two coils, one on each half of its periphery. Current from a cell passed through the first coil caused a galvanometer connected to the second to deflect, but only whilst the current was being switched on or switched off.

(*b*) *Alternator*. A natural (lodestone or magnetite) bar magnet 8 inches long that could slide closely inside a hollow paper cylinder, wound with a coil connected to a galvanometer, caused the latter to be deflected only when the magnet was pushed into, or pulled out of, the coil.

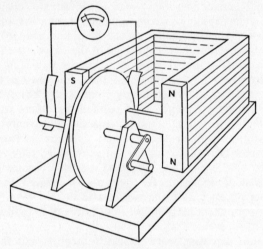

Fig. 3.4 Faraday's Disc Machine, 1831.
(Low Voltage D.C. Generator).

(*c*) *Dynamo*. A copper disc 12 inches diameter and one-eighth inch thick, rotated between the poles of a large permanent magnet (described above in 3.2), generated current collected between metal brushes bearing respectively on the disc's outer edge and on the shaft. In this case the current, indicated by the continuous deflection of a galvanometer connected across the two brushes, could be maintained while the disc was being rotated (Fig. 3.4).

These experiments proved conclusively the dynamic nature of electromagnetism, in that there must be relative movement between magnetic flux and an electrical conductor, in order to produce current or dynamic electricity. It is also interesting to note the contrast between them in apparatus used. The first uses direct conversion of chemical energy into electromagnetism, the second converts the energy of the movement of a ferrite magnet into a fluctuating current, and the third converts rotary movement into continuous current by the agency of a hard steel permanent magnet. In the last two experiments the energy came from the action of the experimenter.

Faraday had already demonstrated earlier that a vertical wire carrying current from a cell will rotate around one pole of a vertical bar magnet surrounded with a trough of mercury into which the lower end of the wire is lightly dipped. This arrangement was later made sensitive enough to move in the Earth's field. It was the first indication that continuous movement can be generated by the flow of current and hence may be regarded as the first electric motor; so this remarkable man can be said to have started all the main branches of electrical engineering without realizing the practical significance, which was beyond his sphere of scientific experiment. But his work was being done while the world's first railways were being built in England, and many able men were ready to follow up the practical aspects in a new climate of public interest. Technical advances were now moving outside factories and mines to influence the daily lives of the whole population.

3.4 Electromagnetic Machines

The first device which rotated on a shaft and should thus be regarded as the forerunner of the electric motor was Barlow's Wheel of 1822, made shortly before Sturgeon's invention of the electromagnet and some years before Faraday's above-mentioned experiments on electromagnetic induction. This little machine consisted of a metal star cut from thick sheet and fixed to a horizontal shaft so that its lower part could rotate between the poles of a horseshoe magnet. The points of the star just dipped into a trough of mercury connected to one pole of a battery, the other being joined electrically to the shaft. Thus a current flowed along each arm of the star in turn, and it rotated by the force of the magnetic field created by the current acting upon the field of the permanent magnet. (Fig. 3.5). Barlow's Wheel can be regarded as the motor version of the better known Faraday Disc low voltage dynamo already described,

6

and modern versions of these in combination are discussed in detail in Chapter 8.

The great force of attraction of Sturgeon's electromagnet inspired many inventors to adapt it as a practical electric motor and the first machine of this kind was made in 1830 by dal Negro in Padua, using a pawl and ratchet mechanism to convert the linear into rotary motion. Sturgeon two years later produced his 'electromagnetic engine' consisting of four fixed coils wound on iron bars mounted vertically at the corners of a square wooden frame. Four corresponding armatures fixed at the ends of arms attached to a vertical shaft were intermittently attracted to the fixed electromagnets by current passed when contact was made at suitably located mercury pools, so that a continuous rotary movement was imparted to the shaft. A somewhat similar set of electromagnets, but with a horizontal shaft and commutator, was devised by Froment in 1845, and seven years later Tobler made the electromagnet equivalent of multi-cylinder reciprocating engine. These designs were all based upon the famous steam-engine pattern and were mainly intended for traction purposes, described in the following section. It is now clear that they could not be operated economically with electric current supplied from available batteries but had to wait for machine-produced electricity many

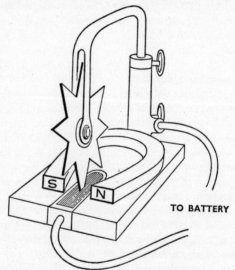

TO BATTERY

Fig. 3.5 Barlow's Wheel, 1822-23.

years later. Only then did it become apparent that such machines would produce rotational power without the need for reciprocating mechanisms, so the main history of electrical machines then merges into the account of the development of the dynamo.

The first 'magneto-electric machine' appears to be that exhibited by Pixii in Paris about 1831. It consisted of a horseshoe magnet rotated by a hand-crank on a vertical shaft so that its poles pass close to the ends of two fixed electromagnets with soft iron cores, the magnetic circuit being almost closed twice each revolution. At first this produced alternating current which was of little value at that time, so that it was modified later to give direct current by the addittion of a primitive kind of commutator suggested by Ampere. The current fluctuated appreciably but this defect was cured by the introduction of the familiar two-part commutator by Sturgeon. In 1833 Saxton used multiple coils and magnets to make a larger machine and this seems to have produced direct current successfully.

Attempts to produce current from practical versions of Faraday's Disc machine, which produced unfluctuating direct current without the complication of a commutator, were limited by the very low voltage that available magnets and speeds of rotation would give. This design was the equivalent of a single turn armature winding, whereas there was no theoretical limit to the number of turns in the equivalent of electromagnets used in machines which generated alternating current, which was then converted to direct current by the commutator. The problem of transmitting electric power dominated electrical machine design, and limited it to what are basically a.c. machines, until the past decade. But there has always remained the conviction among many designers that the simpler Faraday Disc would ultimately be used as the only true d.c. machine.

The first practical use of a dynamo appears to have been electro-medical. Clarke in 1836 wanted to obtain the highest possible voltage and introduced a method of intermittently breaking the circuit, an effect used later in magneto ignition. Electroplating was one of the earliest applications of direct current from batteries and the demand for greater output turned the manufacturers' attention to dynamos. What is now considered to be the earliest commercial dynamo installation was designed by Woolrich and in 1844 installed in Birmingham where it ran successfully for many years. It consisted of a circular bank of cylindrical electromagnets with associated commutator driven to rotate between the poles of a number of large steel horse-shoe magnets installed in a wooden frame. An important feature aimed to maintain uniformity of current was the provision of more coils than magnets, this application being sensitive to current fluctuations which are absent in battery supplies of direct current.

By the middle of the last century the use of the dynamo was sufficiently well established in this general pattern, of fixed permanent magnet field and rotating coils with commutator, that attention was directed to greater output and higher efficiency. In 1856 the shuttle armature was invented by Siemens in Germany which enabled much higher rotational speeds to be used. This was a deliberate departure from the known high efficiency of circular coils to an elongated rectangular shape which greatly improved the magnetic circuit. Earlier tests had shown that the field of the permanent magnet could be augmented by winding coils on the poles and passing current in the right direction, and in 1867 Siemens showed that the use of permanent magnets was not essential for converting mechanical into electrical energy.

This led to a number of inventors in that year claiming to have originated the self-excited dynamo, which gave prospects of machines with much larger output. The difference between the weak fields of the best steel magnets and electromagnets with enough excitation current and turns to bring soft iron towards the saturation limit, was very considerable; and there was less need for long magnetic circuits essential for low-coercivity materials, though this point was not established until many years later by Hopkinson. This extension of the use of electromagnets was probably the greatest engineering advance in this subject and became so universal that few now know that permanent magnets are a possible alternative for the excitation of electromagnetic machines.

The problem of instability of output was still difficult, however, and was solved on a practical scale by the Gramme ring armature in 1870 which started the commercial manufacture of these machines in various countries. Apart from the improvements of the drum armature, the dynamo had reached the stage in which it has remained in terms of basic design up to the present day. Permanent magnet machines continued in use for special purposes up to the end of the last century, mainly for lighthouses lit by electricity where reliability and efficiency were more important than low cost and small size. The first Holmes machine of this type weighed 2 tons with overall dimensions $5 \times 5 \times 4\frac{1}{2}$ feet, contained 120 coils and 36 large compound steel magnets, and was driven by a steam-engine of $2\frac{1}{2}$ hp. This shows how large a low-power electric machine must be when low grade permanent magnets are used.

In view of the importance paid earlier to the lifting ability of the many magnets becoming available, this test was applied to machines with electromagnetic excitation with results that were difficult to explain at that time. A small machine in 1867 excited by a permanent magnet could produce enough current to lift 40 lbs with an electromagnet. If used to excite a larger dynamo to give current that would provide the field magnetic flux for a third and still larger machine, the output could be used to power a large electromagnet able to lift as much as 25 tons. This was 1400 times the load lifted by the first machine, and this is readily explained today in terms of the mechanical power, or its equivalent, required to drive each machine. Magnetism is an intermediate factor or agent in the transfer of power.

These investigations gave an important indication of the fact that there is no upper limit to the power that can be converted by electromagnetic machines if the mechanical problems can be mastered, and this is the basis of the modern power station with a highly efficient and compact machine producing as much as 500MW of 50c/s a.c. power from a vast array of boilers and fuel-handling plant with a capacity of around a million horsepower. All the magnetic flux for this power-conversion link is produced by a relatively insignificant d.c. generator giving the equivalent power of a railway locomotive.

It is beyond the scope of this survey to give further details of the rapid development of fixed a.c. power networks throughout the major industrial countries of the world. Their outstanding success is indicated by the difficulty in meeting increases in demand despite recent gluts of fossil fuels, but it froze progress to a limited pattern. It has been widely noted that important basic developments in electrical engineering stopped about the year 1900.

3.5 Electric Traction

The potentially great, but hitherto limited, uses of electric traction are dependent upon the availability of suitable machines, particularly d.c. motors, and this subject is so prominent in later chapters that a special section is allocated here to its history. It has already been noted that this subject, unlike the unvarying expansion of fixed power supply networks, reaches an early zenith at the beginning of this century and then steadily declines, though electrical batteries and equipment continue to play an important but subsidiary part to the internal combustion engine for starting and lighting, and numerous auxiliary functions.

The first uses of electric motors in traction appear about 1840 with Davidson applying the reciprocating electromagnet design already described to railway trucks using battery power. This propelled a 5 ton load at 4 mph. and this was later improved to 12 tons at speeds up to 18 mph. A year earlier Jacobi in Russia had propelled 12 passengers in a boat powered by a similar kind of motor of 1hp. at 4 km/hr. ($2\frac{1}{2}$ mph.) using 128 Grove cells. There were other examples of similar kind which, from later knowledge, had little prospect of commercial success until the work of Pacinotti in 1860 showed that a dynamo would run as an electric motor with better performance than the reciprocating mechanisms based on steam engine practice. Ten years later, supplies of suitable motors as well as generators began to appear and a great variety of tests were made on both road and rail vehicles. Direct current power could then be made available in required amount, either for direct transmission to tracked vehicles or in storage batteries for road use.

In 1879 Siemens & Halske demonstrated the first electric railway in Berlin which carried a total of over 100,000 passengers with great success. It was found that improved insulation was needed under wet conditions, the track having a centre rail connected to a 130 volt d.c. supply, with return by the running rails. In the following year Edison opened a similar kind of experimental railway one-third of a mile long, and reached speeds of 40 mph. with 12 hp. motors using series field control. During the 1880s the first commercial passenger tramways, underground railway and battery-operated road vehicles appeared, and there seemed to be excellent prospects for railway electrification, although there were formidable transmission problems ahead. This led to an investigation into various novel kinds of a.c. traction motors, because d.c. machines give starting and sparking difficulties if fed with alternating current, and special modifications are needed to minimize the added losses, hysteresis and eddy current, in the stator.

By 1890 a 3-phase machine of 100 hp. was demonstrated and in the following years single phase motors were commercially developed, which started what was called the battle of the systems for railway electrification. This was primarily a choice between the excellent motor performance of d.c. machines for this use versus the advantages of a.c. transmission; the latter was better for long distances yet d.c. traction excelled for suburban and city conditions. But a.c.

traction can be used in either single or three-phase form, with the choice between easy or complex overhead wiring balanced against motor performance and economic factors; special power supplies of one-third or half the power distribution frequency were used to give the required speed level and control. With the added plant and complication these alternatives presented, it was never possible to give a uniform answer to new requirements. Consequently, even after some efforts towards standardization, there are today more than a dozen main alternative systems in use throughout the world, about equally divided into a.c. and d.c. supplies.

However, as in the case of magnetic materials, the middle of this century became a turning point, in that agreement was reached on the best system for the future, by employing the most valuable features of the various alternatives. A.c. supply from the national network is transformed to 25,000 V. for the track overhead wiring in single phase; on the locomotives or trains it is transformed and rectified to an appropriate voltage d.c. supply for feeding to multiple motors, using recently developed static rectifiers of various kinds. But by this time electric rail traction was faced with strong competitors in large diesel engines and gas-turbines with either a d.c. drive or, more recently, with lighter and cheaper hydraulic transmission.

Electric tramways in this country became well established in all the larger centres of population towards the end of the last century and expanded to over 250 undertakings, but nearly all were abandoned by 1950 though some lingered on as trolley buses. Much of this obsolescence is the result of congestion caused by any form of tracked transport in busy streets mixed up with all kinds of motor vehicles as well as pedestrians. The great lesson that now appears to be learnt is the necessity for track transport to be isolated so that it can yield its greatest asset, the carriage of high-density traffic at high average speeds; under these conditions electric propulsion operates at greatest advantage, which the scrapping of tramways and certain railway electrification schemes has done nothing to alter.

The battery-operated road vehicle had an even shorter effective life than the electric tram, though it did not entirely disappear from the streets of this country as happened in America. With the differing levels of fuel and electricity costs maintained in European countries there has always been a market for slow-speed delivery vehicles operating over a limited regular route, such as milk rounds, where long life and ease of control are of relatively greater value.

Batteries of the expendable kind were prominent for all purposes up to the middle of last century when the first storage batteries were developed, and these were commercially available as soon as there were practical d.c. motors to operate from them. Hence many kinds of electric road vehicles were being devised in the 1880s, from a tricycle to a town car or brougham. The latter became well known at the end of the century when their numbers exceeded those of petrol-driven alternatives owing to their reliability, silence, cleanliness and lack of fumes, as well as their ease of control and economy. A typical car weighed $1\frac{3}{4}$ tons with battery, ran at 15 to 20 mph. for distances up to 50 miles per charge, and was propelled and partially braked by two 6 hp. electric motors of conventional commutator type. The controller gave 6 forward speeds and one reverse, with handbrake and regenerative braking, some of these facilities not yet available on the latest petrol cars after half a century and astronomical sums of money spent on research and engineering. Moreover, this electric car had no starting problems and the motors only revolved when the vehicle moved. It is not surprising that electric traction appeared to have an assured future at that time.

In case it should be thought that electric cars were limited to their present pedestrian speeds, this kind of vehicle gained the world's road speed record in 1898 at nearly 40 mph in France, and held it for the following five years when it reached 66 mph. By 1903, however, an American named Henry Ford, who had spent a dozen years in the electric supply industry, raised the speed record to over 90 mph. in a car he had made himself, and it was propelled by a petrol engine with mechanical transmission and almost nothing electric in it. His later renowned efforts to make vast numbers of cheap and reliable cars of similar petrol-operated kind effectively removed all electric alternatives from the roads of his country for over 40 years. He must have been in a unique position to make a choice of design and power source between these two alternatives, and in a large country this may have well been decided by the distance travelled for a single 'charge' of fuel or energy.

This brief account of the rise and fall of electric traction contains no valid reason why it should not be ultimately successful, probably in close association with the fuel-operated prime mover which gives so many miles of travel for its limited bulk of fuel. Electric traction is still at the mercy of the commutator motor which is basically the same as when developed in the days of slow-speed steam engines. While excellent in large size, it becomes progressively worse in bulk and cost per unit power, as well as in efficiency, as the size is reduced to that needed for individual vehicle propulsion, and the author's remedy for this case of retarded development lies in the realm of magnetic materials. But their significant advance took place well into the present century, by which period the design of nearly all self-propelled vehicles had, like fixed electric power supply some time earlier, become set into a rigid pattern; however, this time it was all-mechanical.

3.6 Magnetic Materials

The demand for special magnetic materials for the electrical industry did not become appreciable until the end of the last century and early designers had to rely on stock steels made for entirely different uses. Low-loss sheet soon became important with the introduction of production a.c. transformers, motors and generators without means for limiting the iron losses. Investigations were therefore started in Sheffield towards the end of last century and outstanding progress was reported by Hadfield and others on the properties of silicon steels (1902). With only limited reduction in saturation flux density compared with commercial soft iron sheet, the new alloys gave about threefold reduction of losses, hysteresis and eddy current together, on account of a simultaneous deoxidizing action and increase in electrical resistivity. The disadvantage of brittleness was introduced and this has limited practical progress because these materials must be rolled into large thin sheet to construct high permeability magnetic circuits with limited eddy current loss. The latter is restricted by varnishing the sheet, or otherwise coating it with the thinnest possible layer of insulating material which will not appreciably reduce the iron space factor of the assembled magnetic core, so there is a definite limit, technical and economic, to the progress in this direction.

Though the optimum silicon percentage for lowest hysteresis is over 6%, the best available sheet is now about $4\frac{1}{2}\%$ Si and the cheapest about 1% with a variety of stock thicknesses for the many applications. These were achieved after steady production improvements for the first half of the century and the next great advance came with the introduction of cold-rolling and orienting techniques much later.

Permanent magnet materials made a slower start, resulting from shortages of raw materials in the first World War, but have had an increasingly spectacular advance which justifies more detailed description. The only notable improvement over the commercial hard steel used for centuries of early magnets was the introduction in Germany about 1880 of tungsten steel which gave up to 50% improvement in coercivity and, probably more important, improved the structural stability enough to justify a special purpose magnetic material. Though impressive at the time, this improvement was small by later standards and it can be generally assumed that all major advances in the performance of permanent magnets have been achieved during the past 50 years. The first publication of note on their electrical engineering uses was in 1920 by Evershed and methods of quality assessment with organized research were to follow.

It is therefore important to note that permanent magnets, in spite of their ancient history, are a recent engineering development, with little general appreciation of their best performance and properties. These have been attained by the progressive introduction of so many complex alloys that this account will be restricted to about a dozen of the more important, listed with magnetic performance and composition in Table 3.1. These have been chosen from a list of over 60 different alloys available throughout the world in 1948 (ref. 3.4) which had increased to over 250 only nine years later (ref. 3.5). Owing to the fact that magnetic progress has been generally achieved at the expense of mechanical brittleness and material costs, the commercial demand for early materials remained and the user was faced with a growing list of alternatives for which he generally found a choice difficult; hence added comments in the table are intended to provide some explanation.

All early magnets needed elaborate and prolonged ageing treatment to achieve stability for important uses such as measuring instruments, with special precautions for handling and dismantling, but these have been largely superseded in materials with coercivity exceeding about 40 AT/mm or the cast alloy (alnico group) discovered in Japan in 1931. These in oriented form comprise the great majority of all permanent magnets produced today, giving better magnetic performance in equivalent space at competitive cost compared with the conventional kind of electromagnet. They reached this level in commercial quantities by about the middle of this century when the first moulded micropowder and earliest ferrite magnets were starting to appear.

The last four alloys in the table are special owing to their unusual mechanical or magnetic properties, and are commercially available to a limited extent. The first is known as the Heusler alloy after the discoverer in Germany who produced the first permanent magnet

GROUP	MATERIAL	DATE	TYPICAL COMPOSITION (percentage)	MAGNETIC PROPERTY			REMARKS
				COER-CIVITY H_c AT/mm	REMAN-ENCE B_r Wb/m²	ENERGY PROD. (BH) max kJ/m³	
STEELS (machinable)	CARBON STEEL	up to 1880	1%C (balance Fe)	4	0·9	1·6	cheap and fully available
	TUNGSTEN	1880	6W 0·7C 0·4Cr 0·5Co	5	1	2·4	less available
	CHROME	1917	3·5Cr 1C 0·4W 0·2Mn	6	1	2	cheap
	3% COBALT	1921	3Co 1C 9Cr 1·5Mo	10	0·7	3	better alloys of 9% and 15% Co etc.
	35% COBALT	1921	35Co 1C 9Cr 4W	20	0·9	7·5	expensive, owing to high Co content
CAST ALLOYS (brittle)	ALNI	1931	13Al 25Ni 4Cu 58Fe	40	0·6	11	medium cost but un-machinable
	ALNICO	1934	10Al 18Ni 13Co 6Cu 53Fe	41	0·7	13	highest quality isotropic grade
	ORIENTED ALNICO	1941–1950	8Al 14Ni 24Co 3Cu 51Fe	53	1·25	40	main production grade today
	.. .. HIGH H_c	1945	9Al 21Ni 20Co 2Cu 48Fe	66	0·9	25	ferrite magnets have over double H_c
SPECIAL ALLOYS	SILMANAL (Heusler)	1903	86Ag 9Mn 5Al NO IRON	43	0·05	0·6	costly. Intrinsic coercivity 500AT/mm
	PLATINUM-IRON etc.	1935	77Pt 23Fe (or 23Co)	143	0·45	32	very expensive. Highest H_c. Ductile
	REMALLOY	1931	17Mo 12Co 71Fe	18	1	9	high B_r springy metal
	CUNIFE etc.	1935	60Cu 20Ni 20Fe	50	0·6	15	ductile
NOTES	1.) The above figures are typical and approximate; selected from lists of over 200 different commercial magnet alloys (1957). 2.) Owing to diversity of cost, magnetic and mechanical properties, most materials are still in limited use.						

TABLE 3.1. HISTORICAL DEVELOPMENT OF METAL PERMANENT MAGNETS

without using any ferromagnetic constituents in 1903. This is of particular scientific importance and will be considered further in the next chapter. It also had a much higher coercivity than any other magnet of that time, with an intrinsic coercivity as much as ten times the H_C value, though the significance of these properties has only recently become known.

Though silmanal, with 86% silver, is costly, the platinum alloys of cobalt and iron cost up to a hundred times more than the best alnico alloys, but they give the highest known coercivity and a practical level of remanence compared with that of the silver alloy. Their applications are mainly limited to very small magnets used in precision moving-magnet instruments, for which their high stability and resistance to demagnetizing forces are of great value. Experimental samples of the platinum-cobalt alloy have given energy products as high as $70kJ/m^3$ which were the maximum achieved up to the present decade, when the 100 level was reached with a special alnico alloy having exceptionally good orientation.

The last two alloys in the table give desired mechanical properties with reasonable magnetic performance at commercial prices. Cunife is typical of a group of ductile alloys available in the form of thin sheet or tape, based on high proportions of copper, a non-magnetic metal. The latter feature results in low remanence, shown in extreme form with silmanal, and is a disadvantage in some uses where there are no ready means for concentrating the flux. It will be seen that this was a minor problem for the steel group in the table, and in 1931 a molybdenum-cobalt-iron alloy with superior remanence and energy product, named remalloy, was introduced. This had the merit of mechanical springiness and could be made in thin sheets, so it found an important use for telephone receiver diaphragms of the kind standardized for many years.

Probably the greatest advance in magnetic materials of all kinds, with high and low coercivity, was the introduction during the past 25 years of orientation methods, which increase the remanence and permeability to levels that could not otherwise be attained in commercial materials. In all practical magnetic circuits the flux has a definite path along which it is desirable to have the highest permeability, and it is not important how low the permeability may become in directions at right angles to that path. This was known in the earliest days when magnetic circuits of machines and transformers were built up of bundles or coils of iron wire with its direction coinciding with the magnetic path. The new orientation methods give the same effect by metallurgical processes which promote an acicular (needle-shaped) crystalline formation that can be oriented with the aid of powerful magnetic fields. This is aided by high temperature heat treatments and mechanical working to assist the structural mobility necessary for optimum results. In practice it has entailed the adding of complex manufacturing processes which were fully justified by the outstanding technical improvement and commercial advantage, and there is scope for further improvement in this field. Experimental figures of remanence for oriented alnico as high as $1.45 Wb/m^2$ have recently been announced, compared with the commercial level about 1.25 to 1.35, which is approaching the limit. Further improvements in permanent magnet and low-loss materials lie mainly in the direction of coercivity.

The main purpose of Table 3.1 is to show the remarkable progress in metal magnets, mainly in the historically brief period between 1920 and 1950 during which the average commercial material was improved about tenfold in magnetic performance. This was achieved by the development of dozens of different alloys, most based on considerable proportions of expensive elements such as cobalt, and the variety was necessary to provide the required range of magnetic and mechanical properties. Their increased cost and limitations meant that supplies of the magnet steels had to be maintained for many of their traditional uses. The importance of the new moulded materials described in the following chapters is that all the required properties can be provided with processed variants of one or two cheap and widely available materials, principally iron and its oxides.

3.7 Summary

The most important conclusion from this historical survey is that all the significant improvements in magnetic materials have taken place at a recent period, many years after major developments in electrical machines. These had originally been based on the properties of hard and soft steels produced for other applications and with magnetic properties so poor by latest standards as to make some of their designs obsolescent. The main feature of continuity in electrical machine design is the saturation flux density of iron which, like the conductivity of copper, is similar to the values in Faraday's day compared with the vast improvement in permanent magnets. Hence designs that can still justify the use of electromagnets, with their continuous consumption of power, for excitation purposes will be relatively unaffected by these improvements and this applies mainly to very large machines.

The brief account of early electric traction shows that its relative failure during this century was based upon a variety of circumstances which in no way diminish its outstanding advantages in performance, cleanliness and ease of control for both tracked and road vehicles. It needs a simple kind of electric machine to be used as motor or generator. Large commutator motors give excellent performance with high efficiency in such uses as locomotives and ships, but the performance becomes progressively worse as the size decreases and the weight and cost per unit of power steadily rise to uneconomic heights. The main cause, which will be shown to lie mainly with electromagnetic excitation, could be largely overcome with permanent magnets according to all the earliest designs. These could fulfil the same function without power loss or heat, but the new moulded materials such as ferrites, most suitable for this purpose, operate under entirely different magnetic circuit conditions from all the traditional machines still in general use today.

New magnet materials with the highest coercivity are needed to withstand these arduous conditions and these must operate in shortest magnetic circuits, involving a design based upon first principles. The latter were inevitable for the pioneers and it will be shown later that such designs go back to the beginning, to Barlow's Wheel and Faraday's Disc.

3.8 References

1. Andrade E. N. da C. 'The early History of the Permanent Magnet', *Endeavour*, Vol. XVII, No. 65, pp. 22-28, Jan. 1958.

2. Dunsheath P. *A History of Electrical Engineering*, Faber & Faber, London, 1963.

3. Crowther J. G. *The Social Relations of Science*, Macmillan, London, 1941.

4. Oliver D. A. 'Magnetic Materials. (Progress Rev.) Permanent Magnets', *J.I.E.E.* Vol. 95, Part I, No. 96, December, 1948.

5. Edwards A. 'Permanent Magnets', *Electrical Energy*, January & February, 1957.

6. The Science Museum, London. (Display and Publications.)

Note: Ref. 1 above also appears as Chapter 1 of both Refs. 1. 9. 2. & 1. 9. 3.

4

THEORETICAL BACKGROUND

This chapter deals with the reasons for magnetic phenomena and material performance. It summarizes the work of many scientists during the past few decades, which has only rarely appeared outside conference reports and specialist publications. Too much space would be required to give it the attention it deserves and those interested in this aspect of magnetism are thus urged to examine the literature indicated in the references. Thanks to the efforts of many specialists in this field, it is now possible to give acceptable explanations of what was largely a mystery up to the middle of this century, and to make forecasts of future progress. However, the fact that ideas have recently been modified in the latter respect indicates that there is still much to learn, though the remarkable progress in new materials and methods is an eloquent testimony to the success of this theoretical work and its associated experimental proofs.

4.1 Ferromagnetic Materials

The outstanding importance of Sturgeon's electromagnet, invented in 1825 and described in the previous chapter, was the thousand-fold increase in magnetic flux when soft iron is placed inside an air-core coil carrying current from a battery. The famous experiments with coils and compass needles announced a few years earlier added much more to then existing knowledge, but the practical consequences of the great pull exerted by the horseshoe electromagnet on its keeper were more significant in ultimate results. The force produced from the direct generation of electrical energy in a simple battery was soon greatly to surpass the best that permanent magnets could exert after some centuries of development, but the most striking factor was the unique property at that time exhibited by the most common metal in its ability to multiply the magnetic force so greatly. This provided a sharp contrast to the universal ability of metals to conduct an electric current without displaying any magnetic properties, with this notable exception of iron.

Ferromagnetism was thus the name given to this inexplicable property of greatly increasing the magnetic flux when a magnetizing force is applied to certain substances. Ferromagnetic materials comprise many alloys of iron, as well as iron oxides and compounds made from them. During the present century it was discovered that the presence of iron was not essential, as shown by the development of Heusler alloys. In modern terms a ferromagnetic material may be described by stating that its permeability relative to that of air or of free space is appreciably greater than unity, but this tends to become misleading in describing the latest high-coercivity magnets which approach this value, though being excellent for low-loss materials with relative permeability in the wide range of from a thousand to a million or more.

Although they will not be needed in later chapters, there are other magnetic prefixes which apply to the properties of materials and are of interest for theoretical study of them. They are:—

Para-magnetic with relative permeability slightly greater than unity,

Dia-magnetic with relative permeability slightly less than unity,

Ferri-magnetic with low saturation flux density of the kind found in non-metallic substances of the magnetic oxide and ferrite types.

All non-ferromagnetic materials are either para- or dia-magnetic and these properties are substantially independent of the applied magnetizing force with no known practical value. In physics they are important for correlating the various properties of materials with their structure.

Iron with its alloys and oxides was unique in this ferromagnetic category until the approach of modern times when it was found that the elements nickel and cobalt also possessed this property to a smaller extent. But during the present century it was found that nearly all alloys of iron with nickel and cobalt were strongly ferromagnetic in comparison with other substances (except for a few rare earths). They were fully explored by Elmen and others in the 1920s and it was found that certain nickel-iron alloys could be made to give about ten times the permeability of the best commercial iron if suitably prepared and heat-treated. Later it was found that special purification processes applied in the laboratory could raise the permeability of iron and a few selected alloys to as high as the one-million level.

By the middle of the present century the scope of ferromagnetism had grown to such an extent that a thousand page textbook was needed to cover it adequately (Ref. 1). Bozorth's classic, published in 1951, contained mainly experimental results with as many as 71 pages of references. Most of these investigations were carried out by those primarily concerned with light current applications—chiefly tele-communications—for which magnetizing force and flux density were low and permeability was the main figure of merit. With the limitations imposed by magnetic saturation, this is somewhat misleading for the high flux densities needed in power-handling applications. Thus, nickel-iron alloys with high nickel percentages (permalloys) give around ten times the permeability of commercial soft iron at the expense of about 60% reduction in saturation. The latter property has changed little since it first became important in electrical engineering and the effect of alloying has been relatively predictable; this is a somewhat parallel example to the conductivity of metal. It has therefore become apparent, but only very recently, that the key factor in ferromagnetic materials is coercivity.

Instead of two separate categories of ferromagnetic material, hard or soft, with different technologies, it is now appropriate to include them in a single group and to study the conditions under which coercivity can be maximized for magnets and minimized for low-loss applications. This brings the whole subject into line with the latest scientific developments in atomic and crystal structure analysis. The material is the main subject in the case of both the principal groups of new magnets, micropowders and ferrites, which each have closely similar counterparts in the low-loss categories. In the simplest case it is possible to take the most common ferromagnetic material, iron, and to reproduce all the different magnetic properties of the hundreds of commercial magnet alloys and low-loss alloys by appropriate processing; in addition the iron can be oxidized to form the main ingredient of another family of ferromagnetic materials which are electrical insulators. These are among the principal factors which enable answers to be provided to the following points relating to ferromagnetic materials:—

(a) the reason for the pronounced ferromagnetic behaviour of a very limited range of metals and their oxides;

(b) the cause of the vast variations of coercivity in these materials;

(c) an explanation of the various shapes of their magnetizing and hysteresis curves.

7

4.2 Atomic Structure

During the past two decades the importance of atomic energy has become universally understood by reason of its great destructive and power-producing properties. The same knowledge that produced these results can be used to explain the fundamental properties of electricity and magnetism, so it is of prime importance to this whole subject. In an earlier chapter it was stated that a current of electricity in a conductor consists of a flow of free electrons which are plentiful in metals but are almost absent in the non-metallic substances generally used as electrical insulators. Also, an electric current flowing in a conductor generates a magnetic field around it and inseparable from it, and this must occur regardless of scale or magnitude. Thus the movement of electrons which comprise the current must create their own individual magnetic field as well as the external field generated by them *en masse*.

Every atom consists of a positively charged nucleus with a number of orbiting electrons with negative charges so that the atom is normally neutral, and the number of electrons is different for each element. The lightest is hydrogen with one orbiting electron and this atomic number increases progressively up to 92 for uranium. The electrons move in a manner similar to the planets in the solar system at differing distances from the central nucleus, and at the same time spinning on their own axes in either a positive or negative direction; hence the direction of the magnetic field will either be similar or opposed, according to the spin direction. Two adjacent electrons with opposite spin directions will produce no magnetic field and the effect of many electrons magnetically will be the resultant of their positive and negative spins. This is normally zero in the same way that the atom itself has no resultant charge, but it varies with the atomic structure and is capable of variations from outside causes.

Thus, in the same way that the magnetic effect of a current flowing in a conductor can be small or large according to the conditions surrounding it in terms of ferromagnetic materials, so the magnetic effect of a host of spinning electrons can give a strong or negligible magnetic field according to their pattern and spin direction, the orbital movement being relatively unimportant. The balance of plus and minus spins is generally so close that the resultant magnetic effect is very small and the materials show either para-magnetic or dia-magnetic properties, but a few elements exhibit pronounced spin unbalance owing to their atomic structure and iron is the outstanding example. Also, changes in atomic structure by mixing atoms in close proximity, such as alloying or the formation of compounds, can have considerable magnetic effects in certain limited circumstances.

The atomic structure of iron is shown in Fig. 4.1 which indicates that the spherical orbits of the electrons are grouped in 'shells' around

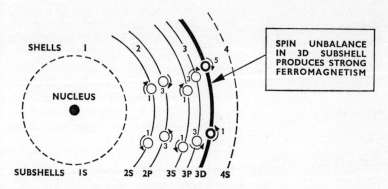

Fig. 4.1 Inner atomic structure of Iron.

the central nucleus. For this metal there are four main shells and some of these are divided into subshells, but all elements are now classified on this basis in up to six shells, with a maximum number of four subshells denoted by the initial letters of their relevant spectroscopy terms (*s* sharp, *d* diffuse, *p* principal, *f* fine). With each element having its distinctive and different number of electrons in this shell pattern, in some shells there may be only one electron which could be filled with the maximum number of electrons in another element. The maximum magnetic effect will occur in a half-filled shell. In atoms of iron the $1s$ $2s$ $3s$ $4s$ subshells each contain two electrons and are filled, as are the $2p$ and $3p$ with six electrons each. Ten electrons are required to fill the $3d$ subshell and iron has only six, which gives the reason why it is strongly ferromagnetic. The outer $4s$ shells contains two electrons which give the electrical conducting property of metal.

Of the remaining ferromagnetic elements, cobalt has seven and nickel eight electrons in the important $3d$ subshell, which explains their lower though still significant ferromagnetism, whereas copper with ten electrons is non-magnetic since the spins are completely balanced. Manganese has five electrons in this group and is normally non-magnetic as an element, but if it is alloyed with high percentages of silver so that its atoms are widely dispersed, manganese becomes ferromagnetic in the form of silmanal. This is one of the Heusler alloys which contains no iron; they have very high coercivity with low remanence, figures being given in Table 3.1.

This brief account of electron spin unbalance in atomic structure provides a relatively simple reason why some substances give strong ferromagnetic properties. It could point the way towards the discovery of new and better magnetic materials, but there is at present no sign of any breakthrough in this direction. Although the number of ferromagnetic elements is small, the possible combinations of them in metallic and oxide form are very great and much development of this kind remains to be done. Explanations of their magnetic performance require some knowledge of crystallography to show the manner in which atoms are grouped together to form solid substances.

4.3 Crystal Structure

Some materials exhibit a definite crystalline form when found in their natural state, with geometric shapes of marked regularity. Others are readily prepared synthetically by means of simple chemical experiments by slow cooling of solutions to form a solid phase, which will indicate the critical conditions involved and the importance of small impurities. These effects occur widely in metallurgy, but generally on such a small scale that powerful microscopes are needed to study them. They are extremely important for the investigation and understanding of magnetic materials, whose performance depends upon crystal size, shape, arrangement and lattice distortion.

The three ferromagnetic metal elements crystallize into three different geometric forms which have an important influence upon their magnetic behaviour. Iron has a body-centred cubic crystal lattice structure which can be most readily magnetized along the edge of a face, whereas cobalt is hexagonal and can be most readily magnetized in its axial direction, but with nickel this lies along a body diagonal of its face-centred cubic structure. These contrasting factors are illustrated in Fig. 4.2 which shows the relative positions of these three crystal shapes for best horizontal magnetization.

This property of a crystal to be more readily magnetized in one direction than others is of the greatest importance in magnetic materials and the recent high-coercivity magnets rely mainly upon this *crystal anisotropy*. Conversely, the lowest-loss alloys have the smallest value of this property, which is in a different sense for iron and nickel; hence certain critical proportions of these two elements in specially heat-treated alloys give the characteristic high permeability and low hysteresis of the permalloys. The crystal structure of such materials was found to be very strain-sensitive and the hysteresis loss

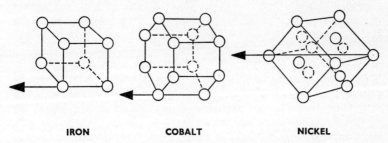

IRON   COBALT   NICKEL

Fig. 4.2 Crystal Structure of Ferromagnetic Metals indicating Easy Direction of Magnetization.

was greatly increased by the mechanical working needed during manufacture, which had to be removed by a subsequent annealing process for materials intended for low-loss applications. All early permanent magnet steels, however, relied upon strain imparted to the crystal lattice of the metal by established metallurigcal processes, originally developed to give the physical hardness with which desirable magnet quality was associated. Crystals of certain ferro-magnetic materials give small changes in permeability and in linear dimensions along the direction of magnetization as manifestations of the effect of strain; this is known as magnetostriction and is utilized in various kinds of instrument transducer.

Crystal structure can thus be of greatest value for providing desir-able magnetic properties for materials with high or low coercivity and became specially important when practical methods of orienta-tion were developed during the past two decades. Here the pro-nounced directional effects could be used to best advantage and much recent work has been devoted to this subject. Most metals are prepared by heating them to high temperature which tends to make them *isotropic*, with a random arrangement to their final crystal structure, so methods of applying strong magnetic fields during the critical periods of cooling were devised to ensure that the majority of the crystals would be oriented in the preferred direction for the ultimate magnetic circuit.

While strain anisotropy has contributed the main source of permanent magnet energy in the past and crystal anisotropy is of such importance to the new ferrite magnets, the third major influence of crystals on magnetic performance relates to their size. This introduces the important subject of magnetic domains; it has been responsible more than any other factor associated with magnetism for producing a coherent explanation of its phenomena and of the performance of ferromagnetic materials.

4.4 The Domain Theory

No effective explanation of ferromagnetism was made before the present century though Ewing published in 1900 his notable work suggesting that all ferromagnetic atoms and molecules could be regarded as elementary tiny magnets able to rotate on their own axes in an applied magnetic field. A model made from a large number of small compass needles provided the means for indicating the approximate shape of magnetizing curves, but it failed to convey the magnitude of the forces needed to magnetize and demagnetize a permanent magnet. This became possible several years later, after Weiss had introduced his domain theory; this started with the assumption that ferromagnetic material consists of a large number of tiny regions or domains which are each normally magnetized to saturation in a closed magnetic circuit, so there are no external magnetic effects. The domain boundaries or walls can be stretched by external fields so that they return to the non-magnetized state when the field is removed, or they can be moved or enlarged; they then give the effect of magnetic remanence with the application of larger applied fields, since the internal magnetic equilibrium of the domain has thereby been upset. Still greater applied fields will cause a rotation of the domains so that their individual fields coincide in the applied direction, giving the magnetic saturation effect.

This is shown in diagram form in fig. 4.3 for a typical magnetizing curve with simple diagrams of the domain movement for these three conditions, from the non-magnetized state at zero up to the fully saturated state. This relates to iron crystals and the domains have been enlarged about 100,000 times, which still allows billions of atoms for each domain and for the domain wall thickness to be many atoms thick in order to explain the required degree of mobility. It will be seen from the intrinsic magnetizing curve that the zone of domain stretching is limited to the small part up to the first bend and the domain growth applies to the major part of the curve between the lower and upper bends which is almost linear for much of this zone. These are the conditions for enlargement of hysteresis loop area and the increase of remanence which is the fundamental factor in permanent magnetism. The final step of domain rotation requires considerable increase in magnetizing force to attain relatively limited improvement in remanent flux.

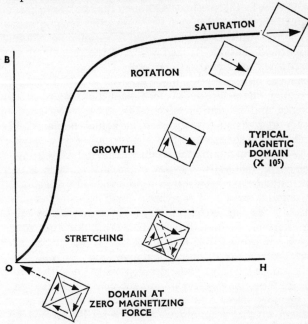

Fig. 4.3 Magnetizing Curve (Intrinsic) of Iron to indicate Domain Theory.

In 1919 Barkhausen discovered that this domain movement could be demonstrated practically by magnetizing a piece of iron with a microphone fixed to it and connected to a thermionic amplifier. As the magnetizing force was increased, a telephone receiver in the amplifier output circuit gave a number of clicks which indicated that the flux density advanced in a series of small jumps instead of uniformly, which might have been expected earlier. This indicated that domain movement was detectable and that a greatly magnified version of the magnetizing curve at the steeper part would be stepped instead of smooth. Ten years later Bitter produced visual proof of the existence of these magnetic domains by a highly refined and enlarged version of the early iron filings pattern used to display the path and distribution of magnetic flux. He used very fine colloidal ferromagnetic powder with prepared specimens that could be examined under a strong microscope, and several later investigators have produced an impressive series of domain patterns under differing conditions by this method. Although the size of metallic domains is so small (between 10^{-4} and 10^{-5} mm.) this technique has added greatly to the knowledge of the causes of magnetic performance and has confirmed the validity and value of the domain theory in an unprecedented manner.

Starting as an assumption made in order to explain the non-linear magnetizing characteristic of ferromagnetic materials with their remanence and saturation effects, this theory developed into the discovery and visual investigation of actual domains. These are generally needle-shaped and they tend to move as a result of magnetizing force overcoming the strain and crystal anisotropy forces in ferromagnetic materials. Various other factors, such as impurities and inclusions, have been shown to influence this resistance to magnetization and these have together contributed to an explanation of the shape of the magnetizing curve with its associated hysteresis loop. Those interested in finding ways of making domains more mobile developed improved low-loss materials while better permanent magnets were made by introducing obstacles in order to prevent domain wall movement. These developments led to the introduction of 'square loop' magnetic materials for new demands such as computer memory cores and indicated an entirely new approach in permanent magnet technology—high coercivity created by micropowders of domain size.

4.5 Crystal Size

Ferromagnetic powders have found important practical uses for many years and it has been noted that finer powders tend to have higher hysteresis loss. The first records of iron powders made by electrolysis into mercury appeared in Japan at the end of last century, reaching the high coercivity for that time of 30 AT/mm, and further work in Russia 30 years later related this to crystal anisotropy. Experimental micropowder magnets of this type were made in both Japan and America in the following years but the most important contribution was the commercial process installed in France at the end of World War II to deal with the raw material shortages which restricted the output of conventional metal magnets. This was the outcome of the important theoretical work by Néel and his associates, who confirmed it by reducing ferrous formate in hydrogen to produce iron micropowders of nearly domain-size, which had been estimated to be around 0.01 micron. It was found that finer particles than this critical dimension tended to be non-magnetic whereas coarser particles had progressively lower coercivity.

By normal powder metallurgy standards these conditions were extremely exacting. Not only must all the particles be the same size, but this was about one-hundredth the average of the finest grades of iron powder being made for powder cores to operate at radio frequencies. Such micropowders are highly pyrophoric, oxidizing instantaneously in air with liberation of heat which presents a hazard on a production scale. In spite of this, a considerable output of the equivalent isotropic magnets to alni and alnico of pre-war quality was achieved. The original micropowders had coercivities in the 40 to 80 AT/mm region but these values were steadily reduced as the compacting pressure was increased in order to make physically strong and stable magnets with practical levels of remanence. However, this indicated a new and very significant innovation in magnet technology; instead of the need to produce a different alloy for a practical range of magnetic properties, one starting material could be produced with any desired ratio of remanence to coercivity from the intrinsic value of the latter up to the low-loss grades, with appropriate increases in the physical density. This corresponded closely to the methods for altering the permeability of powder cores for covering the wide range of audio and radio frequencies described in the next chapter.

This development of micropowder magnets was the culminating proof of the domain theory in grouping magnetic materials into one category and deriving high coercivity by appropriate sub-division. It became strikingly apparent when achieved with pure iron, the classic 'soft' magnetic metal. Theory indicated that this effect depended upon the saturation flux density so that better results were expected with cobalt-iron alloys with up to 50% cobalt. This proved to be the case in practice and most commercial micropowder magnets have been made of this kind of alloy. A preliminary reduction process converted the mixed formates into oxides which were found to have extremely high coercivity, a forerunner of the ferrite magnets which appeared some years later.

While the great importance of crystal size was being investigated in France, Guillaud extended this to the detailed study of manganese-bismuth. He found that particles of below 3 microns in diameter possessed the remarkably high coercivity of 1000 AT/mm at room temperature, and established the dependence of domain-size coercivity upon high crystal anisotropy. This was followed up in America on a practical basis to produce compressed powder magnets of this material with the high energy product of 40 kJ/m³, or about equal to the best commercial alnico in oriented form. However, the cost of the raw materials for this kind of commercial magnet makes it uncompetitive and the corrosion problems are severe enough to limit the long-term stability, so that it is doubtful if these magnets will be manufactured. But, as in the present case of micropowders of iron, the information provided by workers developing these materials has been of the greatest scientific and technical value; in the case of manganese-bismuth it provided the incentive to search for more stable and cheap high-coercivity materials such as barium ferrite with high crystal anisotropy and much higher domain size than the metal micropowders. The approximate relationship between these properties is given in Fig. 4.4.

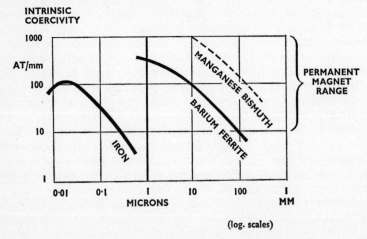

Fig. 4.4 Coercivity (Intrinsic) dependent upon Particle Size.

Powders and micropowders made by the reduction of oxides or compounds in hydrogen in furnaces tend to have nearly spherical shape so that magnetic orientation processes give only limited improvement, especially when compared with oriented metal magnets. To obtain similar results it was essential to revert to an early electrolytic process for producing acicular or needle-shaped particles with a ratio of length to diameter preferably in the 10/1 region. These achieve coercivity by reason of their shape anisotropy which, for high saturation metals such as iron and iron-cobalt, were expected to be in the 400-800 AT/mm level or similar to that of manganese bismuth and many times higher than the best commercial values of ten years ago. For many reasons these have not been achieved and at the time of writing it seems unlikely that more than 30% of these values can be reached by the proposed and attempted methods. However, it would be difficult to use extremely high coercivities, even if they were available, until application techniques have caught up with the progress already achieved in magnet materials. Further information on the recent work on oriented micropowder magnets is given in the latter part of Chapter 5.

4.6 Permanent Magnet Properties

This brief theoretical survey giving the main reasons for magnetic performance has arrived at the stage where the properties of the new materials, micropowders and ferrites, can be explained in terms of their two main anisotropies, shape and crystal anisotropy. The first of these applies principally to metals with high saturation and the second to oxides with low saturation flux densities, but ferrites have the merits of insulator resistivity and freedom from corrosion.

While it is possible from the great volume of published information to calculate the main cause of intrinsic coercivity from known physical properties, this is still of limited value because other factors must be taken into account and these cannot easily be determined except by prolonged experiment. It has already been shown that both particle size and crystal anisotropy influence the properties of barium ferrite, but the shape of typical particles is that of platelets which will act differently from spheres or cylinders.

However, in order to make good magnets it is not sufficient to have a powder with high intrinsic coercivity; it must be bonded into a compact and physically stable mass that can withstand the most severe practical conditions and also provide a useful level of remanence. It is shown later in dealing with applications that low remanence can be compensated in appropriate designs, so that a bonded magnet of relatively low physical density can make efficient use of the somewhat diluted magnetic material it contains. In the case of micropowder magnets, the proximity of particles tends to reduce the coercivity and hence there is a strong incentive to dilute the magnetic material. On the other hand, ferrites are mainly dependent upon high crystal anisotropy for their coercivity and this is much less affected by particle proximity; so sintered ferrite magnets with up to 95% of the pure crystal specific gravity give high coercivity and best use of the

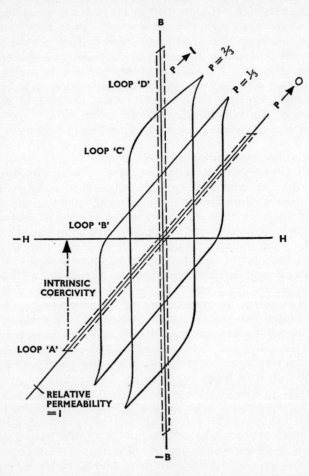

Fig. 4.5 Theoretical Hysteresis Loops for Iron Micropowders with Different Packing Factors (P).

available magnetic energy. These conditions provide good mechanical properties independent of limitations which might be introduced by the non-magnetic additives in the filled or bonded grades.

With the variety of demands for permanent magnets, indicated by the great number of grades which already exist for a comparatively recent material such as barium ferrite, it is essential to see the effect of considerable degrees of magnetic dilution in powder form on the magnetic properties. This can best be shown in a series of hysteresis loops made from a single batch of high-coercivity metal micro-powder in which the differences will be appreciably greater than in the case of ferrites (Fig. 4.5). Curve A shows the powder so diluted with binder that it gives an almost linear hysteresis loop as for an air-core coil but extending to the intrinsic coercivity point. The remanence and working coercivity are almost zero and this would apply to the energy product $(BH)_{max}$; this material would be useless for conventional applications to which this measure applies.

Curve B has about one-third magnetic material by volume and gives an almost linear demagnetizing curve without considerable reduction in coercivity but a low remanence by present metal standards, comparable to ferrite values. Curve C has a pronounced bend in the demagnetizing curve but gives the highest $(BH)_{max}$ value with about two-thirds of the volume occupied with magnetic material. In loop D the density is increased to approaching 100% so that the spaces between the fine particles have been eliminated; the material then has the highest remanence near to the saturation point but nearly zero coercivity. It will have been converted from the permanent magnet to the low-loss grade.

It will be seen that Curves B and C compare closely with those of the typical oriented grades of alnico and high coercivity ferrite given in Fig. 2.7. Between Curves A and B there will be a series of loops which will all have the almost linear demagnetizing curves employed for most of later applications; their magnetic strength will diminish as the proportion of magnetic material is diluted but this will give relatively better resistance to demagnetization as measured by the ratio of intrinsic coercivity to working coercivity. These features are of great potential value when considering new applications which come under very severe demagnetizing conditions, as well as providing materials with unusually low specific gravity with attractions for novel design and manufacture. A good example is flexible barium ferrite sheet.

4.7 Summary

This outline of the theoretical reasons for the magnetic properties of ferromagnetic materials has now provided the main answers to the points raised at the end of section 4.1, with particular reference to the new materials, micropowders and ferrites, which have appeared commercially during the past two decades. These can be said to be the practical results of the great scientific advances in the subject of magnetic materials during this period. In the case of permanent magnets, they provide elegant synthetic processes for reaching desired conditions in place of the traditional trial-and-error methods by which the great progress in the familiar kinds of metal magnet has been achieved. The properties of the latter are now being explained in the light of the discoveries made principally with the micropowder magnets.

While strain anisotropy has played a relatively greater part in the traditional magnet metals, it is difficult to give the added effect of the other causes and this is also beyond the scope of this work. It must suffice that higher coercivities have resulted in special grades of alnico alloys in recent years but these are still about half the best values for ferrites without their economic advantages.

In addition to the advantages of understanding the technology of applied magnetism, there is now the possibility of predicting the trend of future development. Before ferrite magnets became well established in various oriented grades during the past few years, it was natural to look to the micropowders for the next great advance in permanent magnet strength, but the ultimate possibilities are more difficult to attain and there is now some doubt whether the predicted further tenfold improvement is within the revised theoretical horizon. There is still a prospect of other notable advances in the performance of barium ferrite and, from the engineering standpoint, the main attraction is in the economic sphere of low cost in bulk and excellent availability. Attention has been paid recently to the properties of mixed micropowders and ferrites in order to combine the high saturation merits of the former with the high coercivity and insulating properties of the latter, and this subject is included in the following chapter.

4.8 References

1. Bozorth R. M. *Ferromagnetism*, Van Nostrand, New York, 1951.

2. Wohlfarth E. P. 'Hard Magnetic Materials', *Phil. Mag. Supplt. Advances in Physics*, pp. 82-224, 8 April 1959.

3. Luborsky F. E. 'Permanent Magnets', *Electrotechnology*, July, August, September 1962.

4. McCaig M. 'Recent Developments in Permanent Magnetism', *J. Applied Physics*, Vol. 35, No. 3 (Pt. 2), March 1964.

See also reference 1.9.2.

5

POWDERS & MICROPOWDERS

Magnetic powders first became commercially important about half a century ago for telephone transmission purposes, and the subsequent developments in telecommunications and electronics have created a demand for progressively finer grades. When it became known that still finer iron particles in the sub-micron region, known as micropowders, could make good permanent magnets instead of low-loss cores, there was a considerable fund of practical experience available to deal with the severe problems in making these novel micropowder magnets. Although these and some grades of powder core have recently been eclipsed by ferrites of both high and low coercivity, they continue to possess the advantage of higher saturation flux density and thus are important for present and future applications.

5.1 Early Developments

Synthetic oxide magnets were first described about two centuries ago (see section 3.2) and the first low-loss cores made from iron powder appear in publications dated about 1886. Fritts made experiments in their use for dynamos and motors and Heaviside used cores made from iron filings set in wax in order to improve the performance of inductance coils used in telephone circuits. Even with the limited frequency range of those early days, eddy current loss (proportional to the frequency squared) was increased some hundreds of times from the power level to mean speech frequency level, to use modern terms, for equivalent flux density. Iron sheet was inadequate for the new a.c. machines and dynamo armatures then being developed so it was inevitable that telephone circuits would need magnetic cores of a very different character, though the low working flux density made them more amenable to the use of powder techniques.

Eddy currents can also be reduced by increasing the electrical resistivity of the magnetic metal, and this has applied to all the silicon steels and other iron alloys which were primarily developed for lower hysteresis loss. Hence most of the needs for reduced losses in electrical machines and power equipment have been met with laminations made by the well-established processes of the steel industry. The need for more stable magnetic cores for telephony and other purposes could be covered by laminations with an air gap, which tended to flatten the magnetising curve in greatly reducing the relative permeability, so that the inductance value of coils could be made much less dependent upon changes of magnetising current.

By the turn of this century the telephone had become widely used for local calls and there was a growing demand for longer distance circuits. This could be done only by reducing the line resistance with ever-increasing conductor diameter, to which there was a severe economic limit. Theoretical investigation backed by experiment showed that the circuit capacitance imposed the principal restriction, and this could be neutralised to a great extent by the adding of inductance coils at regular intervals along both sides of the line. This operation was called *loading* and the special kinds of inductance used for this purpose were 'loading coils'. It will be clear that these must not add appreciable electrical resistance, whether due to the d.c. resistance of the winding or the a.c. resistance due to core losses (eddy currents and hysteresis); this amounted to the equivalent of a very good power factor in an electrical capacitance. These loading coils had to maintain their electrical properties within close limits regardless of lightning or strong induced currents, and were to be used in such numbers in close proximity that they must have negligible leakage flux, otherwise there would be serious crosstalk between adjacent circuits. This could only be done with ring-shaped coils which produce practically no external field; if wound on an air-core (e.g. a non-magnetic ring of wood), the d.c. resistance of the multi-turn winding needed to give the required inductance value would be excessive, in spite of the absence of a.c. losses in the core. The only answer was a new kind of magnetic core with permeability in the 10 to 100 range and a.c. losses lower than any so far attained, and the future of telephony over long distances depended upon a solution to this problem at a time when there were no satisfactory amplifiers.

This appears to have provided the main incentive to the great progress in magnetic materials which is the main subject of this book. The American company (Bell Telephone Laboratories) which first explored this subject proceeded to make a major contribution during the following decades in the investigation of a host of new alloys, which was followed up by numerous other workers throughout the

8

world. The early history of the loading coil also has important points relating to the recent developments in magnetic materials.

Fine iron wire cores were the first commercial answer to this requirement. The wire was drawn down in diamond dies to as thin as 0.004 inch (0.1 mm.) diameter and wound into large rings of rectangular section with insulation between adjacent layers in order to minimise eddy currents. Compared with a similar kind of core made from coarser soft iron, this gives about one-tenth of the relative permeability in composite form, partly owing to the lower metal space factor but mainly because the wire is hardened during the drawing process. The finished cores were available in two permeability grades, 95 and 65, which gave a more linear magnetising curve than any alternative at that time, and corresponding better stability when used for loading coils, though they were some way from reaching a constant value of inductance over long periods of use in practical conditions. But they met the needs of the time sufficiently well that by 1915 it was possible to speak across the full breadth of America by heavy-gauge loaded line before thermionic amplifiers had been introduced.

It is a surprising fact that the permeability of these low-loss cores was less than that of the best hard steel permanent magnets then available. Also this fine core construction was a perfect forerunner of the modern highly oriented magnetic material, but the wire diameter was 10,000 times greater than that needed for highest coercivity of the single domain kind in metallic iron.

5.2 Magnetic Powders

The search for the desired improvement in stability of the iron wire cores for loading coils indicated that it was necessary to introduce air gaps for this purpose, but these must be infinite in number and uniformly distributed around the magnetic circuit if leakage flux was to be avoided. The only method of achieving this was to make the core of fine magnetic powder which, if metallic, must be coated with a non-magnetic layer of insulating material to reduce eddy current loss and compacted to give the required permeability. The first experiments were made with oxidised ring cores of sheet iron laminations, or of iron wire or tape to give greater surface area for the oxidation process. These had low eddy current loss but the permeability tended to be too low and the hysteresis too high. The alternative was to make iron powder by one of several methods and to coat the particles with diluted lacquer before compacting them; this called for a special process to make powder with suitable properties for this purpose which became the main part of the development. The promise of better performance by the powder method was the deciding factor in changing from the iron wire cores when the supply of the necessary diamond dies was cut off during the first World War, and it was ultimately found that the iron powder cores were superior in every respect.

Many early accounts describe the use of iron powders, generally in the form of iron filings which are readily available in most places, but they usually were ignorant of the need for some degree of compaction in order to attain a useful permeability level and physical stability. At higher flux density conditions the powder tends to orient its particles which may not retain their relative position when the magnetising force is removed, and the best permeability level was less than 10; this is little better than the use of non-magnetic cores in cylindrical coils. The first record of the importance of tamping to compact the powder was in 1914 by Benedikts, who raised the permeability with d.c. magnetising conditions to 90, which was about half the value for the solid metal under the same magnetising conditions. The iron particles in this test were uninsulated, which showed that this material could not be effectively used for a.c. applications, and an insulating layer added for this purpose would reduce the permeability to below the 10 level, with or without tamping. This indicates that a very thin insulating layer is needed and appreciable pressure to compact the insulated powder without the layer breaking down under these severe conditions; it requires considerable refinement of materials and methods which would have been difficult to obtain before this period.

The best-known method of making iron powder at that time was the chemical reduction in a furnace of a pure oxide in a current of hydrogen. Early experimenters tried to insulate the resulting fine powder by oxidising the particle surface in steam under conditions intended to give a very thin coating, but this proved to be mechanically weak and the surface was too irregular. Any attempt to tamp or compress this coated powder would break down its insulating layer, which could be readily shown by measuring the d.c. resistance of the compact. It was found that a lacquer such as shellac would adhere to a slightly oxidised particle and this would permit the use of moderate pressure to make a relatively strong core on account of the binder action, with a noticeable improvement in core resistance. But the permeability tended to be lower than desired and attempts to raise it by reducing the proportion of insulating material as well as by increasing the pressure intensity would give inadequate resistance, though the permeability might be greatly increased. Thin ring cores separately insulated and stacked in the form of laminations gave little improvement if the particle insulation was inadequate.

These early difficulties with the development of the first magnetic powder cores have been given in some detail in order to indicate the magnitude of the task and to explain the considerable time taken to organise a successful commercial process from the first experiments. This was finally achieved by use of an electrolytic process in place of the hydrogen reduction in order to produce the required physical properties to meet the above stringent conditions for loading coil cores. In the telephone industries these became known as 'dust cores' but this name has been superseded in general use to meet the terminology of powder metallurgy, of which the magnetic interests form an appreciable part. In modern terms a dust would be a micropowder which would give very high hysteresis loss, the opposite of what has always been required for telephone transmission demands. Thus the general term now is 'magnetic powder cores', often referred to as iron cores although the important loading coil requirements have been mostly provided with nickel-iron powders of the permalloy group in recent years. Iron powders have continued to be important for radio applications in fine grades made by different processes, which will be described in some detail in view of their continued promise for other uses.

5.3 Iron Powder Cores

The limitations of hydrogen-reduced iron powder for high grade magnetic cores were due to the following:—

(a) The metal was too soft physically and distorted too much under the compacting pressure.

(b) Particles tended to be aggregates with sponge-like properties unsuitable for insulation with thin layers of lacquer.

(c) Large scale iron powder production by hydrogen reduction methods was too costly compared with alternatives.

Consequently the first process for making magnetic powders was based on the electrolysis of a solution of ferrous chloride and ammonium sulphate, using steel electrodes operated at a current density of 12 amperes per square foot ($130 \ A/m^2$). Iron was deposited in the form of thin brittle plates, broken up and ball-milled so that about half of the resulting powder would pass through a 200 mesh/ inch sieve. A final anneal in hydrogen produced a softer and cleaner powder which could be readily treated to take a thin layer of insulation on account of the smoothness, regularity and toughness of the particles.

This kind of powder permitted the use of high pressure compacting processes without breaking down the insulating film on any appreciable proportion of the particles, while the finished core was mechanically strong and had the appearance of solid metal. It was found possible to raise the pressure intensity to as high as 100 ton/square inch, so that the metal particles were distorted into interlocking shapes without destroying the effectiveness of the insulating coating. These extreme moulding conditions called for special dies made from tool steels and large hydraulic presses. The resulting cores had relatively low permeability values of 25 and 60, but these gave a suitable balance between the d.c. resistance of their windings in the comparatively large sizes of loading coil then in general use and the a.c. losses at the standardised test frequency of 800 c/s. The specific resistance of these early cores was about 0.01 ohm. centimetre, or about a thousand times higher than that of the solid metal, with 90% of its specific gravity; but this figure could be varied considerably according to the proportion and properties of insulating material used.

While these first powder cores made in America from electrolytic iron were designed to meet the performance specification drawn up for the iron-wire kind, based upon the electrical requirements of the telephone line, they showed a great improvement in the vital factor of stability. The permeability, and hence the inductance value of the loading coil, would remain much closer to the nominal figure, essential for maintaining good transmission characteristics. In some cases it was necessary to replace the early types of coil because their properties had altered to such an extent during a limited period of time, but powder cores were progressively improved to the point that changes in permeability due to all causes, ageing and heavy superimposed current, became almost undetectable.

Magnetic materials of both hard and soft varieties had been notoriously unstable up to that time and elaborate air-core coils of considerable size and cost had to be employed in many cases, especially in early radio equipment. During the 1920s the thermionic amplifier and electrical filter circuits were developed. These needed magnetic cores of the highest stability for the operation of carrier telephony circuits with a number of speech channels over a single physical circuit. Additionally the introduction of radio broadcasting created a need for cheap tuning and filter cores in vast quantities. These new demands called for iron powders of highest magnetic quality and in a wide range of particle size grading, in order to meet this thousandfold expansion of the frequency band from the limited speech frequency of about 2 kc/s when the first powder cores were introduced for loading telephone cables.

In Germany there were two important new methods devised at that time to improve the quality of iron powder for other purposes, but which were found appropriate for magnetic applications. The Hametag Eddy Mill used chopped wire or other coarsely divided iron of the desired metallurgical quality fed into the opposite ends of a strong cylindrical chamber containing powerful fans which projected this raw material in two colliding streams. The mutual attrition of the particles provided means for both reducing the size and improving the shape of the subsequent powder, giving higher pack density than had previously been possible and reduced contamination in comparison with conventional ballmills. This process did not depend upon the brittleness of the grade of metal used, which is significant in dealing with low-loss metals that are inherently soft in the physical sense. It could equally well handle alloys which had tended to complicate other powder-making processes. The resulting material had a characteristic particle shape of discs with smooth edges which could be effectively insulated with lacquer, so that early loading coil cores in Europe were made by this method.

Another method for making fine iron powder, which ultimately was used in most leading industrial countries of the world, was based upon the iron penta-carbonyl process. This makes spherical particles of a few microns diameter and was specially suitable for radio-frequency applications for this reason, but its outstanding magnetic quality was first proved in the early loading coil and filter core field. Although alloy powder cores based on permalloys, described below, were soon to supersede the early iron kind in American and British markets, carbonyl-iron cores dominated European telephone network requirements for nearly 30 years (until the arrival of low-loss ferrite pot cores). Most of the world's radio sets, however, depended upon this material which continues to compete today with ferrites in certain uses.

Magnetically, carbonyl-iron powder is unusual in being extremely hard physically while having the lowest hysteresis loss of any grade of iron made commercially. No complete explanation has been given for this feature, but it is lost if the material is heated to usual annealing temperatures and the particles become physically soft with hysteresis near the hydrogen-reduced iron level. The average particle size of around one-tenth of typical alternatives gives the required low eddy current loss in insulated form. This is of great practical advantage even in the annealed grades, which are needed for cores with permeability of much greater than 10 (measured on ring specimens). However, the great majority of applications consist of cylindrical shapes in open magnetic circuits for which the low permeability unannealed material is used, giving its full magnetic quality.

Iron pentacarbonyl is a liquid made from sponge iron reacted with carbon monoxide. When heated to above 100°C, it forms iron in the fine particle state and releases the carbon monoxide for further use. The powder falls to the bottom of the large reaction towers and is periodically removed. The average particle size is about 5 microns in the deposited form and this is one of the chief merits of this process which automatically produces a fine powder with high pack density without special grading and sieving processes needed for alternative manufacturing methods. The extreme hardness of the particles means that they do not distort in shape under the highest moulding pressures, which simplifies the insulation process so that cores can achieve resistivity levels of insulators in the low permeability grades. The highest permeabilities in annealed material with inferior loss standards are 50 to 70; these have proved inadequate for the demands for smaller loading coils needing twice these values, which require nickel-iron alloy powders, and the carbonyl process is not able to make this kind of material. The relationship between permeability, resistivity and working frequency is indicated in Fig. 2.2.

5.4 Alloy Powder Cores

The original permalloy was an alloy of $78\frac{1}{2}\%$ nickel and $21\frac{1}{2}\%$ iron produced in thin sheet or strip form with primary applications for the continuous loading of submarine telegraph cables by wrapping high permeability material around the conductor wire. This was discovered about 40 years ago and created much interest because it gave around ten times higher permeability than iron, when subjected to a critical heat treatment, although its main constituent had a relatively low permeability. The reason for this was only discovered some time later and is given in the previous chapter. The physical properties of this alloy, however, are similar to nickel in terms of ductility and freedom from normal corrosion effects and it has a rather low saturation flux density. This and its relatively high cost based on nickel prices has mainly confined its use to smaller components in telecommunication circuits. Here one of its most important applications has been in the smaller and better loading coil cores.

As a result of the high ductility of these nickel-iron alloys, together with their strain-sensitive properties, it was necessary to devise special processes for making them in powder form, and also to produce low-loss cores from this powder. The high pressure moulding process would subject the particles to heavy strain which greatly reduces the permeability and increases the hysteresis loss, minimising the benefits which the alloy was intended to provide. These difficulties are overcome in solid metal, sheet or tape by a final anneal at around 600°C. But the use of alloy powder could give important advantages compared with any kind of pure iron:—

(a) The permeability is much higher under all lower flux density conditions.

(b) The alloy is more corrosion-resistant and mechanically more suitable.

(c) With six times higher resistivity, the eddy current loss for equivalent particle size is correspondingly reduced.

In America the problem of making permalloy in powder form was solved by the addition of embrittling agents such as sulphur during the high frequency melting stage to form the alloy, and this could be augmented by pouring the melt into a suitable liquid at room temperature. The powder was further reduced in size and given the necessary particle shape by appropriate ballmilling processes which produced the desirable high pack density. An annealing process then restored the physical softness of the powder and removed the main impurities.

An insulated powder could then be pressed into a core of high physical density and the strains introduced by this step in the manufacture needed a core annealing process approaching red heat to remove their effects. All earlier powder insulation processes would break down under this temperature level, so it was essential to devise new ways of coating the particles with fine ceramic powders mixed in a temperature-resistant binder. After considerable development a satisfactory insulation method was devised on these lines which would withstand core heat treatment at about 500°C and yield the greater part of the high magnetic quality which these alloys are able to give. The resulting cores were about one-tenth the size of the iron powder predecessors for the same electrical performance but also had considerably better stability. They became available at a time when most telephone circuits were being installed in underground cables with crowded manholes where small size and negligible crosstalk were urgently needed.

In this country a novel method was developed about 1930 for the production of alloy powders of this kind without the need for the melting and embrittlement process. It originally consisted of the chemical preparation of intimately mixed oxides of the constituent metals in the desired proportions by co-precipitation methods, which were reduced by passing them through a tube furnace carrying an opposing stream of dry hydrogen at low red heat. The resulting spongy mass was found to be alloyed to a high degree and could be converted to fine powder of suitable grading and particle shape by appropriate light ballmilling. In contrast to the American process which tended to make a high proportion of coarse particles, this produced a fine powder which needed particle growth for the main applications at speech frequencies. The commercial process developed from this work used high-grade oxides of the constituent metals which were thoroughly intermixed in edge-runner mills, then reduced in hydrogen to give partial reduction followed by a preliminary milling to form the powder into discrete particles of suitable size. This powder was then given a sintering heat treatment to complete the alloying and to convert the spongy structure into smooth solid particles; in this manner coarse powder could be made with a high percentage yield, or the temperatures could be modified with associated milling schedules in order to make finer grades.

This experience enabled the methods to be applied to the successful manufacture of pure iron powder, which could be insulated satisfactorily in order to produce radio cores under conditions of wartime shortage when supplies of Continental carbonyl iron were cut off. A higher quality grade was made in 50/50 nickel-iron alloy with high resistivity and low hysteresis, while a powder equivalent of silicon steel to give intermediate magnetic quality with higher saturation flux density was also manufactured. For the past sixteen years the main product from this plant has been a ternary alloy of copper-nickel-iron of the permalloy group which produces the highest quality powder cores in a range of permeabilities up to 140. The latter grade is mainly used for miniature loading coils known as 'wedding rings', indicating their very small size, which are housed in many hundreds in a container for the loading of the large underground cables which carry most shorter distance telephone circuits. Thus the original process used unsuccessfully to make the first experimental magnetic powders by various workers was ultimately proved capable of manufacturing the powder equivalents of the principal solid and sheet materials in widespread use today.

The plant consumes large amounts of pure hydrogen produced by electrolysis of water, made conducting by caustic soda of optimum proportions. Direct current of 2000 amperes provided by a 3-phase static rectifier makes enough gas for the reduction of several tons

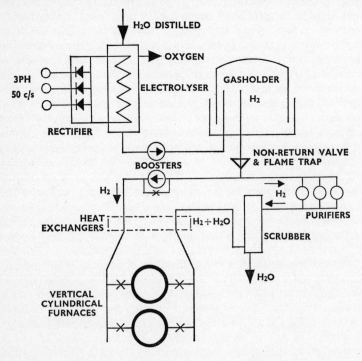

Fig. 5.1 Hydrogen-Reduction Plant for Magnetic Powder Production.

of magnetic powder per week. The mixed oxides are spread in stacks of shallow circular trays and heated in vertical furnace pots that can be removed with hydrogen flowing after reduction is completed, to be cooled in adjacent pits. To deal with the uneven rate of reduction, and hence of hydrogen consumption, the gas is circulated with ample storage and purification facilities, shown in the simplified diagram in fig. 5.1.

Though many of the uses for iron powder-cores in the electronics industries are now provided by ferrites, they have important future possibilities for high frequency power circuits discussed in later chapters. The reduction plant described above is mainly intended for the production of high grade alloy powders used in limited tonnage, but other methods are available for greater outputs at low cost. In particular, brittle iron-silicon-aluminium alloys with lower hysteresis and eddy current losses than commercial sheet materials can be readily produced in powder form and moulded into cores with good saturation values relative to any grade of ferrite. Consisting entirely of plentiful and cheap raw materials, they are the economic equivalent of barium ferrite in the permanent magnet sphere with iron as the main constituent. Consequently they can be included in the general category of iron powder-cores to indicate the kind of high quality that could be made available on a large tonnage basis when such a demand arises. This could not be economically provided by thinner strips and sheets of conventional silicon steels.

It is necessary, however, to examine certain inherent limitations to the relative permeability of powder-cores which must be insulated electrically in order to give the very low eddy current losses usually needed for frequencies up to the radio range. It will be found in power uses, as well as for electronics at mainly low flux densities, that the permeability must be related to the frequency in an inverse relationship; this applies especially to magnetic circuits in the medium power range with airgaps.

5.5 Limitations of Iron Powder Cores

During the 1950s there was considerable activity in the use of electrolytic iron powder of high purity and relatively low cost for a variety of magnetic cores in both insulated and uninsulated state. These were partly inspired by the progress in powder metallurgy which provided the specialised plant and equipment for mass-producing simple or fairly complex shapes at low cost, if the quantity to a particular design and size could be more than tens of thousands and preferably many millions. This would ensure that the high capital and tooling costs could be adequately covered, but it required market conditions progressive enough to withstand the hazards of innovation, yet stable enough to maintain continuity of design for a period of years. Most of the established designs in the smaller products in electrical engineering, such as small motors, were based upon the highly complex patterns of slots, teeth and pole pieces made possible by use of sheet steels, which could not be adapted to the new techniques. In the electronics industries the rapid and unforeseen introduction of ferrites added to the rate of technological change which was unfavourable to components based on iron powder.

Considerable progress was made in producing small pole pieces by sintering pressed powder compacts at temperatures near the melting point in order to achieve the highest possible specific gravity, so that the working magnetic flux density would be close to that obtained with machined solid iron; additional coining operations assisted this objective. But this was a cost-reducing operation and no technical improvement could be claimed for the use of powder methods. The powder could not be insulated in any way in order to reduce losses because the reduction of permeability would be disastrous to the electrical performance, and in the case of d.c. machines it is not necessary to laminate the poles, which carry uni-directional flux.

From the design standpoint it is thus clearly necessary to treat iron powder cores for high flux density uses in the same way as ferrite magnets. Both are inherently low permeability materials and cannot be effectively used as substitutes in the high permeability magnetic circuits on which the whole of present electrical engineering is based. Both can give their outstanding technical advantages only in special machines designed for, and based upon, their special characteristics. Sheet magnetic material provides primary lamination against eddy currents without reducing the permeability along the path of the flux, but the best kinds of magnetic powder with thinnest insulation film must give the effect of an appreciable airgap when made into cores. A spiralled tape core or one made from iron wire will also have an equivalent airgap with consequent reduction in permeability, and this is the penalty for the greatly improved eddy current loss which would be excessive at frequencies above a few hundreds of cycles per second if commercial sheet laminations were used.

The permeability of iron being roughly 1000 times that of air, a relatively narrow gap cut radially in an iron ring will greatly reduce the equivalent permeability of the magnetic circuit. It is convenient to treat the airgap length along the magnetic path as a percentage of the latter; thus a 0.1% airgap will have the same magnetic reluctance, if leakage flux is neglected, as the whole iron ring and their combined permeability will be 500, or half that of the iron alone. A 1% airgap would mean that its reluctance will be ten times that of the iron and the combined permeability will be less than 100; in other words the 99% of the volume of the whole magnetic circuit occupied by iron is now having only a small influence upon the total reluctance. Hence the permeability of a powder core is mainly decided by the geometry and proportion of the small amount of non-magnetic material—insulating film, filler or binder, as well as voids or air—rather than by the magnetic properties of the powder, though the losses of the core will of course derive from the metal.

Airgaps are essential to the magnetic circuits of nearly all transducers operated electromagnetically and the equivalent percentage airgap of their magnetic circuits tends to become larger as their size becomes smaller, for mechanical tolerance reasons. In these circumstances the same argument about the limited importance of the magnetic material permeability will apply, and materials with considerably lower permeability than the 1000 level can be used, but in practice this necessitates the employment of short magnetic circuits to minimise leakage flux. Only in transformers, large machines and certain kinds of choke coil can very high permeability be regarded as a major factor in design.

It is difficult to make calculations or to illustrate adequately by diagrams the magnetic effects of highly subdivided cores of ferromagnetic metals, but a first approximation is given by regarding the particles as cubes of equal size. A ring core is shown in Fig. 5.2 with this kind of subdivision, with the faces of the cubes parallel to each other in radial planes. The non-magnetic or insulating material will then contribute two kinds of effect:—

1. About one-third of it will form an equivalent airgap which will greatly reduce the core permeability relative to that of the solid metal.

2. The remaining two-thirds will reduce the effective saturation flux density of the core relative to that of the metal, about proportionally.

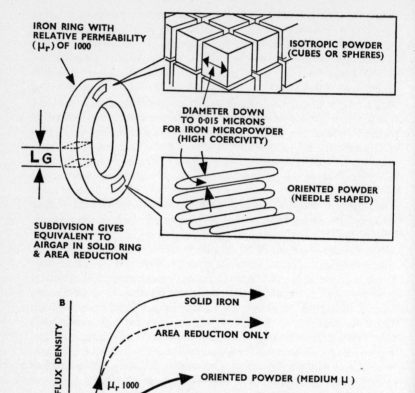

IRON RING WITH RELATIVE PERMEABILITY (μ_r) OF 1000

ISOTROPIC POWDER (CUBES OR SPHERES)

L G

DIAMETER DOWN TO 0·015 MICRONS FOR IRON MICROPOWDER (HIGH COERCIVITY)

ORIENTED POWDER (NEEDLE SHAPED)

SUBDIVISION GIVES EQUIVALENT TO AIRGAP IN SOLID RING & AREA REDUCTION

B — FLUX DENSITY

SOLID IRON

AREA REDUCTION ONLY

μ_r 1000

ORIENTED POWDER (MEDIUM μ)

ISOTROPIC POWDER (LOW μ)

O — MAGNETIZING FORCE — H

Fig. 5.2 Effect of Subdivision on Iron Powder-Core.

The diagram shows the individual and combined effects upon the shape of the magnetising curve; these also apply, but to a smaller extent, to iron wire and iron tape cores wound in a spiral form. In the case of highly oriented needle-shaped particles with length ten times their diameter, the equivalent airgap would be reduced to one-tenth the value based upon cubic particles without altering the reduction of saturation given in (2). In this way the core permeability could be better related to that of the metal.

Typical cores for high frequency uses are made with about 25% non-magnetic material by volume, give about 10% equivalent airgap and result in core permeability in the region of 10. Alloy cores with a few percent of insulation by volume and moulded with highest compacting pressures have values of permeability between 100 and 150 with the metal permeability around the 10 000 level. Powder cores of pure iron made commercially give permeability below 100 with minimum adequate insulation, but higher values are obtained by previously rolling the coarse powder into flakes and using magnetic orientation methods during the moulding process. It may be concluded that relatively simple shapes of iron core at the 100 permeability level could be made in large quantities at low cost for kilocycle frequency power uses up to around 20kc/s.

Permeability values must be related to application: 1000 and higher relates to d.c. and power station frequencies; 100 to higher power-frequencies and to smaller magnetic circuits with airgaps (trans-ducers etc.), and 10 to open magnetic circuits (cylinders etc.) for radio frequencies, with maximum particle sizes respectively in the region of 1000, 100 and 10 microns. The finer grades with lower permeability can be made with normal powder metallurgy plant and pressure intensities by automatic processes in large repetition quantities, but the higher permeabilities need greater pressures and are consequently more expensive; this imposes an economic limit to their further development unless the shapes are very simple and the quantity required very large. The permeability categories relative to their resistivity and applications are given in Fig. 2.2.

5.6 Micropowder Magnets

When it became widely known in the late 1940s that finer grades of iron powder could be made into practical permanent magnets, there was thus a considerable technology available in this special branch of powder metallurgy. However, this involved the further extension into still finer particles and the equivalent of cores with permeability down to 1 (the relative permeability of air), a new concept also for permanent magnets; these traditionally had permeability values in the 100 to 10 range corresponding to the early hard steels and the later high-coercivity alnico alloy magnets. Stated in other terms, this was the first indication of the basic property of future magnets in which the coercivity would be increased to the level of remanence by earlier measurements (in oersteds and gauss) and values of

$\mu_0 H_c$ would approach B_r in modern units. Although these micro-powder magnets, using the name to denote fine ferromagnetic powders of sub-micron size which derive high coercivity from their particle dimensions, did not achieve the practical performance to the predicted extent, they provided the information necessary to achieve it later with ferrite magnets. This subject is thus of the greatest importance to the development of modern dynamic permanent magnets.

The severe post-war shortages of cobalt and nickel for the manu-facture of conventional alloy magnets provided a strong incentive for widespread development work in this field, but the main credit must be given to Néel and his staff of Grenoble University in association with the French metallurgical company, Société Ugine. Within a few years they had developed a commercial process for making the equivalents of the pre-war isotropic grades of alni and alnico. These grades filled an important gap until replaced by the new oriented grades of conventional cast alnico. The subsequent work in this country and America indicated that this could be much more important than a substitute material, so that micropowders could be made into a wide range of magnets with different magnetic and mechanical properties from a single starting material.

Severe development and manufacturing hazards arose from the pyrophoric properties of these very fine metal powders in the presence of air, owing to the great surface area exposed to it. If the particles are small and fluffy enough to be suspended, they may cause an explosion; if dense enough to be collected in a container, the whole batch may suddenly become red-hot in rapidly changing to an oxide, and this can apply in changing also from a lower into a higher oxide. Smooth and regular particles are less prone to this trouble, which is rare for even the finest carbonyl iron powders, but relatively coarse dendritic particles are sometimes pyrophoric and a small proportion of this kind of material will affect a large batch of otherwise stable powder. The only known way of storing and handling iron micro-powders is by immersing them in benzene which is itself highly inflammable and thus adds to the hazard. In association they can set fire to such material as wood, cloth or paper on making contact.

The French process used ferrous formate as starting material, fed into a horizontal rotary kiln furnace to convert it into oxide. This was introduced at the top of conical towers into an upward stream of dry hydrogen, the velocity of which could be controlled to give the required particle size of the reduced powder, together with temperature control at about 200°C. Under these conditions there is little chance of grain growth which would greatly diminish the particle coercivity and the micropowder can be removed at intervals in special containers under benzene. This is then compacted in the wet state in appropriate moulds which have channels for handling the surplus liquid squeezed out during the pressing process. As soon as it is compacted, the micropowder magnet material becomes stable enough to handle without precautions, but needs vacuum-impregnation with a suitable lacquer to fill the pores of the compact and to impart a durable surface finish, in order to meet normal stability and ageing requirements. Thereafter the pressed compacts are magnetised and treated like conventional magnets, but are readily distinguished by their superior finish and appearance, with nearly half the physical density of typical steel or cast metal. Though early production magnets were somewhat brittle and tended to weakness at the edges, this was overcome with experience and improved designs of mould.

Micropowder magnets can be machined by normal workshop methods, such as drilling and tapping, on account of their physical softness. They can be moulded around a splined shaft for producing small rotors which would be automatically balanced on account of the uniform density of the pressed material. Many of the tyre-operated cycle dynamos were made at that period by this method, giving a saving in weight and smooth operation. Other early applications were telephone receiver and loudspeaker magnets to meet specifications drawn up for the early alnico alloys. These called for moderate stability and ageing tests, not being necessarily associated with the more stringent needs of measuring apparatus and instruments.

Attempts were made in England at that time to produce finer grades of iron powder with the equipment outlined in paragraph 5.4 in order to manufacture micropowder magnets with somewhat lower energy products more cheaply than the French process. This showed that the process was too critical for finest oxides when stacked lightly in shallow containers, owing to grain growth. Experiments with French micropowders, however, proved that they could be coated with thin plastic films by the standard methods developed for making radio cores, and the same kind of pressing plant and tools could be adapted for quantity production. Such coated micropowders could be stored safely and overcame the considerable hazards of the French process based on the use of benzene.

9

They enabled the coercivity of the unpressed material to be maintained with higher pressure intensities so that additional grades with lower remanence could be provided. Additionally, the plastic coating material could also act as a binder in order to improve the mechanical strength of the finished product and produced magnets with the electrical properties of insulators. These technical and economic improvements appeared sufficient to justify the development of special grades of magnet for new applications, rather than substitutes for established designs and materials. Investigation showed that this applied especially in electrical instruments and integrating meters which had always been dependent upon various grades of steel magnet, but for these uses the highest degree of long-term stability was essential.

5.7 Micropowder Magnet Applications

While the original main interest in this novel kind of magnet lay in the possibility of using pure iron micropowder in place of complex alloys dominated by strategically restricted and costly elements, the relatively high cost of iron made from ferrous formate or oxalate tended to make the price of magnets high in spite of the great economies that were made when the coated micropowders were used. But the main drawback of hydrogen-reduced micropowders was that the particles were nearly spherical and could not be used in oriented grades which were then being adopted for most alloy magnets. For a given cost of raw material, the latter gave over double the magnet strength of the isotropic alnicos and many more magnets could be produced with available supplies of cobalt and nickel.

Higher saturation flux density will give improved magnetic performance to micropowder magnets and a 20 to 50% alloy of cobalt with iron will give roughly a corresponding improvement in energy product. It was found that these alloys could be made by the above process by using co-precipitated formates in suitable proportions, and this also gave a high-coercivity cobalt-ferrite at the end of the first stage through the rotary kiln (though no practical use was made of this at the time). The relative performance of the two grades of micropowder magnet, high remanence and high coercivity, in pure iron and cobalt-iron is shown in the set of demagnetising curves in Fig. 5.3. The high coercivity grades used the insulated micropowder in the finished product with the advantages of production and mechanical properties given above, while the insulating film was

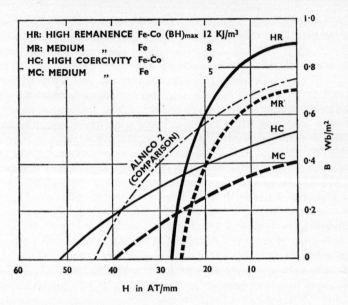

Fig. 5.3 Demagnetising Curves for Isotropic Micropowder Magnets.

removed for obtaining high remanence at a stage when the pyrophoric effect had been avoided. It was found possible to mould composite magnets with pole pieces of soft iron coarse powder or in some cases of solid shaped metal, but the tooling cost tended to be high when producing the equivalent of a standard design.

On this general point, the conclusion with regard to applications is similar to that already given earlier; the best overall results, technical performance for minimum cost, could be obtained by designing the device from first principles in order to use the new techniques to best advantage. This is clearly difficult in an established market and is generally limited to new fields of application.

Unlike all other kinds of magnet, the micropowder type is moulded without subsequent heating and can thus be made in large quantities in automatic presses to very close dimensional tolerances, approaching 0.001 inch. Adding to this novel advantage the great uniformity of physical density of the moulded material, it is possible to make the variations of magnetic performance from the required standard much closer than ever before. This can greatly reduce the relatively high proportion of the total cost of measuring instruments and meters spent upon calibration and adjustment. In the case of small measuring instruments made in large quantities and using conventional metal magnets, it is necessary to calibrate each individually and to mark the dial with special apparatus requiring skilled operation. With micropowder magnets it was found that a predetermined scale, printed cheaply and visually better in requisite numbers, could be assembled in a short time to give first grade accuracy. A somewhat similar case was found in house integrating meter assembly where great uniformity of braking magnets gave corresponding improvement in electrical performance uniformity and, moreover, the large demand for one size of magnet gave scope for considerable economies by automatic production methods.

The chief obstacle to these aims was the imperative need for the highest possible degree of stability with long periods of time and with changing conditions of use. Present magnets have been established for these uses for many decades and considerable time is needed to complete the tests. In these cases a considerable number of electricity meters were in continual operation with specimen micropowder magnets matching standard metal magnets under all required conditions; summation of the differences gave very accurate comparison and it was found that the best plastic-bonded type averaged about three times the required variation limits. This was just inadequate for these requirements though satisfactory for other kinds of use. It was later shown in America that a much denser filler such as lead could give stability values better than those obtained with any kind of solid metal commercial magnets. This had been achieved in about a decade after the first practical micropowder magnets, with completely unknown performance capabilities, had been made under extremely difficult conditions to meet an immediate need.

5.8 Oriented Micropowders

During the past four years, after several years of intensive development, the first oriented micropowder magnets were made commercially available in America under the name 'Lodex' in various grades by magnetic performance and composition. The acicular (needle-shaped) micropowder from which these are made is described as elongated single domain (abbreviated to ESD). It is produced on a considerable annual tonnage by a development of the electrolytic deposition process into a mercury cathode, which was the basis of the earliest experiments in this subject. The anodes are made of the metal or alloy of the desired product, which follows the French work

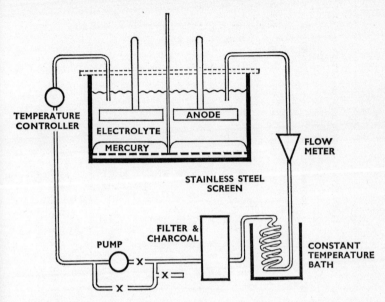

Fig. 5.4 Basic Electrolytic Plant for making Elongated Single-Domain Micropowders.

in making pure iron and cobalt-iron alloy with the latter giving the
same decided magnetic advantage (Fig. 5.4).

The fine powder is deposited in the mercury pool which is removed
for concentrating the magnetic product into a slurry; this is then
compacted under a magnetic field in order to set it in the desired
oriented state and to facilitate protection against oxidation. It is then
embedded in a matrix, which can be either metallic or plastic according to ultimate use, and this also acts as binder and particle separator
(to maintain coercivity) as well as a means for preventing oxidation.
In this way all the material is separated from the mercury and the
latter is returned for further use. The mercury-free impregnated
compacts are either coined to their final shape or are ground to
powder for feeding to powder metallurgy machines, using magnetic
orientation methods where directional properties are required.

A range of magnetic properties is obtained by varying the packing
fraction of the material from 0.2 to 0.5 with both iron and iron-
cobalt for isotropic and oriented conditions. These are given in
Table 5.1 in detail in order to indicate the wide range of magnetic

PACKING FRACTION	ELONGATED SINGLE DOMAIN—IRON						ELONGATED SINGLE DOMAIN—IRON-COBALT					
	ISOTROPIC			ORIENTED			ISOTROPIC			ORIENTED		
	H_c	B_r	$(BH)_{max}$	H_c	B_r	$(BH)_{max}$	H_c	B_r	$(BH)_{max}$	H_c	B_r	$(BH)_{max}$
0·2	78	0·24	6·5	86	0·28	8	96	0·26	8	110	0·33	13
0·25	72	·31	7·2	81	·37	11	92	·33	9·6	106	·45	21
0·3	65	·39	9·6	73	·5	13	84	·41	11·2	100	·57	25
0·35	57	·46	9·6	65	·6	16	77	·48	13	92	·69	27
0·4	48	·54	10·4	54	·7	17·2	66	·56	13	80	·79	28
0·45	38	·62	8·8	45	·79	17·6	55	·65	11·2	68	·9	29
0·5	27	·68	7·2	37	·89	17	42	·73	9·6	52	1·02	26
UNITS	COERCIVITY H_c in AT/mm ;			REMANENCE B_r in Wb/m^2 ;			ENERGY PRODUCT $(BH)_{max}$ in kJ/m^3					

(Converted to MKSA units by author)

TABLE 5.1. MAGNETIC PROPERTIES OF ELONGATED MICROPOWDERS AS FUNCTION OF PACKING FRACTION (*General Electric of America*)

properties that can be obtained from a single starting material by relatively slight modifications to the manufacturing process. For commercial reasons the available grades for sale are restricted to those with optimum performance. As before, the better performance of the iron-cobalt grades makes their use preferable to that of the iron. These are based upon a lead matrix which imparts the high density of between 8.5 and 9.8 gram/cm³, but lightweight grades with plastic binder are also made for those purposes where the highest stability is less important than the weight of the magnet.

It will be seen that in all the grades of micropowder magnet in Table 5.1 the packing fraction is 0.5 or less, so that there is generally a greater proportion of the space in the material which is air or filler-binder than the volume of magnetic metal. In the highest coercivity grades only one-fifth of the volume consists of ferro-magnetic material, so that a relatively costly micropowder on a weight basis may be manufactured cheaply in these proportions with a wider choice of non-magnetic ingredients than had been possible with any earlier composite magnetic core materials. Present commercial grades have packing fractions of from 0.25 to 0.45, the latter giving the highest energy product of 29 kJ/m³, about three-quarters the value for typical oriented alnico. On a weight basis, instead of volume, the new kind of magnet could be made appreciably better than the conventional if light non-magnetic ingredients were used. The Table also shows the wide range of magnetic properties obtainable from a single supply of micropowder, with coercivity from 52 to 112 AT/mm and corresponding remanence from 1.02 to 0.33 Wb/m² for iron-cobalt. Considerably higher values have been obtained under laboratory conditions, but these are still about one-quarter of the ultimate quality expected, though the basis of this deduction has been queried in recent years.

The practical position today must be judged by what is commercially available; in the all-important requirement for highest coercivity for the new applications described later, barium ferrite gives over twice the value of these oriented micropowders with comparable remanence to the ESD-iron. The ESD iron-cobalt gives 25% higher remanence but contains the costly element which would restrict its use for largest-scale applications on economic grounds. Both kinds of new material, ferrite and high-coercivity micropowders, can be made as electrical insulators of similar physical density by moulding processes and represent the modern magnets of the title of this book; they can together be classed as 'moulded magnetic materials'. Though the ESD-iron will have the advantage of moulding dimensional accuracy and machinability compared with sintered ferrites, the recent plastic-bonded ferrite powders have acquired these merits, though at the expense of lower energy product and remanence. Thus both kinds, whether based on iron micropowders or iron oxides, have more in common at present when compared with conventional alloy magnets, and this will become increasingly apparent with the expected future improvements.

A recent extension of this American elongated single domain project attempts to combine the merits of ferrites with those of micropowders in a single material, high coercivity with insulating properties added to relatively high saturation flux density with better remanence levels. The good magnetic properties of cobalt ferrite have been reported from several sources, though they have hitheito received little commercial attention, and the iron-cobalt micropowders made by both the French and American processes can be readily converted to them. If the ESD iron-cobalt micropowder is subjected to a partial oxidizing atmosphere so that the particle surface contains about 12% oxygen, the coercivity is increased nearly fivefold, from 40 to 192 AT/mm for a 57-31 Fe-Co alloy. The commercial grade, Lodex 55, uses a lightweight binder and has the following properties:—

Coercivity 116-132 AT/mm

Remanence 0.58-0.62 Wb/m^2

Energy Product (BH)$_{max}$ 31-33 kJ/m^3 (at B of 0.35 Wb/m^2).

Reversible Remanence Change 0.008%

Specific Gravity 3.8-4.2 gram/cm^3. Electrically non-conducting.

This material is appreciably better than ferrite magnets in remanence with coercivity nearly up to the sintered ferrite level, the energy product being about 30% better. Its physical density is similar to that of bonded ferrite, nearly half the typical metal magnet value. It thus provides a new quality in the whole range of permanent magnet materials, but economically it must be grouped with the cast metal magnets, relying on an equivalent proportion of cobalt to obtain its permanent magnet properties. However, this is a most interesting development in showing the close relationship between the ferrite and micropowder groups of magnetic material and pointing the way to further lines of research.

No details of the cost of making oriented micropowders have yet been published, though the ESD-iron in lower packing fractions is said to compete with ferrite, but the published details indicate a more complex and expensive process for the essential material. The final product is more suitable at the present for smaller complicated magnets of traditional kind rather than the more massive simpler shapes which are required for the dynamic applications described in later chapters. This subject, taken in association with the following account of ferrites, would appear to provide the key to the future of permanent magnets.

5.9 References

1. Speed B. & Elmen G. W. 'Magnetic Properties of Compressed Powdered Iron', *Trans. A.I.E.E.*, Vol. 40, pp. 596-609, 1921.

2. Shackleton W. J. & Barber I. G. 'Compressed Powdered Permalloy: Manufacture & Magnetic Properties', *Trans. A.I.E.E.*, Vol. 47, p. 29, 1928.

3. Polgreen G. R. 'Moulded Magnetic Materials', *Electrical Review*, 13th May, 1955.

4. Falk R. B., Hooper G. D. & Studders R. J. 'Recent Developments in Elongated Single-Domain Iron & Iron-Cobalt Permanent Magnets', *J. of Applied Physics*, Vol. 30, No. 4, pp. 130S-133S, April 1959. See also same Journal Supplement, March 1961.

5. Meyer R. 'Les Aimants Permanents', *Revue Gén. de l'Electricité*, pp. 487-505, Oct. 1960.

6

FERRITES

Ferrite magnets with high magnetic strength are a very recent development from the well-known high frequency grades, and exhibit the same insulator properties. Even more important for all the applications to follow are the exceptional resistance to demagnetisation and the potential cheapness of this new permanent magnet material. Moreover, it is already available commercially in suitable shapes and sizes on a tonnage scale suitable for the smaller power-handling machines and equipment which are the main subject of this book. Hence this novel substance, from an engineering standpoint, requires a detailed description of its derivation and properties in view of the leading position it has quickly assumed in this field. The limitations imposed by its low saturation flux density and ceramic nature, which at first tended to restrict its use to open magnetic circuit conditions, have been overcome to a remarkable extent during the last few years so there now appears to be no limit to its scale of application.

6.1 General Description

The word 'ferrite' has been introduced during the past two decades to describe classes of magnetic materials made by the sintering at high temperature of mixed oxides of iron and of other metals. As oxides they have been known to possess ferromagnetic properties, with both higher and lower coercivity according to the composition and treatment, for many years; but it is only during this recent period that their magnetic quality has been improved to the extent necessary for widespread commercial and engineering use. This is mainly due to the recent great advance in the theoretical and scientific understanding of magnetic materials outlined in Chapter 4. Ferrites form the new scientific group of ferrimagnetic materials with electron spins partially compensated in a manner which results in a lower level of magnetic saturation, generally about a quarter of the figures for iron and the familiar iron-alloys used in power engineering. This disadvantage is relatively unimportant for low flux density operation, which applies to the great majority of uses in electronics and telecommunications where the losses at high frequencies are the dominant factor. It can thus be readily understood why the first important commercial ferrites were developed to meet the demands for telephone loading coils at speech frequencies and were extended into higher frequency grades before the permanent magnet possibilities could be assessed. This development sequence followed closely that of the powder cores and micropowder magnets given in the previous chapter. However, the finished product was much further removed from conventional magnetic materials based upon the properties and processes of ferromagnetic metals, the powder stage being intermediate in several respects. But, whereas the technology for metal powders had to be developed with novel manufacturing processes, ferrites could be made by ceramic methods which were in crude form probably the earliest process invented by man.

In the same way that ferromagnetic metals can range in physical and economic varieties from the finest instrument steels to cast iron, so ceramics can vary from fine porcelain to building bricks. Consequently a magnetic ferrite can have a wide range of qualities according to the skill and experience of the manufacturer and the price level of the product on which he may specialise in this broad field of industrial endeavour. One of the novel features of all these ferrites is their insulator resistivity, and the electrical industry established many years ago a group of specialised factories for the production of a wide range of high-grade insulators. Many of these, for example in overhead power lines, operate under mechanical conditions that could not be approached in earlier materials; hence the chances of new areas of development in ceramics are probably not greatly different from those of metal, the traditional raw material of the engineer. In manufacturing scale, the ceramic industry would seem to out-class all others in the ability to produce vast numbers of identical solid products by automatic methods at lowest cost, so that the suggested scale of application of ferrite magnets in later chapters can be regarded as another specialised field of insulator development and manufacture.

Against the familiar brittleness and poor dimensional tolerances of ceramics, from the engineering standpoint, must be set their freedom from corrosion, lightness and structural homogeneity. In the recent plastic-bonded grades of ferrite magnet, the brittleness is used to advantage to produce fine powder at low cost. This provides a greater diversity of material forms, such as rigid and flexible sheet and mouldings as well as various kinds of extrusion, than has ever been possible with metals. At the present time ferrite magnets can be produced in almost any desired physical form on the understanding that such features as flexibility, close tolerances and best surface finish are obtained at the cost of reduced magnetic performance, mainly in remanence; all these grades have coercivity higher than nearly every commercial alternative, with the corresponding outstanding ability to withstand all practical demagnetising conditions, however severe.

6.2 Low-loss Ferrites

When first developed as telephone components, magnetic ferrites with high permeability and low losses (hysteresis as well as eddy-currents) had a crystal structure in cubic form known as spinel. The most useful magnetic properties were found in compositions typified by the formula $MO.n \, Fe_2O_3$, where M is a divalent metal and n is a small integer; the divalent metals are either magnesium, manganese, copper, nickel and zinc, as well as iron. These can be combined in the form of double ferrites to give relatively high permeability accompanied by low coercivity to an extent unknown and unsuspected before the later 1930s when they were first developed in Holland. The electrical resistivity, in the region of 100 ohm.cm and higher was so much greater than that of metals that subdivision and particle insulation were not needed in order to reduce eddy current loss. The material could be moulded or extruded into the required size and shape and then 'fired' at temperatures above 1000°C to form a hard and brittle solid magnetic core, with specific gravity 4.8 gram/cm$_3$ and saturation flux density of 0.3 to 0.4 Wb/m^2.

The permeability averaged around 1000 and higher values could be obtained by use of highest purity raw materials and by careful control of every stage of the process. For the telephone components at speech and carrier frequencies (approx. 1 to 100 kc/s) it was generally not practicable to use this kind of material in the usual ring form because the permeability was about ten times too high and the stability would be very poor, although the losses might be small enough to meet requirements. It was essential to introduce an air-gap into the magnetic circuit in order to reduce its effective permeability to the 100 level (used for the best alloy powder cores). It seemed to be a retrogressive step to powder the material for re-pressing into an equivalent compact when this was quite unnecessary on loss-reduction grounds. Tests showed that it was possible with this high permeability ferrite to make mushroom-shaped cores which fitted each end of a thin cylindrical sleeve core so that an airgap of appropriate length was formed at the geographical centre of the assembly. A simple coil, wound on a bobbin that fitted closely round the stems of the mushroom cores and totally enclosed in the assembly, would then provide an inductance with negligible external leakage.

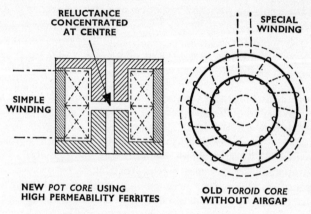

Fig. 6.1 Leakage-free Magnetic Circuits.

This ferrite pot core design is shown in Fig. 6.1 in comparison with the traditional toroidal core with uniform winding, which had hitherto been the only known means for obtaining a magnetic core with negligible leakage flux. It required special winding machines and skilled operatives to apply the toroidal winding uniformly, whereas the pot core could be wound on simple machines more quickly and with greater electro-magnetic efficiency, using virtually all the winding space. Moreover, it was easy to adjust the inductance value of the pot core wound with a fixed number of turns by inserting a thin rod core in the central hole, whereas the toroidal coil could only be adjusted approximately by altering the number of turns by hand. Thus, a very important development in magnetic circuits had arisen from the need to adapt a new and unfamiliar magnetic material to a traditional design, and this trend is repeated later on a larger scale as a result of what were originally regarded as the limitations of ferrite materials.

It is, however, important to note the conditions under which there will be negligible leakage field in Fig. 6.1 for the pot core design: virtually all the magnetic reluctance must be concentrated in the central airgap. This can be achieved only by the following:—

(a) The relative permeability of the core material must be high, about 1000 or more, and the magnetic area of the outer parts should be as great as conditions allow.

(b) The joints between the end cores and the outer core must be a fine ground fit.

(c) The winding must be symmetrically located with the same number of turns on each half relative to a plane through the airgap centre.

It will be clear that these conditions are less severe if a larger airgap is used so that the effective permeability of the assembly is greatly reduced below the 100 level. This applies to the higher frequency applications under conditions where screening against stray flux is also attained by electrostatic methods which are generally impracticable at audio- and lower carrier-frequencies.

The introduction of high permeability ferrites also brought further improvements to a.c. magnetic circuits by the use of cylindrical cores in place of the square or rectangular section made necessary by the shape of assembled laminations. A circular coil gives the minimum d.c. resistance relative to the flux it can enclose and is desirable for all electromagnetic designs, as well as being simpler to wind with high copper space factor. Short cylindrical cores could be made with compressed powder but with limited permeability; ferrites, on the other hand, can be extruded to any desired length and section with minimum tooling costs to give high permeability after the subsequent firing operation (though the value is somewhat lower than in the case of direct moulding). Ferrite rods of this type have been made in large numbers for the incorporated aerials in radio receivers for many years. They can be used to give a wide range of inductance change for a radio tuner, in addition to the small range necessary for a high stability trimmer for a fixed inductance. They have completed the revolution in the wide range of components used throughout the electronics industries, and based upon fixed and varied inductance, which was started with the iron powder cores.

Though many combinations of the ferrite compounds outlined earlier give good permeability levels and low hysteresis loss, the resistivity at radio frequencies of the better materials is too low and a different composition is required. The lower frequency material is generally a manganese-zinc ferrite and for 0.1 to 10 Mc/s a nickel-zinc ferrite gives better results, with 1000 times greater resistivity and about half the permeability. Other grades of the latter material with permeability down to 20 are used up to 100 Mc/s or higher. The temperature at which these low-loss ferrites lose their magnetic properties (Curie Point) is rather low for the high permeability grades, between 150 and 190°C., so that the permeability will tend to fall appreciably if they become warm. This temperature is very much higher, up to 500°C or similar to that of the later magnet ferrites, for the lower permeability grades produced for operation at radio frequencies. (See also Fig. 2.2).

In terms of cost, the raw material content is relatively high and the cost of processing and grinding is also considerable for the pot cores or other versions of nearly-closed magnetic circuits suitable for lower frequency uses. Their merits lie more in their performance and ease of construction, rather than the price difference of the material with iron or alloy powder cores. Although their low saturation flux density rules them out for the high permeability components of magnetic circuits which handle power, the cost of pole pieces or poleplates in this kind of material would be too high and the Curie Point too low for the kinds of application investigated later. Metallic iron in sheet or powder form, with or without minor alloying constituents, appears to be essential on magnetic, mechanical and economic grounds for this flux concentration purpose.

6.3 Early Permanent Magnet Ferrites

Magnetite, black oxide of iron and lodestone are the principal names of the well-known natural material, sometimes found in the magnetised state, which was the original source of magnetic energy up to the early part of last century. The usual chemical formula is Fe_3O_4 and if this is rewritten in the form $FeO.Fe_2O_3$ it will be seen to meet the earlier definition in this chapter of a magnetic ferrite; it could well be described as ferrous ferrite. In its natural state lodestone may have been magnetised to any degree and it is difficult to give reliable figures for its magnetic performance in modern terms, but tests made at the end of last century give coercivity equivalent to that of the available carbon steel magnets with about half their remanence level. A good quality lodestone with coercivity of 4 AT/mm and remanence of about 0.45 Wb/m^2 would have an energy product in the region of 1 kJ/m^3. This was the reason for the earlier comment that the latter measurement could be the basis of a figure of merit for magnetic strength. Thus, isotropic alnico is 10 on this basis and the best oriented alnico so far made experimentally is 100 (the commercial level at present approaching 50) with barium ferrite about 25; all these figures are indications of the progress made since the days of lodestone, as well as giving the energy product in latest units. (See also Fig. 2.8).

As in the case of micropowders and recent ferrites, the properties of synthetic magnetite Fe_3O_4 can vary greatly according to the details of the methods used to make and compact it. In the plastic-bonded grade, for example, the coercivity can be three times higher than the above-quoted level for the natural material, but with only one-quarter of the remanence; this same oxide could give figures closer to the lodestone properties by compacting it with a volatile binder and then sintering at a high temperature. The coercivity value of magnetic oxides of iron was very small up to 30 years ago when they first were used for magnetic recording. Since that time the great importance of magnetic tape consisting of narrow plastic film coated with iron oxide suitably dispersed in an appropriate 'binder' has become widely known for speech and music recording, computer memories, television recording, machine tool control and most other forms of automation. This is now a technology for magnetic recording specialists with its own library of textbooks to which the reader is referred for further information.

Although iron oxides are technically an important branch of ferrites, they are used under different conditions from permanent magnets which require the maximum coercivity and magnetic strength. In magnetic recording the coercivity level must be high enough for life and stability, but not so high that the record is difficult to erase and so that its field causes interference by coupling between adjacent turns in the spool. Experience has shown that this is about 20 AT/mm and the best performance is given by acicular gamma ferric oxide. The familiar red oxide widely used for pigments and many other commercial purposes is normally non-magnetic in the alpha-form, and treatment to give it the required gamma crystal structure will produce the required magnetic properties in the needle-shaped particles about one micron long.

The thickness of magnetic tape averages 0.002 inch (50 microns) of which about one-quarter is magnetic coating, so the density of magnetic material is very low relative to the tape sectional area, especially when the high dilution percentage of the dispersion medium is taken into account. The first magnetic recording, demonstrated in 1900 many years before amplifiers were invented, used steel wire and the further developments for the following 40 years were based upon the use of conventional permanent magnet materials in wire or tape form. Like the early disc records, these had to generate most of their acoustic energy by mechanical methods so the magnetic energy that could be stored in a given length of recording medium was very important. Consequently the recording medium was bulky and difficult to handle. The introduction of plastic tape coated with iron oxide that was of low magnetic quality by permanent magnet standards was only made possible by the refinements and improvements in thermionic amplifiers and appropriate screening against local and external interference. The energy product of the magnetic medium became relatively unimportant and from this point the new technology of magnetic recording tended to merge with electronics and to deviate from engineering concepts of efficiency, referred to in the early part of Chapter 2.

Typical dispersed iron oxide for magnetic recording gives coercivity of 17 AT/mm and remanence as low as 0.07 Wb/m^2. Attempts were made to use the earlier iron micropowders to improve these figures, especially the latter, but the much better magnetic performance did not make the expected improvement to the overall results. The physically soft coating gave much less wear of the recording and play-back heads than the abrasive oxides, but the corrosion problem was severe though tests indicated that it could be solved. Other tests with dispersed iron-cobalt oxides and micropowders of highest coercivity for permanent records indicated that these could be used as master records from which others could be 'printed' by physical contact rather like conventional printing; but these require considerable development which has limited scope when the present low-energy recording tape is available cheaply in a great variety of practical forms. The remainder of this chapter is thus limited to ferrites in the form of solid blocks of permanent magnet material.

The first commercial material in this category was a cobalt ferrite, known as Kato's Oxide, developed in Japan in 1930. It consisted of 50% Fe_3O_4 and 50% $Co.Fe_2O_3$, sintered at 1000°C. and cooled in a magnetic field from 300°C. The resulting material had coercivity of 32 to 47 AT/mm, high for that period, but the remanence was rather low and varied between 0.4 to 0.5 Wb/m^2 with density averaging 3.6 gram/cm^3. An American version of this ferrite, named Vectolite, containing less cobalt and 30% of Fe_2O_3 was found to

10

give more consistent performance and nearly twice the coercivity level with much lower remanence and energy product, the density being only 3.1 gram/cm³. These materials were relatively expensive with a limited number of suitable uses so they must be regarded as low in commercial value though important in a pioneer sense. A plastic-bonded version named Caslox was produced in this country in 1945 with coercivity of 56 AT/mm and low remanence of 0.11 Wb/m²; this was displayed in the form of two flat discs with central holes placed on a vertical glass rod (Fig. 6.2). By magnetising these

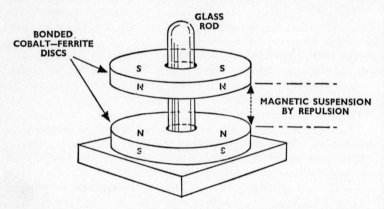

Fig. 6.2 Early Lightweight Ferrite Magnet Demonstration Unit.

discs axially so that the large parallel faces formed the magnetic poles, it was possible for one disc to support the other by mutual repulsion when placed so that adjacent faces were of the same polarity. This simple demonstration unit showed the possibilities of lightweight high-coercivity materials for magnetic suspension purposes.

6.4 Barium Ferrite

By the 1950s the low-loss ferrites described earlier had become commercially available in most industrial countries and experience had been gained in their manufacture as a novel kind of magnetic material and in their special grinding and handling as components. There thus was available a fund of practical experience for the development and production of the permanent magnet versions of this material which the theoretical work could predict, and which had already appeared in the catalogues of some magnet manufacturers. The first permanent magnet grades made with this ferrite background had a considerably higher coercivity than any commercial magnet and appeared at a time when there was a great and rapidly growing demand for focusing units for television receivers. These consisted of a pair of ring magnets surrounding the neck of the television tube in order to focus the electron beam by means of an external control. The magnetic field had to project inwardly in an axial direction in a path that inevitably contained a large airgap, for which a material of highest coercivity was needed in the limited depth of space available. Barium ferrite provided the best technical answer to this novel demand but it also was made from cheap and non-strategic materials at a time when cobalt and nickel were still in limited supply, and the cost of television receivers had to be kept to the lowest possible level. All these factors combined to increase the rate of manufacture of this new kind of permanent magnet in an unprecedented manner to the annual output level of thousands of tons within a few years of the first publication of its patents and properties.

This television demand fell off precipitately when improved methods of focusing by electrostatic control were made available on a large scale so that a large production capacity became available for other applications. This was an unusually favourable set of circumstances for the use of magnets in a new area of development where it was essential to have considerably larger units at much lower prices than had hitherto been possible or economically feasible.

Barium ferrite belongs to a group of materials which were first investigated in 1925 and given the name 'magnetoplumbite'. During the following years it was found that these compounds of either lead, barium or strontium with iron oxides had a hexagonal crystal structure and ferromagnetic properties but these were not fully investigated until 1952 as an extension of the notable work in Holland which had produced the low-loss ferrites a decade or more earlier. These were at first isotropic magnets with low remanence below the level needed for the commercial demands that then existed and this material would probably have made slow progress in the commercial direction if the above great demand for television receivers had not arisen.

A further publication appeared only three years later in 1955 giving details of oriented grades of ferrite magnet, disclosing the relatively simple methods of obtaining nearly three times the magnetic energy from the same cheap and plentiful raw materials. For the first time this brought a technical competitor to the oriented alnico series of magnets which were then becoming dominant in all the main fields of application. With nearly half the physical density of the magnet alloys, ferrites in best oriented grades could give equivalent magnetic energy on a weight standard based upon energy product values designed for mainly static applications, but the full significance of their threefold superiority in coercivity has not yet been fully accepted. The importance in dynamic uses is discussed later in this chapter, but the impact of the new material upon the existing magnet market was limited by the following factors:—

(a) the temperature coefficient of ferrite was about ten times that of most metal magnets, limiting its use for measuring instruments and meters which comprise about one quarter of the market;

(b) the cost of grinding or shaping ferrites to the established designs based on metal magnets would make them too expensive;

(c) the hitherto unknown levels of high coercivity and low remanence of ferrites called for different shapes of magnetic circuit, with short length and large area, which necessitated a redesign to obtain the available magnetic energy, regardless of energy product values.

The latter step is possible only for a very large and continuing demand, and this applies mainly to loudspeaker magnets which comprise half the permanent magnet market; in this field the new oriented ferrites have been very successful, especially in the larger sizes. This subject is followed up in the next chapters.

Barium ferrite consists of over 80% red iron oxide and the remainder is barium carbonate, both freely available in large tonnages at low cost. The ores of both materials are widely distributed in large deposits throughout the world so that the supply could meet any engineering demand that may arise from the numerous large-scale uses outlined later, and under these conditions the price level should fall to that of steel which uses similar raw materials. These economic factors are of the greatest significance as the probable key to the ultimate scale of application. The alternatives to barium, lead and strontium, are also relatively cheap and plentiful by other magnet raw material standards, and recent claims have indicated superior magnetic properties by their use, but these are marginal and have so far not justified special production. At the present time all the leading industrial countries of the world are manufacturing one material for this market, barium ferrite, in a number of different grades which are justified by required differences in magnetic or physical properties. This is a welcome advance in rationalisation compared with the hundreds of different alloys used for metal magnets to cover a more limited range of practical needs.

6.5 Properties of Barium Ferrite

The composition of barium ferrite is given by the formula $BaO.6Fe_2O_3$, which may also be written $BaFe_{12}O_{19}$. In manufacture it is usual to incorporate rather more than the theoretical amount of barium than this denotes, and the ingredients, red iron oxide and commercially pure barium carbonate, are thoroughly wet-mixed in a ballmill and then dried and briquetted. These compacts are fired at about 1200°C. to form the ferrite material, which is milled and sieved to the required size for subsequent pressing into the required finished shapes by use of established powder metallurgy processes and machinery, and incorporating lubricants and binding materials. In designing press moulds for this purpose it is necessary to allow for the considerable shrinkage of up to 20% in linear dimensions for this kind of material, which makes it very desirable to use only symmetrical shapes of simple form with pressing depth considerably less than the linear size. Flat rings of rectangular section and bricks of conventional proportions are the most appropriate shapes and it will be shown later that these can be readily applied to the kinds of magnetic circuit mostly required in the future. The pressing process is carried out with the application of a strong magnetic field in the preferred direction for oriented grades which are expected to become almost universal with these simple shapes. They give nearly three times the magnetic energy with the same starting materials, and a relatively small increase in manufacturing cost. The final firing is slightly higher in temperature than the first and careful control is essential, but the furnacing of ceramics on a continuous feed basis has been explored for other uses and much special-purpose plant has been developed.

Like all other ceramics, barium ferrite is glass-hard and cannot be machined by workshop methods except grinding, and this only with suitable coolants and abrasives. Ultrasonic methods of shaping and drilling are technically feasible for experimental purposes, but are not economically viable for production until ultrasonic power is widely available at low cost (a possibility discussed in detail later).

In the general case of designs based upon a standard range of flat rings, it is generally enough to grind the two pole faces flat and parallel; this can be arranged at relatively low cost for large production runs. The surfaces which are left unground may vary in dimensions by about 2% above and below the nominal value; this may be regarded as excessive by engineering standards, but the cost of grinding where it is not essential may increase the price to an extent not compatible with the design modification that might avoid it.

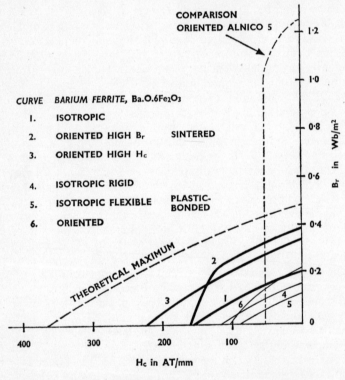

Fig. 6.3 Performance Curves: Typical Ferrite Magnet Grades.

Oriented ferrite magnets are now becoming generally available in alternative grades, high remanence for optimum $(BH)_{max}$ or energy product for static uses such as loudspeakers, or high coercivity for dynamic uses. The latter grade has the almost linear demagnetizing curve which makes it possible for the first time to magnetize the material in the factory with the assurance that the properties will not be appreciably deteriorated in any kind of subsequent use or maltreatment short of fracture. This does not apply to the high remanence grade which is generally treated like the alloy magnets by arranging for the magnetising process to be delayed until the completion of assembly. The pronounced curvature in its demagnetisation characteristic is shown in Fig. 6.3 in comparison with the other isotropic and oriented grades and the bonded materials described below, with their corresponding magnetic performance factors summarised in Table 6.1. It will be seen that all the lower energy grades maintain good coercivity levels above those of conventional metal magnets, as well as exhibiting the linearity of performance described above.

Theoretical considerations shown that the limit to the performance of barium ferrite is reached with remanence at 0.46 Wb/m² and coercivity of 370 AT/mm, which indicates that there is still scope for much improvement. This is mainly in coercivity which could be nearly doubled, and this would also apply to the energy product.

A comparison with typical modern cast alloy magnets is provided at the bottom of Table 6.1 and in Fig. 6.3 in order to show the remarkable change in magnetic properties throughout the whole ferrite range compared with those of metal magnets. For many years manufacturers have striven to improve the remanence by the use of orientation processes and have succeeded in raising it about 30% above that of early magnet steels, whereas the introduction of the early cast alloys made their great advance in energy product by raising the coercivity a number of times, but at the cost of considerable reduction of remanence. The recent introduction and rapid commercial expansion of several different grades of barium ferrite has repeated this trend to a much greater degree; coercivities are all well above the best that metal magnets can provide but the remanence has fallen to about a quarter in the best sintered material and to less than a tenth in the novel flexible material that appeared a few years ago.

This change has called for a complete reassessment of the methods for judging the quality of permanent magnets as components and of the material from which they are made. From this stage onward it is essential to express magnetic performance in terms of two coercivity figures, the working value H_c and also the intrinsic coercivity H_{ci} which denotes the ultimate ability to withstand demagnetization;

GROUP	MATERIAL	DATE	COERCIVITY H_c AT/mm	INTRINSIC COERCIVITY H_{ci} AT/mm	REMANENCE B_r Wb/m²	ENERGY PRODUCTS STATIC $(BH)_{max}$ kJ/m³	DYNAMIC $(B_pH)_{max}$ kJ/m³	DENSITY gram/cm³	REMARKS
HISTORIC	LODESTONE (Fe_3O_4)	from BC	4		0·4	up to 1			very variable
EARLY	KATO'S OXIDE	1930	40		0·4	8		3·6	variable
COBALT FERRITES	VECTOLITE	1933	72		0·16	4		3·1	
	CASLOX (bonded)	1945	56		0·11	1·7		3·2	
BARIUM FERRITE	Gr.I ISOTROPIC	1952	140	256	0·2	8	25	4·9	principal commercial grades.
SINTERED	Gr.II HIGH B_rORIENTED	1955	152	156	0·38	26	46	4·9	
	Gr.III HIGH H_cORIENTED	1959	208	220	0·34	21	62	4·9	
BARIUM FERRITE	RIGID ISOTROPIC	1958	110		0·17	5	19	4	figures vary according to mechanical properties
BONDED POWDER	FLEXIBLE ISOTROPIC	1958	80		0·1	2	8	3	
	ORIENTED (USA)	1961	105		0·21	8	20	3·7	
THEORETICAL MAX. BARIUM FERRITE Ba.O $6Fe_2O_3$			370	700	0·46	43	160		
COMPARISON	ORIENTED ALNICO 5	1945	52	52	1·25	44	50	7·3	main commercial magnets since 1950s

TABLE 6.1. FERRITE PERMANENT MAGNETS: MAGNETIC PERFORMANCE FIGURES

also there must be two standards for energy product, one for static uses (the familiar BH_{max} value) and a new dynamic figure to indicate the performance under variable airgap conditions with a wide range in reluctance. This is the $(B_pH)_{max}$ column in the table which gives the total flux density B_p available when the magnetic circuit is changed from fully-closed to fully-open conditions. This amounts to the B_r value in the case of a linear demagnetizing curve because the recoil loop coincides with it, but in the case of the highly curved characteristic of oriented metal magnets it is given by the limited proportion of the remanence made available by the optimum recoil loop (i.e. when H is zero). The immense practical importance of this new approach to magnets used under dynamic conditions is described later in this chapter.

The table clearly indicates the great advantage in terms of magnetic strength by either method of assessment in using oriented sintered grades of ferrite magnet, which amply justifies the design restrictions imposed by the use of rough and somewhat brittle materials of simple shapes with rather wide dimensional tolerances. Nevertheless, the bonded grades give such advantages in all other respects, and are so well suited to large-scale mass production conditions, that they deserve detailed attention. They have become available commercially only during the past five years and enable permanent magnet techniques to be applied in ways which were formerly scarcely possible. While they are naturally first applied to such elementary applications as novelties and door-closing gaskets, they will find many uses in engineering design as soon as their great potential merits are fully appreciated.

6.6 Bonded Permanent Magnets

A high-coercivity material that can be readily produced in powder form is the best kind for making into bonded magnets because this type of magnetic circuit must inevitably have a high value of percentage airgap as defined in the previous chapter. The advantages of powder metallurgy methods then outlined can be gained to a much greater extent when the effective permeability of the compact of magnetic powder and plastic binder is low, and the linear demagnetising curves of most ferrite grades denote a relative permeability approaching unity, the value of air or free space which is the ultimate minimum.

Micropowder magnets were shown to give their optimum performance when more than half the volume of the pressed compact was binder, filler or other non-magnetic material; a lower proportion of the latter tended to reduce the energy product because the coercivity would be diminished by the proximity effect more rapidly than the remanence is increased. This is an essential feature of shape anisotropy which has little influence when the permanent magnet properties are mainly derived from crystal anisotropy, as in the case of ferrite magnets. Thus, barium ferrite powder can be made to give much better magnetic performance with the minimum amount of binder to hold the compact together than when diluted with enough plastic to make the product flexible. Table 6.1 indicates a difference between rigid and flexible grades of around 2/1 in magnetic strength but, as indicated in the remarks column, this can be decided almost entirely by the desired mechanical performance. The sintered grades can be made with density up to as much as 95% of the perfect crystal value before there is a serious diminution of magnetic quality and 5% of added binder to a hard and brittle powder is much too little to produce a stable compact from the mechanical, and therefore the magnetic, standpoint. Though this is a new subject and there is room for great improvements in both the magnetic performance of ferrite powder and in the methods of forming it into useful shapes, it would appear that the better mechanical and manufacturing properties must inevitably be obtained by the sacrifice of some magnetic energy, though the reduced specific gravity is a compensating advantage in some cases.

A further important consideration in favour of sintered ferrites is the great physical and magnetic stability imparted to a homogeneous product fired at high temperature, and which has a Curie Point near to the highest value for this kind of ferromagnetic material (about 500°C.). A composite material containing plastic binder must be mainly dependent upon the physical properties of the latter material, though recent advances have indicated the possibilities of new substances in this category operating at higher temperature levels than any available plastic.

The first plastic-bonded ferrite magnets had remanence and energy product values in the region of half the isotropic sintered material values but this gap has been closed recently by the introduction of orientation methods which can be more readily applied to ferrite particles than to other kinds of magnet powder. The earliest work in this direction was carried out in Germany over 20 years ago by Baermann, who ground down the considerable amounts of scrap alnico magnets and foundry casting runners into a coarse powder

and added from 3 to 6% of synthetic resin binder. This was placed
in a heated mixing machine of the kind used for insulating powder
cores and the coated powder was then pressed at about 10 tons/inch ^{2}
to the required shape and size and the compacts were heat treated
to cure the resin. Although the resulting magnets had only about half
the energy product of the original solid material, the product had a
considerable market at a time of war shortages under the trade name
of 'Tromalit' and it was found that the high-coercivity grades of
scrap gave best results. Attempts to improve the product by orientation processes did not give enough advantage to justify the added
cost. It was found necessary to modify the design of devices using
conventional magnets in order to provide the greater magnet area
needed to meet a required flux demand. This development was a
useful forerunner to the recent introduction of plastic-bonded ferrite
magnets.

An interesting indication of the practical importance of these
bonded ferrite materials has recently been published in America. It
has been known for over a decade that the performance of small d.c.
motors, which are used in vast numbers for motorcar auxiliaries,
could be greatly improved by substituting ferrite magnets for the
wound fields; this reduced power consumption and heat to such an
extent that the rating could be substantially increased but the problem
consisted in making sintered ferrite in the required annular or
sectional shape. With plastic-bonded flexible sheet, however, it was a
simple process to cut out the required rectangle and fit it closely
inside the outer iron sleeve which provided part of the magnetic
circuit, avoiding costly tools and cutting assembly time. The design
factors of this are dealt with in Chapter 8.

Magnetic gaskets for closing refrigerator doors have provided the
main incentive for the rapid commercial expansion of these flexible
bonded ferrites. These can be automatically magnetised in the factory
with N and S poles in long parallel strips, so that the 'keeper' is
formed by the steel body of the refrigerator when the gasket has been
fixed around the inner periphery of its door. This arrangement
provides adequate area of magnetic circuit (owing to the considerable
gasket length) and a relatively short flux path, so that considerable
pull is applied from a material which is relatively weak by modern
magnet standards. Apart from the desirable replacement of a latch
which may wear and need adjustment, the magnetic gasket applies
its force uniformly around the edge of the door without requiring

a perfectly flat bearing surface and gives the best kind of seal on which the refrigerator performance ultimately depends.

If the set of performance curves of Fig. 6.3 is compared with the theoretical hysteresis loops of Fig. 4.5, it will be seen that dilution of magnets tends to reduce the working coercivity, as well as the remanence, without changing the intrinsic coercivity appreciably, the latter being a property of the ferrite material itself in terms of its crystal size and formation. So the ability of the plastic-bonded grades to withstand severe demagnetising conditions will be even better than that of the sintered grades.

6.7 Ultimate Performance

Ferrite magnets have made such technical progress within a few years that it is desirable to examine their ultimate limitations imposed by theoretical and practical conditions. Theory indicates that the intrinsic coercivity of random particles depends upon the crystal anisotropy coefficient divided by the saturation flux density, and the

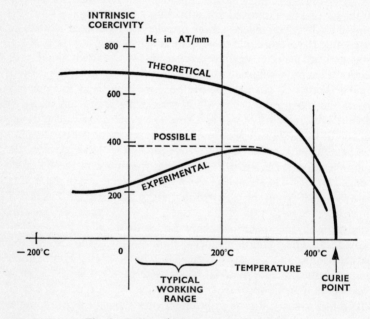

Fig. 6.4 Barium Ferrite: Intrinsic Coercivity.

latter depends upon the temperature, becoming zero at the Curie Point of 450°C. This is shown by the top curve in Fig. 6.4 from −200°C., compared with actual experimental results which are nearly half the value, at an optimum temperature around 250°C. Various explanations have been suggested for this difference and it is expected that material could be made with the optimum figure, approaching 400 AT/mm indicated by the dotted curve. It must be remembered that this is double the present best commercial value. Moreover, it is several times greater than the coercivity of the best commercial magnets produced only a decade ago, so little progress from the application standpoint has yet been possible in this limited time. The best utilization of this remarkable improvement of the most important property of a permanent magnet forms the main subject of later chapters but here the question is concerned only with the ferrite as material.

The low remanence of ferrites must be taken as an inherent property, and any different or improved versions cannot be much better in this respect. It was shown in the last chapter that the highest coercivity grades of micropowder magnets have similar values and this would appear to be inevitable in any future kind of permanent magnet material. Further advance is only possible by producing better intrinsic coercivities and optimising the performance of the compacted magnet in terms of the most perfect attainable degree of size grading and orientation. Much progress has already been made in these respects in the case of ferrites and the much more difficult conditions for micropowders at present seem to be imposing a considerable barrier. Owing to the very low permeability of these new magnet materials, it has been found possible to concentrate the flux by means of soft iron poleplates so efficiently that very low remanence is not the great practical disadvantage which has been assumed in the past. The reason is that all past devices and machines requiring magnets have been based upon low-coercivity materials with much higher permeability. This raises the question of the proper assessment of material quality.

The first requirement of a permanent magnet is that it shall be permanent. To this end it must be structurally stable and unaffected by corrosion, and the coercivity level must be as high as possible; by these standards sintered ferrite magnets are the best up to about 250°C. Most alloy cast magnets have around double the Curie Point of barium ferrite and could operate at correspondingly higher temperatures but this point is of limited practical value, even for power-handling applications which operate on a specified temperature rise basis. The changes in the ratio of remanence to coercivity, which occur in commercial ferrites with temperature variations within the working range, are only temporary and the performance at a given temperature remains constant. The higher temperature coefficient of ferrites makes them unsuitable only for measurement uses but the cost of shaping the material to the exacting tolerances would tend to make them uneconomic. This market is more suitable for metal and micropowder magnets.

In terms of severity of operating conditions there are three groups:—

1. magnets working under static conditions;
2. magnets working under normal dynamic conditions;
3. magnets which have to withstand demagnetising forces comparable to their own working coercivity.

The first two have been already considered in general terms; the third appears later for combinations of electromagnet and permanent magnet where the flux of the latter is frequently reduced to zero, but must return to its original value when the current in the electromagnet is switched off.

Up to the 1950s all commercial magnets operated with coercivities in the range 10 to 50 AT/mm and maintained their properties by careful handling and ageing, but principally by using them under conditions of very limited demagnetisation. In the case of dynamic magnets in group 2 high coercivity was almost essential and the limitations at that time of available materials in this respect greatly restricted progress. Group 3 could not have been considered without material with intrinsic coercivity much higher than the working value, and Table 6.1 shows that isotropic barium ferrite of 10 years ago had almost a 2/1 ratio. The magnets of group 2 require high working coercivity alone and a lower limit of 100 AT/mm appears to meet the conditions, to which all the ferrite grades apart from the flexible bonded kind comply. In addition they must yield the maximum flux from fully-closed to fully-open magnetic circuit, which is provided by the almost linear demagnetising curves of Fig. 6.3; this is the dynamic energy product (B_pH_{max}) given in Table 6.1, and first proposed five years ago (ref. 4). The comparable values of static and dynamic energy products in this table show that the latter give a different order of quality from the conventional $(BH)_{max}$ figures, in that Gr. III sintered ferrite is 25% better than the oriented alnico given for comparison, though the alloy material is over twice the quality for static uses by the usual standards. Allowing for the density of the ferrite being two-thirds the alloy figure, the advantage of the ceramic magnets on a tonnage basis for dynamic uses is about 2 to 1. A corresponding improvement in the status of the other ferrite materials relative to the lower coercivity metal magnets with pronounced curves in their demagnetising characteristics will be obtained. The latter tend to have values of intrinsic coercivity H_{ci} so close to the working values that it is necessary to give only the H_c figure.

The Gr. II ferrite gives its high remanence and static energy factor at the expense of the dynamic performance, though it comes close to the alloy figure in $(B_pH)_{max}$ and 25% lower than Gr. III. It cannot be magnetised in the factory during manufacture without losing some of its energy later and is more susceptible to change for other reasons that apply to metal magnets. Its important uses for loudspeakers are mainly based upon lower costs in large quantities, and this is the main incentive for developing other static uses with ferrite magnets.

The above factors show that the greatest field of application of ferrites is new dynamic developments which depend upon high coercivity, and these rely upon the near-linear demagnetising curve with its high $(B_pH)_{max}$ value and relative permeability approaching 1. The added need for high ratio of intrinsic to working coercivity in certain uses can be provided by the lower remanence grades. These points are shown in Fig. 6.5.

6.8 Economic Factors

Engineering being ultimately an economic activity, it is essential to keep cost levels, present and estimated future, in constant view. It has already been recorded that all permanent magnets from earliest times up to the middle of this century have been expensive commodities because of their rarity or owing to the relatively high cost and frequent supply restrictions on their essential ingredients. Since 1825 it has been much less expensive, as well as technically superior, to provide magnetic fields by the continuous dissipation of great amounts of electric power in complex windings unless there was a strong reason, such as remote or portable uses, for employing permanent magnets. The steady increase in the cost of power and the rapid increase in magnetic strength during the past decades of alloy magnets have brought these two alternatives into balance.

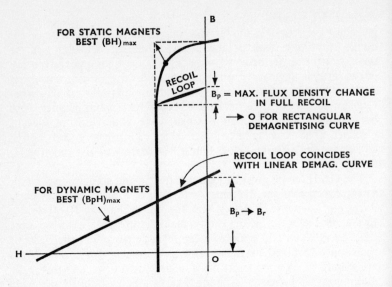

Fig. 6.5 Shape of Optimum Demagnetising Curves, for Static and Dynamic Magnet Conditions.

Twenty years ago the astonishing news that good permanent magnets could be made from ordinary soft iron powder, if fine enough in particle size, held out the promise of steady magnetic fields being provided without the continuous and costly expenditure of electrical energy. But this has proved to be more difficult than early results indicated and, as in the recent instance of atomic energy, did not take into account the further great advances in conventional methods and materials; best results were dependent upon the use of considerable proportions of the element which contributed the main cost of metal magnets (cobalt). However, the required economic answer was soon to appear from a different direction and in an unexpected guise, iron oxide, using the prime ferromagnetic element in a more stable and less processed form than the metallic.

Barium ferrite, being more than 80% iron oxide, is economically in the category of a steel in relation to its raw material cost and ranks with a tonnage ceramic from the manufacturing standpoint. Barium carbonate is already produced annually in England alone in quantities exceeding the 10,000 ton level at a price which makes it relatively unimportant to the ultimate cost of this new ceramic. Thus, unlike micropowders and magnet alloys, it is possible to make realistic estimates for the cost of barium ferrite in simple mass-produced shapes of the kind already mentioned in any required quantity. Moreover, the limit will be imposed by the demand and not, as hitherto, on the availability and material cost.

The source of iron oxide for most magnetic ferrites has hitherto been synthetic pigments, of which world production is some hundred-thousands of tons annually. In recent years the proportion used for magnetic purposes—magnetic recording media and inks as well as ferrites—has risen steeply and now exceeds 10% of the total. High permeability cores must use pure raw materials but permanent magnet materials could tolerate considerable proportions of certain impurities of the inert or 'filler' kind; they could thus use a variety of by-products which are at present valueless. An example is the great quantity of sub-micron iron oxide produced in the new 'tonnage oxygen' steel-making processes. Roughly 1% of the output of steel was at first blown away but, since the passing of the Clean Air Act of 1956, it must be trapped in large filters. In this country alone the output of this waste oxide is expected to exceed the 100,000 ton mark in a few years, and in some cases it is being pelletised in order to return it to the furnaces.

Preliminary tests to make ferrite magnets from this by-product without appreciable purification showed that it gives high coercivity but the expected rather low remanence. This indicates that it could be considered for the ultimate large-scale production of ferrite bricks for the magnetic railway project described in Chapter 10. Owing to the sticky and fluffy nature of this kind of oxide, which makes it difficult to handle and transport, it would be desirable for the bricks to be made where the steel is produced; this process would be similar to the making of refractory bricks in various ways and could possibly be integrated with the main production. The ultimate price of these magnet bricks is the main factor in the capital cost of the project.

At present ferrite magnets are sold at prices in the non-ferrous metal range but these could be brought down to the steel level with greater demand. Already it is claimed in America that this kind of plant can be built with a high degree of mechanisation for single-purpose demands, a considerable advance over anything possible with conventional metal magnets; this will be apparent from the brief description of the process for producing oriented grades of barium ferrite given earlier. A finished ferrite magnet of the high-coercivity grade can be magnetised in the factory by a simple

11

condenser-discharge process which uses negligible power compared with that needed for the processing of the material.

In making an economic comparison between ferrite magnets and their electromagnetic alternative, it is not sufficient to compare a ceramic substance with a metal, whether copper or aluminium today (or steel in the future). The conductor metals have to be drawn to wire, insulated and wound into coils and connected to a source of electric power, usually direct current supplied from an expensive rectifier. After this considerable material and capital cost, no magnetic flux will be produced until the electromagnet is fed from a continuous supply of electric power which contributes an additional running cost.

With the permanent magnet, the magnetic field is provided continuously for an indefinite time at no further cost in either power consumption or maintenance. It is always available for work at full strength with a degree of safety, reliability and freedom from trouble which are of great additional, if unmeasurable, economic value. There can be few cases on record of a new substance having such striking advantages over a traditional alternative in such important fields of application.

6.9 References

1. Snoek J. L. *New Developments in Ferromagnetic Materials*, Elsevier, London and Amsterdam, 1949.

2. Went J. J., Rathenau G. W., Gorter E. W., van Oosterhout. 'Ferroxdure: A New Permanent Magnet Material', *Philips Technical Review*, Vol. 13, pp. 361-76, 1952.

3. Stuijts A. L., Rathenau G. W. & Weber G. H. 'Ferroxdure II & III: Oriented Magnet Material', *Philips Tech. Review*, Vol. 16, pp. 321-8, 1955.

4. Sixtus K. J., Kronenburg K. J. & Tenzer R. K. 'Barium Ferrite Magnets', *J. Applied Physics*, Vol. 27, pp. 1051-57, 1956.

5. Hotop W. & Brinkmann K. 'Applications of Barium Ferrite Magnets', *E.T.Z.(A)* Germany, Vol. 80, No. 17, Sept. 1959.

6. Smit J. & Wijn H. P. J. *Ferrites* (Book), Philips Research, Holland. Cleaver-Hume Press, 1959.

Part 2

NEW APPLICATIONS

7

MODERN MAGNETS IN PRACTICE

Apart from the general introduction, the first Part of this book has outlined the latest information on magnetic materials—chiefly the new kinds of permanent magnet—as material and components. The aspect now changes to the relatively unexplored subject of the best way to use their valuable properties in medium-power engineering, the sphere of application for which it will be shown that they are eminently suited. Conventional uses have recently been fully covered in the books listed at the end of Chapter 1, mainly as components for traditional designs of device, apparatus and small machine.

Here the novelty of the new magnet materials in both physical and magnetic properties calls for a different approach. They cannot be treated in isolation as components because they do not comply with traditional design conditions. It will be shown in this chapter that they can be used in a new and extremely valuable manner to combine the merits of both electromagnet and permanent magnet in what will be referred to as the *ideal magnet*. This is an assembly rather than a component; it has the high-coercivity material with iron poleplates to concentrate the flux and generally also incorporates a high current-density coil to link it with the associated electrical circuit. The permanent magnet provides the basic flux indefinitely without use of power and without the dissipation of heat. This extremely simple and highly efficient arrangement is used in the next chapter as the groundwork for the development, from first principles and elementary requirements, of a wide range of novel electrical machines and equipment; these are in the less familiar linear form as well as in the range of well-known rotary designs.

But the new ferrite magnets also make possible the use of magnetic suspension—the support of loads by magnetic repulsion—on any desired scale; this, in association with linear propulsion, can provide great advances in the much-needed field of track transportation which are described in Chapter 10, following a separate chapter on improvements in rotary machines. The future prospects of these developments and their expected effects on engineering and allied subjects are outlined in the final chapter.

7.1 Permanent Magnets and their Function

The user of permanent magnets for power applications requires the maximum flux in the minimum space at lowest cost, with no detectable loss of magnetic strength during a many-year life regardless of the severity of the demagnetising forces encountered. This assumes low leakage and this kind of flux is also undesirable for the troubles it may cause, apart from the waste of materials. Barium ferrite is the first commercial material to give these properties and is thus the only kind of magnet that can be described as really permanent. Though it has much lower remanence and saturation flux density values than any kind of traditional metal magnet, the working flux density in a machine or device can be increased to any desired practical level by the use of poleplates in suitable form and shape, the limit being based upon the saturation of the poleplate ferromagnetic material and the leakage flux pattern imposed by the design and working details. These conditions apply also to electromagnets but in a more intangible manner, owing to the considerable proportion of the space taken up with windings, which are non-magnetic.

The flux from a very low remanence grade of ferrite magnet, for instance the flexible grades of plastic-bonded barium ferrite powder, may be concentrated to high densities by use of thin sheets of mild steel, but the arrangement becomes unwieldy for most uses where compactness is desirable, and the leakage flux becomes greater as the area of the surfaces of the poleplates is increased. It is always advantageous to use magnet material with the highest available remanence value in order to reduce its volume, and hence the area of poleplates; but for the kind of application under discussion it is not satisfactory to sacrifice coercivity or linearity of demagnetising curve to gain flux density. Though traditional figures of merit treat remanence as equal to coercivity, the latter is several times more valuable, dependent upon the severity of the demagnetising conditions, in dynamic applications. This point becomes most apparent when it is necessary to control the flux from a high-coercivity material by the usual kind of electromagnet based upon conventionally insulated wire; the current density has to be increased to the region of ten times the usual design figure and special cooling methods must be used to prevent the coil from being burnt-out. It therefore became necessary to develop special kinds of coil which could be operated at these high current-density conditions, or in other words to raise the 'equivalent coercivity' of such electromagnets up to the high levels recently attained by the latest ferrite permanent magnets.

This point clearly shows the urgent need for a practical and self-explanatory unit for coercivity in place of the traditional *oersted* (which was stated by a critic to have only tombstone value). Moreover it must be readily related to working conditions, conveying the impression of high current *intensity*. Unfortunately the new MKSA unit is sometimes given in amperes per metre (A/m) as a very large figure with no association with the coil that must invariably be used to give the required concentration of magnetic field; also, a coil or conductor a metre long has little relationship to practical sizes used in this kind of work. Hence, for the permanent magnet values of magnetising force and coercivity which figure prominently through this book the units are given in ampere-turns per *milli*-metre (abbreviated to AT/mm). The 100 AT/mm level is a convenient lower limit for the high coercivity materials which will withstand the kind of severe demagnetising conditions to be found in the moving parts of power machinery; all sintered grades of ferrite magnet are well above this limit. The figure and unit provide a clear picture of a closely-wound coil carrying a very high current density.

If a ferrite magnet is regarded in this way, giving the equivalent service of an electromagnet so compact relative to the power it dissipates that elaborate cooling must be used to prevent it being destroyed, its remarkable potential value can be at once understood. For it provides this service indefinitely at no running cost, with complete reliability and with no temperature rise. Moreover it needs no power supply or rectifier unit. The control of an electromagnet usually involves high switching voltages and consequent arcing which limits the life and provides a main reason for breakdown during operation. In contrast to this impressive list of advantages for the cheap and unpublicized permanent magnet, it is perhaps surprising to note the attention given to the recent alternative way of producing a magnetic field without expenditure of power—by use of an extremely complex superconducting coil cooled down at great expense to near Absolute Zero temperature.

From the great mass of practical and theoretical information summarised earlier in this book the future trend of development in permanent magnets clearly emerges. By further improvements in the alignment of crystals with optimum domain dimensions and highest crystal anisotropy, considerable further increases in both remanence and coercivity can be expected, but especially in the latter which could be more than doubled to approach present values of intrinsic coercivity. To the user this means, in the oriented grades which will become almost universally employed, thinner bricks and flat rings to give the same magnetic flux, with a reduction in poleplate and pole face area for higher remanence under a given set of operating conditions. But the properties of this kind of permanent magnet will be completely different, from those of any pre-1950s commercial product which has been described by that name, in five fundamental respects:

1. Relative permeability approaching unity, the figure for air.

2. Nearly-linear demagnetising curves.

3. Insulator resistivity.

4. Intrinsic coercivity appreciably higher than the working H_c value.

5. Soft iron poleplates for flux concentration give good mechanical protection and magnetic screening.

These mainly unforeseen characteristics, added to the need they create for new kinds of high current-density coils associated with them, comprise the 'modern magnets' of the title of this book. This does not imply that the present extensive range of metal magnets is obsolescent, for they have no rivals for many of the traditional light-current applications, but it means that a considerable part of present-day machines and equipment based on the electromagnet will be greatly modified and ultimately superseded by unfamiliar designs and shapes based upon the provision of permanent magnet excitation. The author's contention that this can be achieved only by fundamentally new designs based on first principles, is derived from the above factors which demand a novel kind of magnetic circuit; in this the mean path length must be very short.

7.2 Short Magnetic Paths

The practical demand for a required value of flux to be maintained across a given airgap, whether by permanent magnet or by a coil carrying current, calls for a definite value of magneto-motive force in ampere-turns. The manner in which this is provided decides the length of the magnetic circuit: the very low coercivity steels required a long circuit of the familiar horseshoe shape, while conventionally

insulated coils had to run at relatively low current density and therefore required a magnetic path of what can be called medium length.
The recent appearance of permanent magnets with coercivity nearly
a hundred times higher than that of the hard steels and many times
higher than the 'equivalent coercivity' of any commercial winding
has created the unforseen need for a short magnetic path. With all
the required m.m.f. provided in as little as an inch or a few centimetres of that path, the mean magnetic path length must clearly be
reduced to similar proportions, say within about 10 centimetres, if
the flux is to be used efficiently.

It must be remembered that this very high coercivity is partially
attained by the use of materials or composite structures with low
remanence and the use of poleplates to concentrate the flux is
essential. They must be of appreciable area for this task and, for
this reason also, it is essential to limit the extent to which they project
from the body of the permanent magnet material. Any coil associated
with them must therefore be designed to operate at the highest
possible current density in order to save this valuable space within
the magnetic path; compared with conventional coils they will have
large diameter and small cross-section, which allows for the better
cooling conditions needed by the high current intensity. This shape
fits well into the large area and small length of magnetic circuit,
so that the whole assembly becomes disc-shaped, a compact and
convenient contrast to the traditional barrel shape of electrical
designs.

This new shape is found in practice to give many advantages,
notably in reduction of leakage flux owing to the small space available
for this notorious cause for low efficiency in smaller machines and
equipment. While this is a continual drain of valuable power for
flux produced by electromagnets, most permanent magnet designs
of the past had little useful flux compared to the amount of leakage
flux. This is the magnetic equivalent of a large shunt across an electric
battery which bypasses most of the current before it reaches the load
(in this case the airgap) where useful work is performed; but leakage
flux is invisible and it is usually difficult to measure or sometimes
even to detect. For nearly a century the pioneers of electrical engineering failed to understand its significance, and this still applies in most
smaller machines and devices.

This misunderstanding of so vital and fundamental a subject is
partly the result of using the electric circuit analogy too literally,
with the relative permeability of air and other 'non-magnetic

material' being regarded as insignificant. Their unity value may appear so in comparison with the soft iron parts of the magnetic circuit around the 1000 permeability level, and components such as hard steel magnets and powder cores in the 100 region, but air occupies far more space and extends in all directions. Consequently traditional magnet design calculations include a leakage factor of from 2 to 10, with even higher values for open magnetic circuit conditions; the best commercial metal magnets, such as those used in the largest numbers for loudspeaker assemblies, use only half the available flux and most other applications waste much more than they use. This can be readily understood in the instance of the early horseshoe magnet with long limbs to provide enough m.m.f. for practical purposes with the low-coercivity materials then available; the volume of air in the cylindrical surrounding space, forming the main leakage paths, is very many times greater than that of either the hard steel or of the working airgap at its narrow poles. Although the flux from the latter is often assumed to issue from their tips, in practice it extends for an appreciable area along the sides. As the coercivity of metal magnets was progressively improved during the past 40 years, the limb length could be correspondingly reduced with the resulting improvement to the leakage factor, but with the best alloys of today the flux comes partly from the sides as well as from the ends; only in the case of very high coercivity substances, such as the ferrite magnets, does the flux emanate from the pole faces only, resulting in unusually low leakage factors if the magnetic circuit is very short.

If the magnetic path length has to be so greatly reduced, there comes a point in rotating machines at which the flux direction must be changed. This is shown in Fig. 7.1 for the magnetic circuits of typical 2-pole machines, from the earliest commercial designs and the present equivalent, with transverse rotor flux, to the proposed future shape with permanent magnet excitation from a large flat ring of barium ferrite now becoming available. It will be seen that the future design is based on a 90° change in the flux direction to that parallel to the shaft, and space is available for a concentric coil for controlling the flux. This is a very efficient arrangement which could be used with materials of the highest possible coercivity, but is entirely novel as a design and is followed up in the next chapter for possible applications. At this point it is introduced to indicate the next stage in the development of the ideal magnet, with most of the flux being permanent and leakage minimized.

MAGNETIC CIRCUITS

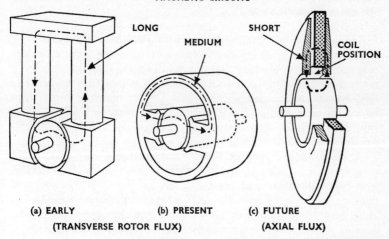

(a) EARLY   (b) PRESENT   (c) FUTURE

(TRANSVERSE ROTOR FLUX)   (AXIAL FLUX)

Fig. 7.1 Typical 2-pole Machines.

The early design is clearly based on the horseshoe shape and Edison's first dynamos had even longer arms than those shown, to give highest possible m.m.f.; but the efficiency was worse than that of compacter machines and it was proved by Hopkinson that most of the top part of the windings produced magnetic flux which by-passed the rotor. The present type of machine in fig. 7.1(*b*) is made with a shortened magnetic circuit by use of the circular surrounding return path, short poles and elongated rotor-stator construction, but this entails the use of difficult and less efficient coil shapes, with appreciable leakage remaining at the ends and in the poorly-used internal airspaces. This diagram should be compared with Fig. 2.8 'Evolution of Magnet Shapes' in order to show the comparable reduction of their mean flux paths in permanent magnets, the long and medium lengths relating to hard steels and recent alnico alloys respectively.

In Fig. 7.1(*c*) the use of the shortest magnetic path brings other advantages besides the efficient use of high-coercivity materials; it provides a convenient disc-shaped assembly of good mechanical strength and low cost with excellent natural cooling properties. The ferrite ring-magnet in Grades I or III material are supplied with pole faces ground flat and parallel in the fully magnetized condition and the poleplates can be cemented in position with epoxy resin to avoid fixing holes, with a high current-density strip-conductor coil filling the space between them.

7.3 Comparison of Electromagnets with Permanent Magnets

During recent years the improvement in the strength of permanent magnets has been so rapid that many still regard them incorrectly as inefficient substitutes for electromagnets. It is therefore desirable to devise a means for comparing them. This comparison must show where the new ferrites and metal magnets stand in relation to the traditional wire-wound coils and the experimental high current-density kind.

A typical electromagnet operated from direct current supplies used a winding space roughly equivalent to the core area, and the soft iron core will saturate at approximately 2 Wb/m². If this core and winding are replaced by permanent magnet material with high coercivity level, it could almost fill the space and the equivalent remanence of the electromagnet could therefore be taken as half the above figure or 1Wb/m². This is the value for early hard steel magnets. To obtain the equivalent coercivity of the electromagnet coil with normal cooling, a current density of 2 A/mm² would apply, and in a typical multi-turn coil of round wire with conventional insulation this will provide a magnetizing force of about 20 AT/mm, corresponding to the coercivity of the best grade of cobalt steel first produced nearly 40 years ago. If the coil current was doubled so that it became very hot, the equivalent coercivity would be at the level of pre-war isotropic alnico alloys and the post-war oriented grades give still higher values, as well as remanence figures 25% over the equivalent electromagnet level.

Hence permanent magnets had drawn almost level with electromagnets of traditional design and construction three decades ago and are now about three times better. This applies mainly to the best alnico alloys which almost correspond in terms of remanence and coercivity and their ratio. Ferrites have one-third of the above equivalent remanence figure for the electromagnet but over ten times the equivalent coercivity for the oriented Gr. III used in most of the later experimental work described here. This explains why coils had to be developed with ten times greater current-density values than usual, and why a thin ferrite ring magnet can do the work of a bulky multi-layer winding ten times longer in axial dimensions, though its area will be three times that of the core-plus-winding section.

The outstanding advantage of the electromagnet is the ability to control the flux in either direction from zero to many times the saturation value of iron, the limit being mainly imposed by the destructive effect of the heat generated and the enormous pressures exerted by high magnetic fields. If the figure of 2 A/mm² given above for a naturally cooled multi-layer coil of commercial round copper wire is to be increased ten times to give equivalent coercivity to the ferrite magnets, it must have special construction with artificial cooling for continuous operation; a bare copper wire with 100 times this present current density figure will melt in the isolated conditions

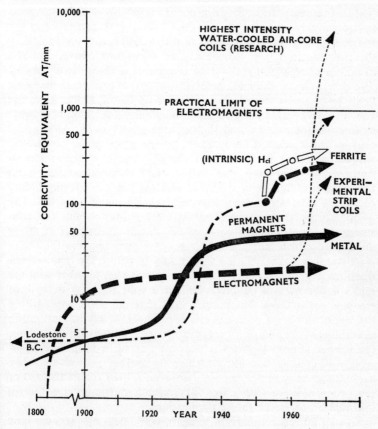

Fig. 7.2 Progress of Permanent Magnets and Electromagnets Compared.

of an installed fusewire for protecting a typical domestic load. Much development work is being done on high intensity electromagnets with special cooling which run at even higher current densities; these are described later. It is therefore possible to produce electromagnets for controlling the flux of the highest coercivity magnet materials which may be developed in the future, and they could be built into the assembly of the kind shown in Fig. 7.1(c) to give the ideal magnet.

All the factors relating to the comparison of electromagnets with permanent magnets in the past and present are given in Fig. 7.2, which gives equivalent coercivity up to the highest possible value, plotted since the beginning of this century, with an indication of the earlier trend. The comparison between metal magnets and electromagnets is also roughly representative of their overall performance, and the ferrite figures should be reduced to the metal magnet level to allow for their much lower remanence, as mentioned above. But the coercivity comparison is the most important in this general subject. The curves clearly show the great advantages of producing magnetic fields by consumption of electric power up to the 1930s. Then the new cast alloy permanent magnets brought about such improvements as to close the margin, and the oriented grades gave a substantial lead in recent years. Compared with these advances in permanent magnet materials the history of the electromagnet shows almost static performance since its invention, being mainly dependent upon the saturation flux density of iron and the current-carrying ability of copper wire, which have changed little during that period. The great improvements now taking place are mainly in new coil construction methods and the use of new materials such as anodised aluminium which can operate at much higher temperatures than were possible earlier. These are necessary to permit the high current densities required to match the ferrite coercivities, together with the much better natural cooling obtainable with the new designs of machine using them. The curve shows that these are approaching the upper limits of practical electromagnets, based on saturation conditions of the best ferromagnetic materials with artificial cooling; the further tenfold increase is possible only with air-core coils of reinforced construction using such costly cooling methods that they are commercially impracticable. However, a brief report (below) of the progress in this direction for research purposes gives useful information for some future applications.

To sum up this comparison, modern permanent magnets are now so much better than conventional electromagnets that it is desirable to employ them for all basic magnetic flux requirements, such as the excitation of machines, using the minimum of added electrically-generated flux for control or other essential operational uses. In the case of ferrite magnets, the control coil can be incorporated with the poleplate assembly, owing to the high coercivity level, and the flux can be controlled down to zero, if necessary, provided that the intrinsic coercivity is much higher than the working value. This will need a special design of coil, such as anodised aluminium strip preferably wound on edge to make it self-supporting, to permit the use of current densities up to 10 or 20 A/mm² without artificial cooling. Smaller changes in the permanent flux could be made with the use of conventional coils and materials for insulated conductors. This arrangement will give the lowest possible heat dissipation and energy loss, hence higher ratings or smaller sizes, by combining the advantages of both methods for maintaining magnetic fields.

7.4 High Intensity Electromagnets

Magnetism generated by the motion of electrons has been shown to provide the fundamental reasons for the performance and properties of magnetic materials; for the same reason high intensity magnetic fields are essential in most aspects of research into atomic structure and nuclear energy, in such apparatus as cyclotrons and thermo-nuclear generators. Up to recent times these intense fields were pro-vided by large iron-core electromagnets with specially shaped poles to give optimum flux concentration, and water-cooled coils dissipat-ing kilowatts of power to give high magnetising force. The limiting factor to this arrangement is the saturation flux density of the core material which cannot exceed 2.4 Wb/m² in the use of the best ferromagnetic metal. If there is no ferromagnetic core the limit is imposed by the I^2R loss of the coil, which rises steeply as the current increases, but air has no saturation limit to the magnetic flux density it can maintain. For most research work the volume of this field can be small; a few cubic centimetres of space inside the coil is adequate for most purposes, but a tenfold increase in flux density is desired compared with the best obtained with the most powerful iron-cored electromagnet. This presents a very difficult problem in heat dissipation and mechanical construction.

To reach a flux density of 10 Wb/m² (from five to ten times the typical airgap value in electrical machines) in an aircore coil with an internal diameter of only 20 mm requires a current density as high as 1000 A/mm² or more, about ten times the current intensity to melt a copper fusewire of average size. This has been achieved by forcing water through a large number of small holes in the conductor with a flow of hundreds of gallons (1 gall. is 4.5 litres) per minute, and this consumes power in megawatts. These figures give some idea of the enormous cost of this kind of experiment and show that practical flux densities in machines are not likely to rise much above the 2 Wb/m² level.

Pressures exerted by magnetic fields vary as the square of the field strength. For this maximum engineering level of flux density they are relatively low at around 100 lb/inch² or 10 kg/cm² which do not need special construction for the electromagnetic circuit associated with these intensities of magnetic field. But tenfold increases raise the pressures to tons concentrated in these small coils and they will distort, or even explode under pulse conditions, unless they are specially reinforced. This has been the fate of costly equipment of this kind and the experience has led to new methods of metal-forming into complex shapes by applying an intense electromagnetic discharge through a suitably made jig.

Cooling problems can be minimised by the use of pulsed power or intermittent discharge circuits which require simple apparatus, but this gives high intensity fields of only milliseconds or microseconds duration which may not be appropriate for the experimental work in hand. Such methods have produced the highest known field of 1000 Wb/m² but of very limited duration, and 10 Wb/m² is the highest for continuous operation at the present time. This represents a magnetising force of 8000 AT/mm and so is appropriate for including at the top of Fig. 7.2, with the 1000 AT/mm level marked as the practical limit for electromagnets of the kind considered in this book.

Superconducting magnets are the latest development in high intensity fields and give considerable promise for becoming the best way of obtaining still higher figures by cooling small coils down to temperatures close to Absolute Zero, which causes their electrical resistance to become almost negligible. The original idea behind this work was put forward half a century ago but only recently have materials been discovered which can retain their superconductive properties in the working range of current densities between 100 and 1000 A/mm². An example is niobium-tin alloy drawn into wire and heat-treated to give the mechanical properties for it to be wound into a coil for operation in a vacuum flask cooled with liquid helium. This is also a very expensive process and is expected to remain suitable only for experimental work.

This information shows that there are still spheres of application for special electromagnets which are beyond the abilities of permanent magnets, arising from the absence of saturation limits in air-core coils. Where there is a winding on a ferromagnetic core, it is always possible to increase the flux density, though marginally, by passing more current up to the heating limit, as the above developments show. This effect is small for materials with appreciable permeability, but can be important when the relative permeability approaches the unity value of air; this applies to the ferrite magnets and other materials of equivalent coercivity. So the proposed use of the magnet-coil assembly could provide higher flux densities, with the coil flux aiding the permanent field, than could be done otherwise without costly cooling arrangements. Practical applications dependent upon B^2 could be greatly improved with a small increase in B near the saturation point.

7.5 Magnetising Methods

The vital link between electromagnets and permanent magnets is the fact that both receive their energy from electric current, the latter in the form of an intense pulse during the magnetising process. In the case of permanent magnets which are also good electrical insulators, such as barium ferrite, the amount of energy imparted to it approaches the theoretical minimum for this purpose, and this is small by power engineering standards. But the production and maintenance of magnetic fields by electromagnets is incredibly wasteful if permanent magnets could be substituted for the task, and the trouble caused by the unwanted heat generated by this waste of power greatly increases the handicap under which electrical machines and equipment have to operate.

Although the amplitude of the magnetising pulse is much smaller for the range of metallic permanent magnets than that for ferrite magnets, on account of their lower coercivities, the high conductivity of metals causes induced currents that oppose the rise of the magnetising energy. Consequently far more power is needed and this applies especially to larger pieces of magnet material. The peak value is generally based on a multiple of the intrinsic coercivity of each material, being roughly 50 AT/mm for the hard steels, five times greater for oriented alnicos and 1000 AT/mm or more for the latest ferrites. In spite of this, the magnetising of barium ferrite has proved to be simpler than that of any earlier magnet for the following reasons:

12

1. the very high resistivity of both sintered and plastic-bonded grades;
2. the physical need to use simplest shapes, especially for oriented grades;
3. with linear demagnetising curves, magnets can be magnetised in the factory where they are made, without fear of subsequent loss of strength.

Metal magnets are sensitive to handling and require to be magnetised after assembly of the apparatus in which they are used. This demand calls for complicated jigs and special plant at the user's factory which adds to the cost and involves risks of subnormal performance when the operators are not well versed in the magnetic behaviour of such materials. The great diversity of sizes and shapes of magnet, as well as the multiplicity of alloys developed during the rapid advances throughout most of this century, have tended to prevent the rationalization desired by the majority of users of metal magnets. In contrast, ferrites start with this great advantage.

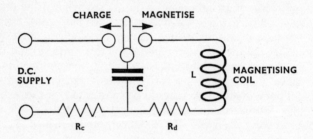

FOR UNIDIRECTIONAL DISCHARGE: $R_d > 2\sqrt{\dfrac{L}{C}}$

Fig. 7.3 Condenser Discharge Magnetiser.

The magnetising process for the above conditions is done with a simple condenser discharge circuit shown in Fig. 7.3, which can be operated from a.c. mains supply through a metal rectifier or a d.c. supply. The resistance value in the charging circuit decides the rate of charge, while that in the discharge circuit will give unidirectional current if its ohmic value is greater than $2\sqrt{L/C}$, where L is the inductance of the magnetizing coil in henries and C is the capacitance in farads. The discharge time of some milliseconds is short enough to avoid heating difficulties. With the normal time allowed between successive magnetising operations, the rate of charge can be prolonged to the point that the current taken is small enough for the apparatus to be transportable and to be run from a single-phase power point. A commercial equipment of this kind weighs 145 lbs. or 0.3 Kg and requires only 30 watt to operate it.

Magnets of up to $4 \times 2 \times 1$ inch (approx. $10 \times 5 \times 2.5$ cm.) can be magnetised in this apparatus, with thinner pieces requiring mild steel plates to fill the gap, though a good fit is not essential. For magnetising ferrite bricks on a repetition basis, over a ton can be handled for the consumption of only one unit (kWhr) of electric power. It can be calculated that over a *million* times more power would be needed to maintain the equivalent flux in electromagnets in typical electrical equipment or machines operating during average life. This is some measure of the great improvements in efficiency that could theoretically be achieved if permanent magnet excitation became generally used, in addition to the elimination of heating, arcing at switches, provision of d.c. supply equipment and risks of burnt-out coils, to which reference has already been made.

Large ring magnets of the kind used in rotating machines described in Chapter 9 can be magnetised with their poleplates and mild steel pieces to close the magnetic circuit around a special magnetising coil. For barium ferrite the manufacturers specify a magnetising force of 10,000 ampere-turns per centimetre of magnet path length, which could be obtained from a d.c. mains supply if available. If the maximum current were only 10 amperes it would need 2,000 turns which could be of relatively thin wire, because the current duration can be as short as practicable if the resistance is low enough. For most experimental purposes, however, magnet makers will supply samples of appropriate ferrite grades in the fully magnetised condition, which avoids the risk that they do not give their full capabilities owing to insufficient power. For large-scale use of these magnets it is better to have special magnetising equipment made for them so that they can be transported and unpacked before this process is carried out, and then magnetised with the poleplates in place to give the optimum flux-path conditions.

Demagnetising equipment for metal magnets has been essential in the past, for maker and user. There are various ways for doing this operation such as the gradual removal of the magnet from a powerful a.c. field. In the case of very high coercivity materials this requires such costly and massive apparatus that it is usually uneconomic. This is very easily avoided in ceramic magnets because the Curie Point is less than half the firing temperature and such materials can be demagnetised merely by heating to a temperature above the 500°C. level. In practice this is seldom needed because of the general simplification of assembly brought about by the use of such shapes as bricks and flat rings in oriented grades.

Plastic-bonded ferrite powders in the form of strips and sheets require special patterns of magnetisation in order to keep the magnetic circuit as short as the applications allow, and to cover large areas of pole face. Two typical methods are shown in Fig. 7.4, the first with flux issuing on one side only and the second on both sides; the first is suitable for gripping or door-closing uses while the second can be fixed by its attraction force to a sheet steel base to make a strong mechanical unit. The latter forms the now familiar noticeboard with papers held by sheet steel strips in what is known as a

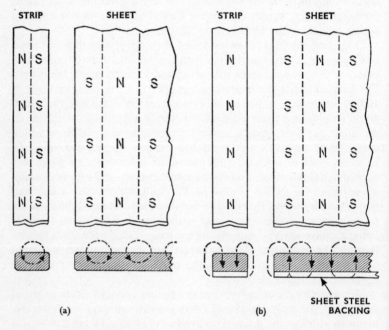

Fig. 7.4 Magnetising Patterns: Plastic-bonded Ferrite Powder Material.

magnetic sandwich. These patterns are produced by special magnetising jigs at the time of manufacture and do not require any
attention by the user, who may not know where the poles are unless
he makes appropriate tests. They are marked with the traditional N
and S figures on the sketch to explain the flux direction but this
shows how far this convention has departed from its original
significance together with the word 'pole', which has finally become
invisible like the flux itself.

7.6 Modern Magnetic Circuits

These novel conditions imposed by high-coercivity materials must
inevitably be reflected in the design of electrical machines and equipment which can benefit from their merits. While multiple strip
magnetisation makes it possible to have permanent magnets in the
form of large sheets, flexible if necessary, for the first time, it is also
necessary to determine the optimum conditions for magnetic circuits
with single paths. This can best be investigated in relation to the
traditional alternative, as drawn in Fig. 7.5; this shows a keeper of
mild steel being attracted across a small airgap with early hard steel
and recent ferrite permanent magnets.

On the left is a long-limbed horseshoe and on the right a ferrite
block with poleplates, which can either be part of a long row or else
part of a large ring-magnet, used to concentrate the flux at the right-
hand side. The airgap length and area, L_g and A_g, are the same in
each case so that the reluctance is $L_g/A_g\mu_0$ on the assumption that
the gap is short enough to neglect the fringing effect at the edges for
the first analysis. To simplify the situation further, leakage flux is
neglected which (as indicated above) can be justified only in the case
of ferrites with the short magnetic circuit shown in the diagram. The
length and area of the flux paths in the magnet material are respectively L_m and A_m for the steel and L_M and A_M for the ferrite, with
corresponding values of relative permeability at 100 and 1.

The general principles of magnetic design were outlined in Chapter
2, based upon working values of flux density and magnetising force
(B_d and H_d) obtained from the makers' published demagnetising
curve for the appropriate material. The magneto-motive force was
$L_m \times H_d$ and the total flux $A_m \times B_d$, the ratio m.m.f./flux being the
reluctance of the magnet itself; this had to be equated to the airgap
reluctance given above ($L_g/A_g\mu_0$) for optimum static conditions.
Theoretically this could give, with the appropriate leakage factor
mentioned above, the required size of magnet to provide a specified

flux or flux density across a specified airgap. If a more complex magnetic circuit was to be designed, as for an electric motor, it was necessary to add the various items of reluctance round the circuit in the manner used for electro-magnetically excited machines; in these circumstances the reluctance of the magnet was $(L_m/A_m\mu_m)$ where μ_m was the permeability of the magnet material.

However, with the pronounced curvature of the demagnetising curves there were many ways of arriving at results dependent upon the position of minor hysteresis loops and appropriate recoil permeabilities, which have taken up much space and involved several calculations in the many publications and catalogues that have dealt with this subject. This brief summary of a very complicated procedure is given to indicate the amount of work involved in arriving at a theoretical design which might have little relationship to the performance of the final product. Suppliers of permanent magnets usually stressed the need for relying on practical experience in the use of leakage factors, and in testing a prototype before proceeding with an experimental design; this must be so when the leakage flux probably exceeds the required working value, often by a considerable proportion.

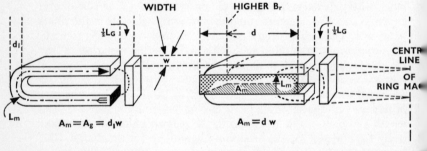

(a) EARLY HORSESHOE MAGNET   (b) FERRITE MAGNET (BRICK OR RING SHAP

Fig. 7.5 Magnetic Circuit Comparison.

Ferrite magnets have fortunately greatly simplified this situation for several reasons, but principally by virtually eliminating the permeability factor which always complicated the reluctance calculation, since the permeability of a high-coercivity material with linear demagnetising curve is about the same as that of the airgap and other 'non-magnetic material'. Also in a short magnetic circuit with the main parts of the lowest possible permeability, the reluctance of pole-plates and practical joints can be neglected; so there remains the most elementary relationship:

$$L_M/A_M = L_g/A_g$$

Moreover, the linear demagnetising curve gives the same recoil permeability along its whole length and this is also unity, while the working values of flux density and magnetising force (B_d and H_d) can be calculated readily from the remanence and coercivity figures supplied by the manufacturer (B_r and H_c). Above all, the prospects of low flux leakage make the calculation a reasonably profitable exercise, though it will probably never attain the accuracy and reliability that are taken for granted in most electrical circuit calculations.

The shape of horseshoe magnet in Fig. 7.5 is based on the convenience in making it from rectangular bar, but has little to recomment it from the magnetic design standpoint. To deal with the high leakage factor the width at the mid-point (d_1) should be considerably greater than that at the poles, with a gradual change intermediately; this is done for expensive applications such as magnetron magnets which generally must have the minimum weight consistent with performance. The corresponding dimension (d) in the ferrite magnet is the depth of the material away from the airgap which, for unit width of material at right angles to the plane of the paper, equals A_M ; it will be seen that (d) has to be about three times greater for plastic-bonded ferrite powder than for the oriented sintered Gr. III material. The poleplate thickness depends upon the degree of flux concentration required and could be about d/12 and d/4 for the stated materials; a high flux density gives greater leakage but results in a lighter assembly, so this factor must generally be decided on the overall requirements. It is magnetically correct to taper the poleplates so that the flux density is at its optimum value (i.e. in terms of permeability) but this may be too costly and flat plate or sheet mild steel with rounded outer edges, as shown, is often adequate.

Leakage flux is reduced when a long row or large ring of magnet material is used instead of the rather shallow block illustrated, because the side leakage is virtually eliminated. The outside edge leakage can be minimised by recessing the poleplates as well as by tapering or rounding their outer surface so that only a minor fraction of the flux is wasted; by reducing the air space adjacent to the airgap to the lowest practicable value, it is possible to reach flux utilisation efficiencies considerably better than any attained by other methods. This is often decided by application conditions, however: if it is necessary to provide a holding magnet with a large 'throw' requiring a considerable range of operating distance, the volume of its magnetic field has to be great and a considerable volume of material is needed with a comparable distance between the poles to match the range. In other words, the dimensions of Fig. 7.5(b) have to be magnified and this need not be uneconomic with commercial ferrites which have low-cost raw materials. But where it is feasible to reduce the equivalent airgap length, if possible with the use of multiple magnetic circuits, it gives much better value in terms of material utilisation.

7.7 Loudspeaker Magnets

The best way to examine the recent progress in permanent magnets from the application standpoint is to survey loudspeaker development. This market has been using about 40% of the total world production of magnet material and the intense competition has resulted in a valuable appraisal of its optimum performance in economic and technical respects. Practically all the loudspeakers needed for radio, television and the other many forms of sound and music reproduction during the past thirty years have used the moving coil principle, requiring a narrow annular airgap carrying the highest flux density that could be economically maintained. This airgap flux density decides, not only the acoustic output for equivalent volume, but its ability to reproduce transients with appropriate damping; a high gap density is also desirable in nearly all other electromagnetic designs and so the following information is highly relevant to all applications to be discussed later. Although the loudspeaker is generally regarded as a use of permanent magnets under static conditions, because the flux generated by the speech coil is relatively small compared with that maintained in the airgap, the power handled in the larger versions can be several watts and the device is comparable to a small electric motor.

Up to a few years ago most loudspeakers used the best grade of oriented alnico alloy, generally in cylindrical form with a 'pot' type of return magnetic circuit in soft iron, which gave a flux utilisation efficiency in the region of 50% with best values of 65%. This gave gap densities varying from 0.5 to 1.0 Wb/m^2 for magnets weighing from 10 to 100 grams, or nearly up to $\frac{1}{4}$ lb., and gap volumes of from 0.1 to 0.5 cm^3, which met most of the quantity demand for smaller sizes. To provide larger sizes and greater gap densities various com-

plications in magnet shape were introduced and ring magnets with a
centre soft iron pole were employed, but the latter arrangement
reduced the efficiency to 35% owing to the high external leakage
which was also troublesome in many uses. However, this permitted
flux densities in the 1 to 1.2 Wb/m^2 region for large assemblies with
magnets weighing some kilograms or pounds, but at a considerable
cost from both the viewpoints of high usage of expensive raw
materials and the loss of twice as much flux as that doing useful work
in the airgap.

When the first barium ferrite magnets became available ten years
ago there was a strong economic incentive to apply them to this
large market, but the low remanence of the isotropic material made
the assemblies rather heavy for a demand where lightness is important. It was necessary to provide ten times the magnet area,
with the extra poleplate bulk required, though the magnet length L_M
was halved compared with the oriented alnico magnets, and this
made the ring design with centre pole of soft iron the only practical
method. The performance and efficiency were found to be better
than expected by earlier outlooks because the airspace between the
centre pole and the inside of the ferrite ring could be greatly reduced
on account of the low permeability of the new ceramic material;
also this enabled as high as tenfold flux concentration to be achieved
by cementing poleplates to the pole faces of the ferrite ring which
had been ground flat and parallel.

As soon as the high remanence grade of oriented barium ferrite
(Gr. II, Fig. 6.3) became commercially available, this design could
be made competitive in size, the magnet area being reduced by 60%

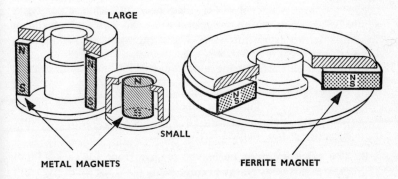

Fig. 7.6 Typical Loudspeaker Magnet Units.

and the ring thickness by 30% on account of the higher working coercivity value. There was no obstacle to the development of larger assemblies because the raw materials were cheap and the additional cost of orienting the crystal structure was small, in comparison with the great benefits in magnetic strength for equivalent weights of the ceramic material; this applied still more to the assembly weight since the mild steel used for the poleplates is nearly 60% more dense than barium ferrite. The arrangement in practical form is shown in Fig. 7.6 compared with smaller typical metal magnet assemblies using a cylinder and ring of oriented alnico. The ferrite ring projects slightly beyond the periphery of the poleplates to minimize external leakage; the inner mild steel pole is shaped to give optimum flux concentration as well as to take a brass centering ring to ensure that the airgap is uniform in length at all positions. The robustness and simplicity of construction are apparent and this shows the disc-shaped magnetic circuit in contrast to the traditional drum or barrel outline.

Table 7.1 gives sizes and magnetic performance of 8 standard ferrite ring magnets in Gr. II material, with 20/1 range of strengths, suitable for a wide variety of loudspeakers with airgap diameters varying from 15 to 65 mm. and gap lengths from 0.75 to 1.25 mm. By also varying the poleplate thickness from 3 to 1.25 mm. it is possible to give many different degrees of flux concentration in order to obtain a high flux density for each ring magnet, and two sets of figures are given for each to provide typical working values. Two comparison sets for central cylindrical alnico designs are added. It will be seen that the efficiency of flux utilization varies considerably according to how well the volume of magnet matches that of the airgap: too large a magnet will create unnecessary leakage flux but a relatively large gap of suitable proportions can give high efficiency if the flux density is not too great. The average efficiency of all sizes and both materials is about 50%.

From this table the following important conclusions may be drawn:

A. Large ferrite ring magnets can give flux densities as high as 1.75 Wb/m^2 at fairly low efficiency but good figures of 1.5 with very high efficiency. These are about double the flux densities of the smallest ferrite rings.

B. The efficiency must be halved to give from 1.2 to 1.5 times greater flux density, the average being 40% for small gaps and 60% for large.

C. Ferrite rings give generally higher flux density for similar size than alnico centre cylinders, although the latter were known to give nearly twice the efficiency of alnico rings used with the same arrangement as the ferrite assembly.

D. The results tend to confirm earlier statements that high-coercivity materials give lower leakage than alternative methods of maintaining magnetic fields, owing to the use of short magnetic paths enclosing the least airspace and to the screening effect of the poleplates.

It will be clear that a much higher efficiency of flux utilisation will tend to nullify the value of figures of merit based upon the performance of permanent magnet materials isolated from their ultimate magnetic circuits. The ability to maintain gap densities appreciably higher than those in common use for equivalent sizes of magnetic circuit gives prospects of much improved performance for this reason alone, apart from the other benefits obtained.

7.8 Electro Mechanical Forces

The details given of the performance of loudspeakers are typical of the problems in electrical machines: conductors moving in a small airgap with the objective of obtaining the greatest mechanical force from a given amount of electric power. In the speaker coil the vibration acts against air pressure, the acoustic load, whereas an electric motor applies starting torque and movement, through continuous rotation, to a mechanical load. Both devices operate by the interaction of the magnetic flux generated by the current in a coil or coils with the excitation flux; this could be produced electromagnetically but is much better maintained continuously by permanent magnets.

The principle of operation of both electromagnetic systems is the flux-cutting rule that the force depends upon the product of the flux density and the current (BI), and the resistance of the moving coil will be reduced as the flux density is increased because this will also reduce the diameter of the centre soft iron pole over which the coil moves. Hence the square of the flux density (B^2) is taken as a figure of merit in assessing the loudspeaker as an electro-mechanical transducer, in addition to the functional advantages mentioned above. This explains why in Table 7.1 there are several examples of what may appear to be limited gains in airgap flux density at the expense of the loss of about half the flux that could be carried by a somewhat

TABLE 7.1. FERRITE LOUDSPEAKER MAGNETS (*Mullard Ltd.*)

MAGNET Gr. II	FLUX mWb	MAGNET DIA-METERS cm	MAGNET L_M cm	MAGNET A_M cm²	MAGNET V_M cm³	WEIGHT kg	TYPICAL AIR-GAP L_g cm	TYPICAL AIR-GAP A_g cm²	TYPICAL AIR-GAP V_g cm³	GAP FLUX DENSITY Wb/m²	GAP FLUX mWb	EFFICIENCY OF FLUX UTILIZATION %
1	0·25	4·5×2·2	0·8	12	10	0·05	0·075 / 0·083	1·4 / 2·0	0·11 / 0·17	0·9 / 0·75	0·14 / 0·16	55 / 64
2	0·5	6·0×2·4	0·8	24	19	0·1	0·075 / 0·093	1·4 / 2·4	0·11 / 0·22	1·35 / 1·03	0·21 / 0·26	42 / 52
3	0·75	7·3×3·1	1·0	36	36	0·17	0·082 / 0·1	1·65 / 3·7	0·14 / 0·37	1·5 / 1·05	0·25 / 0·42	33 / 56
4	1·5	10·2×5·1	1·0	66	66	0·32	0·1 / 0·115	3·2 / 10·0	0·32 / 1·15	1·25 / 0·8	0·42 / 0·78	28 / 52
5	1·5	10·2×5·1	1·4	66	92	0·45	0·1 / 0·12	3·2 / 10·0	0·32 / 1·2	1·4 / 0·9	0·47 / 0·88	31 / 58
6	2·0	12·1×5·7	1·2	90	108	0·57	0·12 / 0·125	7·6 / 13	0·9 / 1·7	1·2 / 1·0	0·93 / 1·36	47 / 67
7	2·5	13·4×5·7	1·4	114	160	0·79	0·12 / 0·125	7·6 / 13	0·9 / 1·7	1·45 / 1·2	1·1 / 1·6	44 / 64
8	5·0	18·4×7·3	1·85	224	410	2·1	0·125 / 0·125	11·2 / 25	1·4 / 3·1	1·75 / 1·5	2·0 / 3·9	40 / 78
COMPARISON: ORIENTED ALNICO 5.												
9	0·27	1·75 dia.	1·1	2·5	2·7	0·02	0·073	1·8	0·13	0·64	0·13	50
10	1·15	3·7 dia.	2·45	10·6	26·0	0·19	0·1	5	0·5	1·0	0·55	47

NOTES: MAGNET WORKING VALUES: FERRITE B_d 0·22 Wb/m²; H_d 116 AT/mm; ALNICO B_d 1·1 Wb/m²; H_d 42 AT/mm.

FLUX UNIT CONVERSION: 1 Milliweber (mWb) is 10⁵ maxwell or lines (earlier units).

(Efficiency calculations and conversion to MKSA units by author) larger gap. What happens to the extra leakage flux in these cases is that it builds up a barrier around the gap to sustain the high density within it and in these terms it cannot be regarded as waste; in this way it will be seen that the length as well as the area of the magnetic circuit, with the non-magnetic space it encloses, must also be minimized in every possible manner. The proof of this is given by the figures: the ferrite magnet assemblies have attained a flux density level as much as 50% higher than the best metal magnet alternatives, and when this is squared it shows a performance that is more than doubled.

Improvements in a similar direction can be expected in motors or other electromagnetic designs, but only by complete changes of the kind outlined earlier in this chapter. In smaller d.c. motors of today about 30% of the excitation power appears as leakage flux which does not reach the rotor although the airgap flux densities are about half of the best in Table 7.1. Though substantial advantages have already been claimed for ferrite magnet replacements of wound poles in small machines, mere substitution at still lower flux densities is yielding only a small part of the potential value of this new ceramic material.

The advantage of high values of flux density squared, B^2 rather than B, which apply to loudspeakers is also well-known in the design of lifting magnets and similar devices. The tractive force is given by:

B is flux density in Wb/m^2

$$\text{Force} = \frac{B^2 A}{2\mu_0} \text{ newtons, where A is the pole area in metres}^2$$

μ_0 is permeability of free space
$(4\pi.10^{-7})$

In a more practical form this becomes approximately:

Force in kilograms$=4$ B^2A with A in centimetres^2

This simple relationship is very useful for showing the importance of high flux densities in electromagnetic designs, and it is practically valuable for measuring the strength of permanent magnets by pulling away a keeper from their poles by means of a spring balance calibrated in kilograms. This provides a quick and cheap method for calculating flux density as well as the performance of magnet assemblies.

Fig. 7.7 gives values of the pull exerted at flux densities up to the saturation limits of best available iron and iron-alloy, in metric and English practical units. The working flux densities of both metal and ferrite magnet loudspeaker assemblies, in comparison with airgap densities in electrical machines, are given below to indicate the importance of high values of B^2. Considerable further improvement

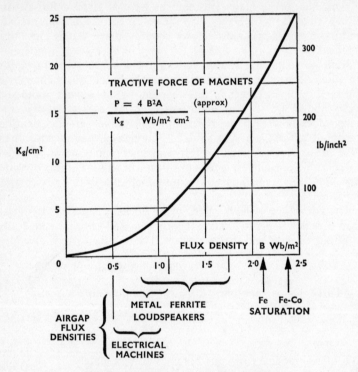

Fig. 7.7 The Tractive Force of Magnets, showing the importance of (Flux Density)^2.

would be possible with the use of cobalt-iron alloys at the pole tips, but these are costly in both materials and manufacture. They are in considerable commercial use, however, for small units and could be more widely adopted in new designs that can give economic advantages by increasing the working flux density in poleplates. With these low permeability ferrite materials, the working density can also be raised by adding electromagnetic excitation to the permanent flux.

The lower part of Fig. 7.7 indicates the range of flux density in the airgaps of present electrical machines in comparison with that of the loudspeakers, and it will be seen to correspond roughly with that of the alnico assemblies which have a similar kind of magnetic circuit in the 'medium length' category. However, the ferrite assemblies which rely on the shorter magnetic paths have extended the range well towards the upper limits imposed by the saturation of ferro-magnetic metals that could be used for poleplates. There seems no reason why similar improvements could not be applied to the machines if suitable novel designs for them can be evolved, though the problems are considerably more complex than in the case of the electro-mechanical operation of a loudspeaker of the moving coil type. Much work has been done in recent years on printed circuit motors in which only the armature winding revolves, the whole magnetic circuit being fixed as in loudspeakers; latest designs use larger ferrite magnets in disc-shaped assemblies with the rotor in the form of a large plastic disc on which the winding and commutator, for d.c. motors, are printed on the surfaces. These provide an interesting link between the traditional kind of rotating motor and the loudspeaker regarded as an elementary form of linear motor.

The B^2 effect in Fig. 7.7 which has been seen (in the case of loud-speakers) to lead to a sacrifice of flux utilisation efficiency, also applies to the design of tractive equipment and devices which rely on the pull of electromagnets. Examples are lifting magnets, relays and similar linear motions of restricted travel in which the pole face is generally tapered in order to give the highest possible flux density at the area of contact of the load—the airgap. While the leakage flux is undesirable in permanent magnet circuits because it represents inefficient use of material, it is far more serious in electromagnets where it forms an added drain of power and source of more unwanted heat throughout the working life of the equipment. These severe penalties in the desirable aim for highest possible working flux densities are thus a considerably greater deterrent in all uses of electromagnetic excitation, and provide an added incentive to the wider employment of permanent magnets for these purposes.

7.9 The Ideal Magnet

The practical information given in this chapter has shown that the recent introduction of high-coercivity permanent magnet materials on an engineering scale means far more than a further technical and economic improvement. It gives prospects of producing the *ideal magnet*, using the word in its original and widest sense as the best way for maintaining a magnetic field for practical purposes. Hitherto the electromagnet has served the dual purpose, virtually exclusively in engineering applications, of generating the magnetic flux as soon as it was required and of changing it to perform useful functions which could be controlled from near or far. Its applications have been an outstanding success when made in the form of large machines, in which its efficiency is inherently high, or in small machines in which its remarkable convenience has outweighed such technical matters as low efficiency and poor material utilization. However, transmission links of short length on the medium-power scale invariably consist of non-electrical alternatives with low bulk, lower cost and higher efficiency.

Even with the limited experience so far gained with the available range of ferrite magnets, with their threefold coercivity advantage over the best metal magnets and up to ten times the typical electromagnet equivalent, these new ceramic materials give every indication that they can transform this situation if used in their most appropriate manner. This has been summarised in the terms of a short magnetic circuit, as contrasted with the long and medium traditional alternatives developed during a period when specialised magnetic materials were non-existent. It is therefore essential to re-examine all present designs of the smaller electrical machines and equipment from first principles combined with laboratory tests on this new basis of the ideal magnet, and this is done in the following chapter. For this purpose it is desirable here to enumerate the qualities it may be expected to possess:

1. The ideal magnet will contain the means for maintaining, concentrating and controlling the magnetic flux in a single unit (i.e. combining the present functions of electromagnet and permanent magnet).

2. All the basic flux (excitation) will be provided by highest coercivity permanent magnet material.

3. The mean flux path will be as short as possible.

4. The incorporated electrical component (conductor or coil) must be suitable for operation at about ten times present current-densities, to comply with 3.

5. Materials and designs will be suitable for maintaining highest operating (airgap) flux density with small leakage field.

These arrangements provide a disc-shaped structure with excellent natural cooling, in which the permanent magnet component assists the heat-dissipating action mainly performed by the poleplates. Moreover, these mild steel parts provide good mechanical support and protection to the ceramic material. The assembly will be cheaper in materials and manufacturing costs than the present less efficient alternatives and may ultimately operate at twice their average flux density level; hence it will be much smaller and lighter to perform a specified task or to handle an equivalent amount of power.

In short, instead of its hitherto rare and ephemeral nature, magnetic flux can become for the first time a cheap, permanent and plentiful commodity for use on any required scale at high density.

7.10 Reference

Bitter F. 'Strong Magnets', *International Science & Technology* (U.S.A.), April 1962, pp. 58-64.

8

NEW DESIGNS

The direct application of the ideal magnet principle to electromagnetic machines and equipment, involving new basic conditions such as short magnetic circuits and a change in the traditional rotor flux direction, necessitates a complete reappraisal of fundamental designs. In this chapter this is done by adaptation of the simple arrangement illustrated in Fig. 7.1(c) with latest materials and technology and, where possible, this is confirmed by experiment. This work was carried out with the early isotropic barium ferrite which was suitable for use only in fixed positions, such as machine stators; but the valuable results and favourable conclusions gained enabled more practical and compact designs to be evolved, using the latest oriented grades of that ceramic magnet material. These are strong mechanically, as well as magnetically, and can be used in rotors to operate at the highest required speeds (described in later chapters).

8.1 First Principles

The simpler kind of electromagnetic machine operates by the interaction of two magnetic fields: one produced by the current in the armature and the other by the field winding, which is known as the excitation. Its performance depends upon their product in terms of flux *density* B and current I so that it can be expressed simply as (BI). If losses are neglected, the current is the electrical equivalent of the mechanical power supplied to the machine as a generator or the mechanical output as a motor; the power to operate being the product of this current and the voltage to overcome the resistance of the circuit within the machine. When run as a motor, the machine produces a back- e.m.f. (in accordance with its generator function) which increases with rising speed until it equals the applied voltage, equilibrium conditions depending on the load.

The new factor introduced by the recent remarkable advance in high-coercivity magnetic materials is that the excitation can now be permanent, thus removing an appreciable part of the losses, especially in smaller machines. This also greatly simplifies the design and improves the performance in several important ways. Hitherto the power supplied to an electric motor had also to generate the field, the first term of the BI product, as well as essential armature current, so the efficiency has been lower than technically possible. The field windings produce unwanted heat and leakage flux which accentuate the disadvantages at which electrical machines operate relative to their mechanical and hydraulic alternatives. If the merits of the ideal magnet could be applied in new designs of electrical machine which use the qualities of these new materials to best advantage, there is no theoretical reason why their performance should not equal that of the traditional non-electric methods which at present dominate most short power transmission links.

In the above brief summary of the operating principles of generators and motors, the historic explanation has been used, based upon conductors moving in a magnetic field and cutting (or linking with) its flux; this uses the concepts of the famous pioneers, Ampere and Faraday, and its present supporters will rightly claim that these descriptions have survived one and a half centuries of outstanding progress. The explanation gives too little attention, however, to the fact that the mechanical forces (for motors) are the result of magnetic effects in narrow airgaps where flux concentration is of great importance, and the current acts as the agent for producing them. It flows through the armature coils as magnetising force (in the familiar AT/mm units) for generating a magnetic field to react with the excitation flux. This is therefore the reaction of two magnets rather than the movement of a current in a magnetic field, and one of these must be an electromagnet fed from a source of energy if it is to perform work for prolonged periods. Two permanent magnets could produce only one reaction movement unless mechanical power is supplied to replace them in a position to repeat it.

Electrical machines of past and present can thus be treated as means for the interaction of two electromagnets while those of the kind to be described here will consist of one electromagnet for the armature and a high-coercivity permanent magnet for the field. Their performance will depend upon the practical degree of coupling between them, or flux utilisation efficiency, which will be much more important for the armature because its leakage represents a continual waste of power whenever the machine is running, unnecessary excitation leakage from a permanent magnet being solely an inefficient use of materials.

If the above BI product is altered by expressing its current in terms of the flux it creates, as the operating electromagnet to react with the permanent field in this new description, it will produce a B^2 term in the simplest case. This then corresponds to the traction magnet performance of Fig. 7.7, which can be applied to one magnet (electro- or permanent) with its keeper, or to two magnets of the same kind, or to one of each kind. The moving coil loudspeaker, described as a simple form of linear motor, is one permanent magnet with an electromagnet in close association, for which B^2 is regarded as its figure of merit. The ideal magnet of the previous chapter is another form of close coupling between the two kinds of magnet to which this could be applied, and will be the basis of a number of new designs to be considered here.

With one term of the BI product, or one of the two interacting fluxes, becoming available at virtually no running cost it may be thought economically desirable to make it much greater than the other, on which the efficiency will mainly depend. This applies, for example, to a very sensitive moving coil instrument using a large permanent magnet to measure tiny currents which could not be detected by their magnetic effect alone; but power conditions are different from light current technology in such instances. In mathematical terms, when the sum of x and y is constant their maximum product occurs when x=y and it falls rapidly when their difference becomes large; this fall is about 60% for a 10/1 difference but only 10% for 3/1, so the latter is the kind of ratio to prove useful in practice. Further, an appreciable penalty is imposed by extra size and weight, especially in mobile applications, so the cost of large permanent fields cannot be neglected even though they may be cheaper than much smaller fields produced electromagnetically.

Advantages to be gained by the use of permanent excitation are proportionally greater for smaller magnetic circuit sizes because their magnetising force varies as their linear dimension, with the resulting flux depending upon this dimension squared. Hence the amount of flux per unit of power becomes progressively less as the machine size increases, and the latest power station generators require as little as 0.5% of their output power to excite them. Conversely the substitution of ferrite magnets for field windings in small d.c. motors has raised the efficiency by 15% although the magnets were being used under inappropriate conditions which employed only a part of their available strength. Much greater improvement can therefore be expected in designs which use them to full advantage for small and medium-sized machines, which corresponds to the practical point that their application is best justified economically in standardised products made in large numbers, owing to the high tooling and other fixed costs associated with ferrite magnets.

These fundamental factors have been given at the outset on this little-explored subject to illustrate the magnitude of the changes from present design procedure. They necessitate increases in such performance figures as current density, flux density and temperature rise, which can only be settled after much time and development has been devoted to the new designs. These must also be related to latest practical needs, expressed in the form of suitable targets for performance, size and cost relative to present standards.

8.2 Practical Needs

Among the many possible uses of new magnetic materials, the most important appears to be the provision of small, light, cheap and efficient means for the inter-conversion of mechanical and electrical power. The merits of electricity in this direction have now been widely known for nearly a century, especially in all kinds of fixed installations and in larger forms of mobile applications. The latter can combine the present generally separated functions of propulsion, braking and unified control with long life, low maintenance and freedom from noise, dirt, fumes and wear; these widespread advantages could now well be extended to what will be called the medium-power sphere.

For these purposes the medium-power range is taken mainly to comprise the 1 to 100 kW machines and their equipment, in order to match the output of the great majority of mass-produced prime movers with simple forms of 'electrical transmissions'. This power range will correspond to mechanical units approaching the 1000 hp level owing to the differences in rating and prevailing efficiencies. While the greatest ultimate market for these proposed new electrical products will be as replacements for conventional mechanical and hydraulic alternatives, they would have many other uses for mobile power equipment and could be developed into linear equivalents.

Of the alternatives discussed in Chapter 2, direct current is the most appropriate form of electric power for these mobile applications owing to its storage capability and its outstanding performance for traction purposes, which require a wide range of preferably stepless speed variation. This stems from its acyclic nature; it can be generated in a high speed dynamo and used in a slow speed motor without difficulty. Alternating currents of any frequency have pronounced cyclic tendencies which are most appropriate for fixed speeds, and also for simple and cheap induction motors; but d.c. machines have hitherto been the most expensive and cumbersome with poor level of efficiency in the smaller sizes. It is around 60%, at the lower part of the stated medium-power range, so that a generator-motor combination used as an electrical transmission would lose more power than it transmitted and can thus be regarded as impracticable at present in these sizes. Large d.c. machines of the same design have up to 95% efficiency which makes their use in this manner very attractive, so there is nothing wrong with electrical methods as such, but only in the smaller sized units.

The magnetic reasons for this severe reduction of efficiency in the smaller sizes have already been given in terms of electromagnets. Large machines can not only afford electromagnetic excitation, but also special cooling methods and, in the case of power station alternators, the advantages of rotating electromagnets to provide their magnetic field. Their recent history of progress by steadily increasing the size well beyond any forecast limits is a good example of the unexpected possibilities in the improvement of electrical machines.

But no present d.c. machine could use rotating field magnets because the rotor has to employ a commutator attached to the armature for converting the rotor current to a.c. This is the only known method for meeting any required terminal voltage by using the armature winding as a kind of transformer; it imposes heavy penalties in cost, weight and size as noted above and, together with the electromagnet inefficiencies, is responsible for the poor performance. This design dates back to the end of last century when the main preoccupation was the power station coupled to tramway and railway electrification schemes, all dependent upon high distribution voltages to close limits. These do not apply to isolated mobile transmission units connected to a single prime mover and probably using an electric battery, which could well operate at a far lower voltage. While direct current has many advantages for this use it is also desirable to investigage the a.c. alternatives in view of recent developments in higher frequencies, and in many kinds of static rectifier for converting to d.c. power and also for controlling it.

In matching prime movers for power it is also necessary to operate the new electrical machines at equivalent speeds because this will give the desirable reduction of size and weight per kilowatt. Present designs are restricted by their complex rotor windings and commutators, so these should be eliminated and substituted by a robust alternative. Also the present cost per kilowatt rises steeply with reduced size so that it is not feasible economically to use, in place of a single motor, two with each of half the power, and out of the question to use four of one-quarter the power. Yet this economic subdivision of motor units is extremely desirable for propulsion-braking systems which should also be small enough to instal inside the wheel hubs.

It is now possible to arrive at some main target figures for the new electrical machines, based upon latest prime mover performance and present conventional designs:—

1. Size and cost to be reduced to about one-tenth that of present d.c. types.

2. Losses to be at least halved with efficiencies from 75% to 90%.

3. Rotors to run at present prime mover speeds and peripheral velocities, e.g. up to 1000 rev/sec and 1000 ft/sec (300 m/sec).

4. Designs to be capable of economic subdivision; i.e. two or four small motors to cost not greatly more than single machines of similar total power.

If item 3 can be reached it will go some way towards the reduced size of 1, which will assist the price reduction for quantity production conditions. The remaining size reduction and loss improvement should be reached with the greater efficiency introduced by permanent magnet excitation and the resulting reduction in generated heat, the use of higher current- and flux densities and the excellent natural cooling of the ideal magnet assemblies.

8.3 Homopolar D.C. Machines (Acyclic)

Faraday's Disc (Fig. 3.4) was the first dynamo ever made, but the first electric motor appeared about 9 years earlier and is known as Barlow's Wheel (Fig. 3.5). The latter is given less attention today than it deserves, but some of the features have reappeared only during recent years: the points of the rotating metal star increase the current density where it is most needed at the zone of highest flux density, and their tips dipping in mercury provide a low resistance contact of limited frictional drag. Such liquid metal rotating contacts have become very important during the past decade for large heavy-current generators to be described later. However, for this stage of the investigation it is desirable to regard the rotating star as a metal disc with solid sliding brush contacts, so that it is the Faraday Disc in reverse; this is in order to indicate that these two great inventions were basically reversible. They form a convenient starting point in this search for the simplest and best method for inter-converting mechanical and electrical power, though originally intended as scientific demonstrations. (Fig. 8.1.)

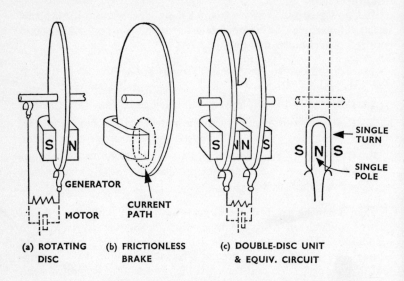

Fig. 8.1 Evolution of Low-Voltage D.C. Machine and Braking System.

Their significance became at once apparent to many able practical men, as described in Chapter 3, but mainly in the direction of multi-turn electromagnets after the impressive demonstrations of Sturgeon and Henry in weight-lifting. In our language the voltage of these rotating discs was far too low and the coils gave the effect of a large number of discs in series; the higher voltage meant more power where it was wanted. The alternatives of much stronger magnets and far higher rotational speeds, which are now available to us in thousand-fold measure, could not then be considered. But the disc rotating in the magnetic field returned for practical use at the end of that century as a frictionless brake which did not require brushes because the currents generated could be confined to a low-resistance circuit round the magnet poles (Fig. 8.1b). Since that time this kind of brake has been used for many electrical measuring devices and is practically universal for electrical integrating meters; it can be seen in domestic meters which provide the number of units on which electric supply is charged for payment.

Sliding electrical contacts proved to be the main problem in rotating disc machines, especially through the shaft in both the above cases. For magnetic and corrosion reasons, steel is undesirable as a contact metal whereas the periphery gives ample space and suitable surface. A double-disc arrangement (Fig. 8.1c) in the form of a bobbin-shaped rotor gives the following advantages:

(a) the brushgear is identical on each side;

(b) the rotor conductor can be insulated and also isolated from the shaft;

(c) several such shallow units can be mounted on one shaft and connected in series to raise the voltage to a working value;

(d) the machine can be designed to run at the highest required speeds.

The equivalent circuit of this design is shown to be a single-turn armature 'winding' encircling a single magnet pole, so this kind of machine is described as homopolar (or sometimes unipolar). The short magnetic path with flux passing to and from the rotor in the axial direction is clearly most appropriate for excitation by high coercivity ring-magnets, with poleplates projecting inwards to cover the main area of the discs apart from their periphery.

The simplicity of this design is matched by that of its performance calculation:

Voltage = Total Flux in webers × Speed in rev/sec.

To give a practical example, a pair of the largest ferrite ring-magnets in Table 7.1 together give a flux of 0.01 weber, and a flux utilisation of 80% can be assumed for these efficient conditions. It thus requires a speed of 125 rev/sec for each volt generated and the highest specified speed (for small gas turbines) gives 8 volts per double-disc unit. By the use of very low resistance external circuits, currents of up to thousands of amperes can be generated, with corresponding power of several kilowatts; these are the required conditions for vehicle propulsion, which could be arranged with short transmission lengths of large-section conductor. The working voltage would best

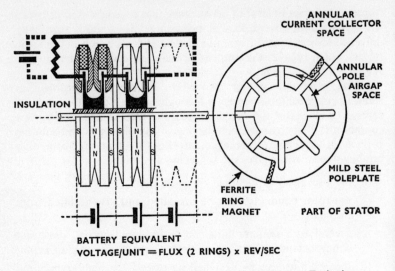

Fig. 8.2 Low-Voltage D.C. Machine with Ferrite Magnet Excitation.

be that of the present battery supply for starting, lighting and auxiliaries and this can be generated at the lower speed of a petrol engine by a machine with a number of series-connected units. Under these conditions it would be desirable to enlarge the capacity of the battery so that it could also be used to assist in the propulsion and to meet peaks of load, when this kind of machine is used in the form of motors as well as the generator in a new kind of electric drive or transmission system.

The actual shape of the suggested ferrite ring magnet of the above example is unsuitable for this use; it would be necessary for the outer and inner diameters to be 20 and 12 centimetres to give the same flux and to allow space for the rotors inside it. Fig. 8.2 shows the kind of assembly of a number of units in one machine with electrical series connections between them made through radial slots in the poleplates, which also minimise flux distortion in concentric directions. Though there are greater limitations to voltage control and adjustment in this type of machine compared with conventional alternatives, this is of minor importance for the proposed use in isolated single circuits. The arrangement can be compared to a battery built up of a number of cells connected in series, the voltage of each cell being fixed by its materials and chemical reaction regardless of size.

But a larger machine of this kind gives increased voltage according to its excitation flux, and this increases roughly as the square of the diameter for equivalent magnet quality.

Conversely, there is a lower limit to the practical size of this kind of machine owing to the minimum voltage dropped at the sliding electrical contacts with the rotor, essential to its operation. Commercial copper-graphite brush materials are made to give a minimum contact drop of 0.1 volt so that a pair of such contacts would form an appreciable part of a generator output giving less than about one volt per double-disc unit. But, although the brushgear or current-collecting problem has always dominated the design and performance of this kind of machine in the past, the conditions at these very low voltages are far less severe than for conventional applications. This subject is dealt with in the next chapter but there appear to be good prospects of reaching a satisfactory answer for machines down to around one kilowatt with practical efficiency values. This range covers the main demands for individual propulsion of vehicles and even of their wheels individually, for which the above design will be found most appropriate.

From the standpoint of permanent magnet applications it will be seen that this simple homopolar d.c. machine uses the latest high coercivity materials to best advantage and at highest efficiency for excitation purposes. This would not have been practicable at earlier times with the use of any grade of metal magnet.

8.4 Direct Current Braking

Frictional braking has made such progress throughout the century, mainly as a result of research in friction materials, that its inherent limitations are often overlooked. Except for stopping from slow speeds, braking forces should be related to speed by dynamic methods which remove most of the energy away from the braking mechanism, and conserve it by some regenerative system. In particular, the stored energy from deceleration should be made available for the accelerating stage which normally follows it. Frictional braking is purely wasteful, tends to produce intense heating where it is least wanted, causes wear and consequent maintenance which, if neglected, can become hazardous.

Early electric propulsion for both road and rail—tramways and electric cars as well as main line, suburban and underground railways—showed that a close approach to this dynamic regenerative ideal for braking could be achieved in practice, though by complex and costly methods. These economic penalties were the direct result of electromagnetic excitation; it was essential to have magnetic fields at full strength in the motors for braking to be effective. This situation was of special significance in the case of the series-wound motor which soon became the preferred design for traction purposes, on account of its high starting torque. With heavy starting current the flux density is appreciably higher than that which can be maintained during continuous running owing to heating limitations but, in contrast, a shunt field winding must maintain a substantially constant flux density. This is the reason for the considerable differences in the shapes of their torque-speed characteristics, though both have important advantages relative to alternatives for traction.

If a series motor is to be used for dynamic braking it is necessary to have appropriate field winding switching and to ensure a power supply to provide the essential magnetic flux, with the necessary precautions to see that the risk of failure is minimised. While these conditions can be provided on a large scale, such as a railway, it can well be understood that regenerative braking with conventional machines is regarded as uneconomic for road vehicles. For safety reasons also, the magnetic flux should be present at full strength at all times; this shows the great importance of permanent magnets for this purpose if they are really permanent to withstand the severe operating conditions, mechanical as well as electrical. For economic reasons also, this subject could not be considered before the arrival of the high-coercivity ferrite materials during the past decade. Their merits go well beyond the vital safety need; it is now possible to have the simplest form of two-terminal machine which will automatically give electrical braking without switching. The performance of the permanent magnet field is similar to that of the shunt winding when the machine is running, but the flux in the latter disappears when the supply is off and has to be built up in a period of some seconds when required; compared with non-electric alternatives the performance of series-wound machine is only marginally better than the conventional shunt types used for traction purposes, and present information points to the permanent field as being superior to either in its ultimate form. If the temporary boost to the field is needed for starting, it could well be given by an added winding, as in the case of the ideal magnet, but this would appear unnecessary if the full benefits of the permanent field are employed in each wheel, in a manner described later.

In electrical braking the propulsion motor acts in reverse as a generator driven by the momentum of the vehicle in slowing down or in descending a gradient. The machine is connected to an electrical load, which can be a resistor or a battery of lower voltage, and control of this braking effect can be obtained by suitable changes of the circuit resistance. For a fixed value of the latter, the power absorbed will depend upon the vehicle speed and this will therefore apply to the decelerating forces. Hence dynamic braking, the most useful form in practice, can be automatically applied by an electrical propulsion system using permanent excitation. It becomes progressively less effective as the speed is reduced and disappears as it comes to rest, so it must be supplemented with frictional braking for the later stages and for parking. However, the duty required for these slow-and-stop uses is relatively light and would contribute little to the needs for adjustments and replacements in present conditions.

To see how an electrical brake operates in practice it is desirable to revert to the most elementary form in Fig. 8.1 b, described as the frictionless design. The conductor disc revolving in the magnetic field generates heavy circulating currents whose magnetic field reacts with that of the permanent magnet to produce a drag of the kind that would occur if the disc were immersed in a viscous fluid. This effect would be increased if the flux density through the disc were raised by the use of stronger permanent magnet material, or by reducing the airgap clearance, but these give little scope for practical control. If magnets are progressively added until they cover the whole surface of the disc, the drag reaches a maximum and then falls off because the path for the circulating current will have become restricted, with the result that its resistance will rise. There are thus limitations to adapting this frictionless brake arrangement for power uses, though it is excellent for instruments and meters.

The double-disc design of Fig. 8.1 (c) can provide the answer. If the return electric circuit can be taken outside the conducting disc, the whole surface (apart from a peripheral strip for current collection) can be used for this magnetic braking. The sliding electrical contacts at the edges are then the low-voltage equivalents of conventional brushgear, and this arrangement has the following advantages:—

1. most of the energy generated can be dissipated externally;

2. the braking effect can be applied and controlled remotely and externally by simple electrical methods;

3. frictional effects, appreciable for heavy currents, can be used for final slowing and stopping in vehicle dynamic braking;

4. ferrite ring-magnets are used to best advantage, as in the virtually identical motor application (Fig. 8.2);

5. the disc-shaped assembly is suitable for installation with its incorporated step-down gearing inside the hub of the wheel it controls.

The final design is therefore the same if this is approached as a better motor or as an improved brake. Powered by a battery, the motor will increase in speed until the back-e.m.f. equals the battery voltage less the volt drop due to losses; if (as part of a vehicle propulsion-braking system) the speed is further increased by running down a hill, the machine will act as a generator and the voltage will rise to the point that current is returned to the battery. This action will provide corresponding braking effect without switching or other kind of driver-operated control. This automatic braking effect is due to the use of permanent excitation and is a further advantage over shunt or series field windings. The main problem to achieve practical success is the development of current collectors with low frictional and resistive loss so that the very high efficiency that is theoretically possible with this design can be approached for the range of operating conditions. In such a short d.c. circuit sliding contacts can be the only significant source of loss. Working at about one-hundredth the average voltage of conventional carbon-based brushes, it represents far less severe working conditions and the problem appears to warrant a different kind of solution to give the best ultimate results.

8.5 Magnetic Clutch

Work done in the development of new kinds of frictionless magnetic clutch led to the a.c. alternatives of the above d.c. machines and brakes, for both techniques were incorporated in a single design. For this discussion a magnetic clutch means one in which the magnetic field is part of the chain of power transmission; this is to distinguish it from an electromagnetically controlled friction clutch, which uses an electric power supply solely as a convenient method for the remote control of a well-known mechanical device. This has the same set of disadvantages as friction brakes, in terms of wear, local heat dissipation and somewhat unpredictable performance.

In practice the friction clutch has generally a less arduous task than the brake because the power dissipated in it depends upon the *difference* between the speeds of the driving and driven shafts, and in vehicles this can be minimised by the skill of the driver. The remarkable performance for low cost is largely due to the great progress in friction materials developed to meet these conditions. But they cannot approach the ideal of hydraulic or magnetic systems in which slipping is part of the essential operation and yet does not cause progressive wear. In both of these alternatives it is possible to dissipate the power externally and to provide remote control, with elaborations to give some measure of torque conversion, so that future developments appear to lie in their direction. The hydraulic analogy to the basic magnetic field in such a system will become apparent in this connection. The flow in the circuit is the equivalent of the current produced, alternating to match reciprocating pumps and direct current for rotary pumps. The acyclic nature of the latter is most appropriate for the infinitely variable gear requirements in which a prime-mover runs at its optimum constant speed and the load can be varied in torque and speed over the widest range required for vehicle propulsion conditions.

In essence this can be regarded as a slipping clutch with no restrictions imposed upon it, but torque conversion represents efficient use of the energy whereas it would be wasted under slip conditions. If it could be stored in an accumulator and returned when needed, this would become a practical proposition. An electric generator coupled electrically to a motor (the 'petrol-electric' drive for buses of half a century ago) gave the same effect with a complication of machinery. The main query is how this desirable end can be achieved with the simplest method and highest efficiency.

An interesting starting-point to this search was the development in America by Rabinow about 20 years ago of a magnetic fluid for this purpose, iron powder immersed in oil. When placed inside a glass tube with a coil wound on it, the mixture would solidify when direct current was passed to magnetise it but it would at once return to its former fluid state when the current was switched off. This principle was used to make a number of magnetic clutches with excellent operating qualities for light current uses in instrumentation and for servo-mechanisms where exact performance was needed.

Plans were then made to develop larger clutches of this kind for vehicles, machines and ships but these have by no means come up to expectations. The heat generated in power conditions tended to force the abrasive magnetic fluid from the airgaps to the bearings and later designs used solid lubricants such as graphite in place of the oil. Some of these clutches have been provided as optional extras for small European cars in the form of automatic transmissions which do not appreciably reduce the fuel consumption efficiency. Though they need current to operate them, this continual drain on the battery is stated to be within its capacity. The chief criticism of this kind of car transmission is, however, the complexity and consequent expense: it requires two such magnetic clutches with the equivalent of a manual gearbox and special control circuits. There would seem to be good prospects for the development of an electric drive without the use of mechanical gears but based upon excitation by permanent magnets of the latest kind to give the essential simplicity and high efficiency.

A study of these magnetic powder clutches raised the doubt of whether the iron or alloy powders were necessary, though this would involve a change in the basic design. Information given in earlier chapters indicates that the magnetic permeability of non-compacted iron powder, i.e. in the form used in these clutches, is very low and would not greatly reduce the reluctance of their magnetic circuit. The main factor was the airgap between two mild steel discs, one fixed to the driving shaft and the other to the driven shaft. If the flux between them were maintained permanently by a fixed surrounding ferrite ring-magnet with suitable poleplates to transfer the flux to the periphery of the rotor discs, power would be transmitted between them without physical contact if they had a uniform set of radial grooves cut in them.

The explanation for this is that any relative movement between the two steel discs would increase the reluctance and the excitation would create a strong restoring torque. If there were considerable slip between them, the flux pulsations so generated would set up eddy currents which would give further restoring torque by electromagnetic induction. The operation of declutching is performed by passing a direct current from the battery through a fixed coil between the poleplates inside the ring-magnet, and of such value that it temporarily neutralises the permanent flux.

Experimental small clutches of this kind were at first made in simple form and construction from early television focusing ring-magnets which had a high value of intrinsic coercivity relative to their working H_c and withstood the severe demagnetising conditions without noticable alteration. These provided interesting examples of the transmission of mechanical power without physical contact in a frictionless manner, but with the novel additional advantage that no power was dissipated to achieve this desirable aim; current was applied only occasionally, for declutching purposes, as a means for control.

8.6 Experimental Clutch Unit

Though originally planned as an improved version of the iron powder clutch invented by Rabinow, the following unit was the means for developing new kinds of high current-density electromagnets for the control and neutralisation of the magnetic flux maintained by a ferrite magnet with poleplates, of the kind shown in Fig. 7.1(c); the only difference was the use of two rotor discs and the required double bearings for supporting their shafts on each side. The adjacent radially-grooved faces of these discs in mild steel modulated the permanent flux as soon as the clutch slipped, so that a rough kind of alternating current was generated in the actuating coil. This current could be dissipated externally in a resistor and thus gave the a.c. equivalent of the d.c. braking system described above; this generating action by modulation of the excitation flux of a fixed magnet-coil arrangement, known as an inductor alternator, is described in the following section as a further application of ferrite magnets. These points explain the importance of this work to the whole of this subject, especially in forming a comparison between the a.c. and d.c. power alternatives as well as a connecting link between them.

A diagram of the operation of the experimental unit is shown in Fig. 8.3, the battery being introduced to reduce or neutralise the permanent flux for control purposes. The coil was wound with anodised aluminium strip slightly narrower than the space between the poleplates, which gave a high conductor space factor of over 90% dependent upon the number of turns and therefore on the necessary applied voltage. This material and the good natural cooling of the design enabled the required tenfold increase in current density to be attained, giving working ampere-turn values up to 2000AT needed for this purpose. As indicated earlier, this applied current is only needed at full value for the relatively infrequent operation of declutching, but it is claimed that the anodised layer of only a few microns thickness will withstand temperatures limited by the melting point of the metal (about 500°C); so this kind of high current intensity coil could be developed to perform this type of flux control on a more continuous basis if required. The extensive experimental work also showed that the Gr. I isotropic magnets, with intrinsic

14

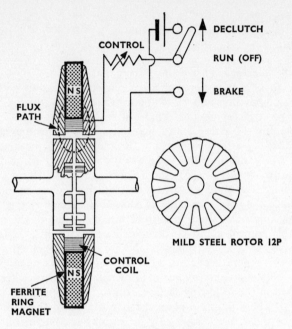

Fig. 8.3 Experimental Magnetic Clutch.

coercivity nearly twice the working H_C value of 140AT/mm, can withstand this frequent temporary neutralisation of its magnetic flux without any practical reduction in its strength.

Without the coil and its applied current the design is a simple magnetic coupling which acts as a mechanical fuse: it will transmit up to a certain torque decided by the flux density and the operative area of the steel discs. Above this level of applied braking torque the driven shaft will slip but there is some restoring torque produced by the eddy currents in its steel disc, on the principle of the d.c. brake circulating currents. Hence the slipping can be confined to periods of overload, and heat will be generated at these periods only, normal synchronous drive conditions absorbing no power with permanent excitation from the ferrite ring magnet.

By incorporating the coil alone, some of the dissipated power produced under slipping conditions can be extracted and used to operate an overload alarm. The supply of direct current enables the point at which slipping occurs to be varied downwards to zero (i.e. declutching) by opposing the permanent flux, or upwards to the saturation level of the poleplates by reversing the current direction. In practice the maximum torque could be nearly doubled compared with the switch-off value, but this could be used as a short term measure with full current; the considerable a.c. power generated under these very high flux density conditions with the high torques needed to brake the driven shaft would heat up the external circuit including the battery, unless the latter were shunted by an appropriate capacitance.

This simple form of permanent magnetic coupling acts as an a.c. brake in reverse drive conditions, with the dynamic performance dependent upon speed as in the d.c. system; but this is frictionless because the electrical power resulting from the absorbed load is induced without any kind of physical contact between driving and driven members. The current appears in the mild steel discs as heat (eddy currents) and also in the closed circuit formed by the coil connected to its resistance or other kind of external circuit. In one test unit the rotor discs each had 12 radial slots which modulated the permanent flux 12 times each revolution; at the moderate operating speed of 25 rev/sec (1500 rpm) the frequency of the generated current under maximum braking conditions with one rotor disc locked was 12×25 cycles/sec or 300 c/s. This is six times higher than the usual mains supply frequency and the waveform will be far more irregular, resulting in harmonics of this frequency appearing in considerable proportions. As the magnitude of induced currents depends upon the frequency squared, these practical conditions give high eddy current losses indicated by the appreciable rise of rotor temperature with little of the power being transferred to the external circuit.

These experiments showed that the new ferrite magnets could be used for the efficient generation of high frequency power owing to their unfamiliar insulator properties. These would prevent the formation of eddy currents, even in massive pieces, when the magnets are used to provide continuously pulsating flux, whereas metal alternatives cannot be used in this way because of their high conductivity. Nevertheless, the remaining part of the magnetic circuit required to convey and to concentrate the flux must be made in a form to minimise eddy currents if the available power is not to be dissipated within it. Mild steel cannot be used and silicon steel laminated cores of the kind used for power frequencies are not good enough for the higher loss conditions of the working speed range. Some kind of iron powder-core material with high saturation flux density is needed and this subject is discussed in the h.f. alternator section.

In the normal clutch application conditions the generated frequency, being proportional to the *difference* between the driving and driven shaft speeds, will be fairly low and the currents of limited duration, so a simple design in mild steel is feasible. But when used for prolonged periods as a frictionless brake, with prospects of recovering some of the energy, a more elaborated design using low-loss magnetic materials becomes necessary. This could well become a motor rather than a clutch, to give full propulsion and braking based upon alternating rather than direct current, and using the induction motor principle; but the logical next step in the development sequence is the inductor alternator based upon the use of ferrite magnets. This gives a more efficient means for the conversion of the mechanical energy into alternating current with the use of only one rotor.

The various models of experimental clutch made in this programme, varying in size from 4 inch cube (10 cm) to three times this dimension, proved it possible to have an adequate range of completely free movement of the driven shaft under declutch conditions to allow for practical variations such as temperature rise. This results from the nearly linear shape of demagnetising curve for this ferrite magnet material. The transmitted torque can be varied by adjustment of the maximum flux density, which can provide variants of this device for use as mechanical fuses or overload alarms.

8.7 High Frequency Alternator

The method of generating alternating current by the use of rotating iron inductors to create cyclic pulsations in an electromagnetic field has been known and used since the early days of power stations. With the equivalent of fixed armature windings as well as fixed field coils and no moving electrical contacts, it is basically the simplest kind of a.c. machine, the rotor being merely the set of inductors in paddle-wheel construction. But in practice its full simplicity can be attained only when excited with permanent magnet material possessing insulator properties.

Though it was finally superseded at the end of the last century by flux *reversal* machines (with adjacent poles of alternate polarity) which were found to give more efficient flux utilisation for power station work, the inductor alternator has continued to be manufactured for higher frequency applications. Its simple rotor design can be made with the equivalent of far more poles than the wound kind, and can operate at much higher peripheral speeds for this purpose. Today many machines of this type are used to generate power at 10 000 c/s or higher for special processes such as the heating or melting of metals by eddy current methods. Early high-power radio transmitters used such machines for frequencies up to 100 kc/s.

But such machines were and are complex and expensive, being generally made to special orders and designs. In addition to the need for a special direct current power supply for excitation, it is essential to use complicated magnetic circuit shapes in the stator in order to maintain the total flux at constant value; otherwise there will be power losses back through the excitation circuit. The flux must be made to pulsate or swing from one path to another by the use of appropriate grouping of stator slots, so that the simplicity of the rotor is outweighed by the complexity of the stator. Especially in smaller units high frequency power made in this way must inevitably be costly.

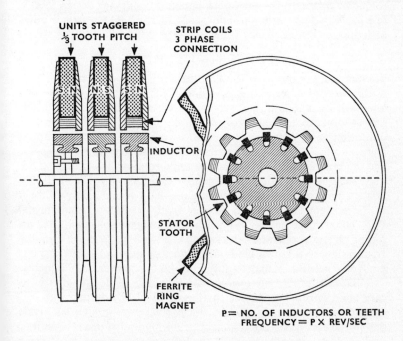

Fig. 8.4 3-Phase Inductor Alternator, 12P Type

The simple manner in which ferrite ring-magnets can be used for this kind of machine is shown in Fig. 8.4. This uses the ideal magnet principle with inwards-projecting poleplates having teeth to correspond with the rotor inductors, enclosing the stator winding between them. As the rotor revolves, pulses of magnetic flux enclose the coil every time the inductors pass the teeth at the point of minimum magnetic reluctance. When the inductors are midway between the teeth it is important that there is enough air-space between them to give high reluctance so that the flux *change* is as great as possible. The design details are most important because the performance depends upon the proportion of available flux that can be used effectively; though it does not have such an effect on the operating efficiency with permanent excitation, it greatly affects the bulk and cost of the machine.

Conventional alternators with flux reversal obtained by the use of alternate N and S poles in their excitation field produce one cycle of current for each *pair* of poles, but this requires only one pole (inductor or tooth) for each poleplate in the inductor design to give one cycle of flux variation, and hence of current. So with P poles or inductors the frequency generated is given by:

$$\text{Frequency in c/s} = P \times \text{revs/sec.}$$

Though the amplitude of the flux variation in one direction is half of that for flux reversal, the doubling of the frequency gives the two alternative methods of a.c. generation the same theoretical output, but in practice the inductor design is more prone to poor flux utilisation when separate excitation is used. The advantages should be reversed when permanent magnets are employed for this purpose, and this could apply to maximum extent if rotating fields can be used.

By shaping the tooth contour relative to the section of the inductor and the airgap between them it is possible to give a sine waveform to the current generated to meet normal alternator requirements. With either fixed or rotating permanent magnet field there are no sliding electrical contacts, an important advantage over the Faraday Disc design, so that this kind of machine can qualify for the simplest kind of electrical design to meet the mobile power requirements.

It is most important to note that this kind of design, if it is to gain the desired benefits of small size for large output specified earlier, must operate at high frequencies (by power standards). While this introduces many development problems it also opens up a new field of electrical applications in the lighting, heating and processing

fields to be described in the next chapter. The use of the conventional
50 c/s frequency, or even the low multiples such as 400 c/s, limits the
machines and transformers to the present kind of large and bulky
units with complex windings which are satisfactory for the present
great majority of fixed uses but are unsuitable for future mobile
power. Though the proposed designs could operate at any desired
frequency in the lower kilocycle range, there are several reasons why
it should be ultrasonic, or in the 10 to 20 kc/s zone. This provides best
conditions for the most important new developments and it avoids
many of the serious noise problems encountered in the higher audio
frequencies.

Fig. 8.4 illustrates a 12P rotor to match that of Fig. 8.3, but this
could be increased to about 20P before the flux utilisation efficiency is
seriously reduced in smaller machines, and it could be much greater
in larger machines. The limit will be the mechanical bursting strength
which depends upon the peripheral velocity. With rotational speeds
in the 200 to 1000 rev/sec region, 100P to 20P designs would be
respectively needed to give the highest proposed frequency of 20
kc/s. At this frequency only one turn of the stator winding in a
ferrite magnet with flux of 0.01 weber (equivalent to a pair of
magnets in the d.c. double-disc unit example) would produce a
voltage of $0.01 \times 20\,000$V or 200V, equivalent to present mains
voltage. This is necessary for many of the new lighting developments
as well as more economical use of present systems, but transmission
and voltage transformation would also be relatively straightforward,
in sharp contrast to the d.c. heavy current system.

An important practical point is the starting difficulty of a single
magnet unit of this kind, owing to the severe 'cogging' or the force
holding the rotor in the lowest reluctance position with inductors
opposite the teeth. This is the force which drives the clutch without
power consumption (Fig. 8.3) and it can be temporarily released in
the same way by passing a direct current of required magnitude
through the coil. A better design is a three-unit machine on one
shaft, as shown, with their inductors aligned and their teeth staggered
by one-third of the angular tooth pitch. In this case the cogging forces
are neutralised and the rotor can be easily revolved. The machine
then gives the equivalent of a three-phase output and can be connected in the conventional manner for present power supplies.

The search for the simplest kind of electrical machine has thus
also arrived at the ultimate limit reached with the d.c. alternative,
one pole and (in this case) windings down to one turn for each basic

unit. The two alternative conditions now become low-voltage with heavy current to transmit power with d.c. machines, and ultrasonic frequency at mains voltage (or other required values) for a.c. power, both being capable of operation up to highest prime-mover speeds. In place of the current collection problem dominating the d.c. system, the magnetic losses of the conducting or non-ferrite part of the magnetic circuits will be the deciding factor in the economic future of kilocycle electric power.

8.8 Rotary Actuators

So far in this chapter the discussion has centred on the use of permanent magnet excitation of rotating machines using a continuous supply of power for the inter-conversion of mechanical and electrical energy; it now turns to single operations or movements of limited travel and duration. Unless some kind of latching mechanism is used, the employment of electromagnetic attraction for closing contactors or similar power controls represents an even greater waste of power with its resulting design complication than in the case of field excitation for machines. The holding operations, on or off, can be done with permanent magnets and power is only needed for the short duration of the mechanical movement, and can be provided by a pulse of direct current. The actuating coil can thus be designed for high current-densities with the resulting great size reduction, and reliability is greatly improved because the control is not at the mercy of power supply fluctuations or failure: it can operate from a small stand-by battery since very little power is needed.

The inductor alternator design of Fig. 8.4 can be used in this manner as a stepped-control rotary actuator, using d.c. pulses in a star-connected three-phase circuit to neutralise momentarily one magnet unit; at the same time it strengthens one of the other magnets by passing the current in the direction opposite to that of the first in relation to the permanent magnet polarity. This action provides a powerful torque to move the rotor into the next equilibrium position with no current flowing, with teeth of the stator poleplates opposite the rotor inductors in their new place. An elementary kind of rotary switch with three-phase electrical connection to the machine can provide the control for forward and backward movement on the appropriate step-by-step basis. While the tooth/inductor contour of an inductor alternator to give a sine waveform causes free rotation, other contours will provide the effect of the familiar ball-and-socket location device so that the rotor is held firmly in each step position until pulses are injected into the coils to release and move it to a new position.

Alternatively, two such inductor machines coupled electrically by three-phase connection could operate as an electric drive, one converting the energy driving it into electrical power used to propel the other synchronously. This could be applied to certain uses where the speeds had to be closely related but would be unsuitable for the acyclic requirements outlined earlier in this chapter; high speeds will again involve high frequencies and the problem of restricting the losses in the non-ferrite parts of the magnetic circuit. These do not apply to the actuator uses for which mild steel is adequate, and suitable contours for giving differing mechanical performance can be tooled and produced in quantities at low cost.

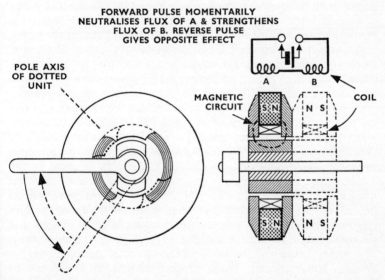

Fig. 8.5 Pulse-Operated Rotary Actuator with Ferrite Ring-Magnet Double Unit.

The above example of the inductor three-phase alternator design used with a rotary switch and battery to give multi-point rotary actuator performance is probably the most elaborate kind required and much simpler designs can be evolved for elementary controls.

Small ring- or disc-magnets of ferrite with poleplates having the equivalent of only two teeth will give the essentials for a two way rotary movement in pairs, with the teeth of one unit displaced angularly from the axis of the other unit (Fig. 8.5). (One unit with a coil-spring return mechanism is the simplest form but the merits of all-magnetic systems are such that this would be regarded as a retrogressive tendency.) In the case of long-travel rotary actuators it is a similar problem to holding magnets which have to operate over considerable distances: the volume of the permanent magnet material must be large enough to match the volume of the magnetic field to be maintained. The smallest and least expensive units will give relatively little linear or angular movement and can be operated by pulses of shorter duration, but the operating cost difference between small and large units will be unimportant. To meet the variety of practical demands it will be necessary to have a number of alternative designs with differing shapes of poleplate contour. This gives a range of holding force values relative to the travel angle or distance, the flux being concentrated for the former and spread out for the latter.

Permanent magnets used for polarised devices such as directional relays give somewhat similar service to the above actuators and the principle has been known and employed for many years, but mainly for instrumentation with negligible power consumed. Even under these conditions it was necessary to complicate the design by separating geographically the permanent magnet and the actuating electromagnet to avoid demagnetisation. The new features made possible by the latest high-coercivity materials are the extension of this principle to power applications and the simplicity of design achieved by the combinations of both kinds of magnet into a single unit, the ideal magnet. Further, the use of permanent flux was costly as well as limited, so that it was confined to small linear movement of the kind typified in the relay. It is now possible to think in terms of large and stronger fields at low cost, which can do far more in a better manner. The rotary actuator, like the rotating electrical machine, has an inherent advantage over linear alternatives that the airgap can be kept small and constant in magnetic length, so there is freedom of mechanical movement at low or fast speeds with low magnetic reluctance for excitation and operational purposes. In other words, the shaft/bearing system provides a very simple means of accurate guidance between fixed and moving parts, with small frictional loss.

For this general reason electromagnetic designs have been primarily rotational and have required gears and mechanisms to give linear equivalents in a clumsy and costly manner. This is the opposite of fluid systems which are at their best in cylinder/piston designs and need cranks, linkages, flywheels and other complications to produce rotary motion; all reciprocating prime-movers are examples, but major progress was achieved when direct rotary motion was attained first in steam turbines and later in gas turbines. Progress of equivalent importance can be expected in the ultimate development of linear electromagnetic equivalents of rotary machines.

8.9 Track Systems

All the applications so far considered in this chapter meet practical requirements which have been known and used on an increasing scale for many years. The proposed new version of them are all similar in the respects that they are derived from the ideal magnet principle and have the same simple construction based on the use of ferrite ring-magnets and their associated circular poleplates, to concentrate the flux where required and to provide mechanical protection. But, though their principle is generally the same their linear versions are quite different, it is thus better to approach this subject from the functional angle.

Since man discovered in prehistoric times that it is better to spend time and effort in the preparation of a track for travelling along a regularly used route, rather than struggle through undergrowth and swamps, there has been a growing demand for track systems of improved kind. This also demanded increasing diversity. At first roads carried all land traffic, people and their loads, which became of considerable weight with the steady improvement of the wheel and its associated structures. Later, canals were made for moving heavier loads slowly, railways for increasing the speed (and hence the volume and value of the traffic) and overhead ropeways for mountainous conditions; each of these became a special-purpose track.

Railways became the classic example of the special track. But they inherited the tradition from the road of heavy wheel construction for both support and guidance; in a modern railway coach as much as two-thirds of the total weight goes to this non-essential purpose. Further, there is an upper limit to the economic rotational speed of wheels decided by centrifugal force (bursting speed) and gyroscopic effects, with resulting vibration which complicate the construction of both track and the vehicles that travel on it. It is therefore desirable to define an ideal track system, matching the similar approach to modern magnets and electrical machines, in order to find how the new materials and methods can be best applied to this problem.

In its simplest form a special-purpose track can be an overhead ropeway providing both support and guidance to a container or vehicle suspended from it. To give sideways stability this system is best duplicated and can be elaborated into a rigid rail grid construction for greater loads and speeds. The importance of the overhead system is that it can operate at any speed safely, using the many benefits of electric mains power in a simple manner. This will avoid the wastage of valuable land essential for conventional roads and railways. But it must be of lightweight construction in terms of vehicles and track, and must thus carry its load in small but frequent portions, if it is to be economically viable. The ideal propulsion will be, therefore, linear force applied from the track so that the vehicle contains no moving parts, engines or fuel.

With all present knowledge available, these ideal conditions can be provided only with a combination of linear electric motors and magnetic suspension by the repulsion principle. This has been known for most of the present century but it has only come into the realm of practical engineering since the arrival of high-coercivity permanent magnets at low cost with unlimited availability. Linear motors have recently been publicised for use in more conventional ways, for small machines up to main line railways, but here they will be regarded as an integral part, with permanent magnetic suspension, of the ideal track system. While the transportation use is of greatest practical significance, the principle could be equally applied to small devices such as linear actuators.

Linear motors have been graphically described as rotary machines cut radially to the axle or shaft and rolled out flat. What was the stator becomes the track and the rotor becomes the vehicle; it is evident that the track can be extended to any desired length and any number of vehicles can then travel along it. The track can become part of a network so it has ceased to be a machine in the accepted sense and has become a 'track system'. It is essential, however, that it should be regarded as a machine in principle, in order to equate its performance with that of the well-known rotary designs. The great difference between the two lies in the loss of the simplest form of guidance, inherent in the shaft/bearing construction, when changing from rotary to linear designs. The great possibilities of the latter are diminished if they are associated with traditional supporting methods

—wheels, axles, bogies, springs and the rest—which can now be replaced by a weightless medium, magnetic flux.

Magnetic suspension can be provided by continuous rows of ferrite magnet bricks laid along the track in order to apply a constant force of repulsion to similar rows of magnet bricks fixed underneath each vehicle with similar poles adjacent. This force can support unloaded rafts of sheet steel, fitted with these bricks, at a height of about an inch or some centimetres above the track with only limited restraining or guidance means. This is required to keep all the vehicle magnets vertically above those on the track, so that the downwards force of gravity is neutralised to give equilibrium conditions. These conditions are maintained if increasing loads are applied up to the point of physical contact of the two sets of magnets. With the latest grade of oriented ferrite this maximum force of repulsion (given by the tractive force formula of Fig. 7.7 in reverse) is roughly 1000 kilograms or 1 ton per square metre. Allowing for enough clearance to give free sideways movement of the vehicles along the track, about half this force is available to carry payload and this amounts in English measure to well over 100 lb/ft^2. The dynamic possibilities of such a transportation system were proved out successfully a few years ago with a small model monorail (developed by the author). This was driven by a single rubber-tyred wheel powered by the smallest kind of

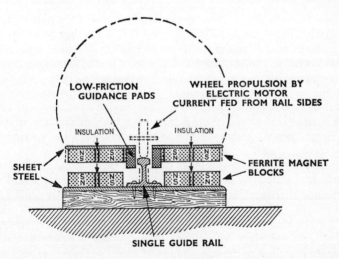

Fig. 8.6 Early Small Model of Monorail supported by Magnetic Repulsion.

d.c. motor used for conventional model railways, and with current collected from insulated conductors fixed along each side of the rail (Fig. 8.6).

It became clear from this work that the relatively small force required to propel the vehicle sideways could be provided by a linear version of the homopolar d.c. machine described earlier, if all the track and vehicle magnets had the same polarity on their operating surfaces. This would entail a low-voltage heavy current supply along the track but the vehicles would require only flat conductor plates to travel just above the track magnets; these would then serve as a massive form of continuous excitation along the whole system, giving maximum efficiency conditions as well as economy of materials. This arrangement provides the essentials for the ultimate achievement of the ideal track system outlined above, a combined linear motor with magnetic suspension to propel vehicles without any moving parts. This is followed up with economic assessment and proposals for further development in Chapter 10, which also gives the history of both subjects.

8.10 Summary

This review of the main directions of development which modern magnets may be expected to take must be seen in correct perspective. In some ways the chapter heading could best be described as earliest designs brought up to date by the use of high-coercivity magnetic materials. The main field of application will be seen to lie in the direction of mobile power, or transportation in its widest sense; this applies especially to the ultimate versions of track systems developed in the nineteenth century and automotive engineering in the twentieth. But the basic electrical principles of this chapter generally anticipated the principal mechanical engineering achievements so that, paradoxically, it is not a programme for the introduction of new electrical methods and machines so much as a need to explain why they were not used earlier.

In this chapter the answer has been derived in terms of the form in which electricity is used. It indicates that direct current and low-frequency alternating current at mains voltages, originally needed for power distribution purposes, are applicable to fixed conditions; then the bulk, cost and efficiency of consumer machines and equipment are of relatively less importance than the cheap power and convenience provided by the magnitude and extent of the power network. By contrast, mobile power demands the simplest and smallest of electrical machines, operating at speeds to match the latest prime-movers. On the small scale needed for individual vehicle propulsion these cannot afford any avoidable waste of energy, such as electro-magnetic excitation; they should operate at efficiencies up to the level of non-electric alternatives.

To achieve this aim it is essential to use permanent excitation, but in a way that gives optimum material utilisation of the new ceramic magnets which can, for the first time, provide this cheaply and effec-tively regardless of the severity of operating conditions. The proposed designs operate under the most favourable magnetic conditions but the electric power has to be in unfamiliar form: either low-voltage direct current or high frequency alternating current. For individual isolated circuits of the kind in which they will flow, the control con-ditions are much less exact than the network requirements but new developments are needed in each case for commercial success. The first kind of power requires suitable sliding electrical contacts to carry the heavy direct currents from stator to rotor, and the second requires cheap magnetic core material with low power loss at the high working frequencies. Much information is already available on these subjects and both are well within the capabilities of modern development programmes; these subjects are followed up in the next chapter in the case of rotating machines, with other particulars of the considerable practical progress in these applications during recent years.

It is important to note that low-voltage direct current is the kind of power produced by the direct conversion of fuel energy into electricity, such as fuel cells and thermo-electric generators, which are thought to have applications in this mobile power sphere. Also conventional traction batteries are used more efficiently in this form than when many such cells are series-connected in order to raise the voltage to meet the demands of present machine design.

With the choice of a number of alternative designs and two kinds of electric current it is necessary to give the main attention to the most appropriate form for the task being considered. This is clearly direct current for mobile power owing to its storage capability in cells and batteries as well as its known merits for traction uses. In low-voltage form it is essential to keep the electrical circuit as short as possible for high overall efficiency but this is the normal condition of an electric drive for vehicles. With latest semiconductor rectifier units it is also now economically feasible for fixed and track installations to convert a.c. mains power to low-voltage d.c. at the point of usage in order to meet these conditions.

In contrast, frictionless magnetic clutches may become of limited importance if simple and efficient electric drives by generator-motor combinations are available; it will then be better to use electric control with all the known advantages of dynamic braking, partly in regenerative form when a battery of appropriate size is also incorporated in the circuit. This is the main feature of the next chapter and, in linear form with magnetic suspension by ferrite magnet bricks, in Chapter 10.

8.11 References

British Patents 889 625 (magnetic clutch), 933 925 (high-frequency alternator), 936 151 (rotary actuator) and 867 045 (magnetic 'railway').

9

ROTATING MACHINES

Considerable progress has already taken place during recent decades in the application of permanent magnets of both metal and ferrite varieties to the improvement of conventional designs of rotating electrical machine. Additionally, there has been much progress in the past few years in practical versions of large d.c. homopolar generators which are of particular significance for the smaller designs with ferrite magnet excitation (proposed in the previous chapter). Since these must inevitably operate at low voltage with heavy current, it is also necessary to examine the circuit conditions that would apply to the mobile applications for which they are intended, particularly for road vehicles in propulsion-braking systems. Finally the simple high frequency alternator and its possible future uses are briefly discussed.

9.1 Excitation by Metal Magnets

The historical survey (Chapter 3) stated that all electrical machines up to a century ago had to rely on the use of low-coercivity hard steel horseshoe magnets for the 30-year period to the invention of electromagnetic fields. These adopted the same kind of long magnetic circuit until later in the century when the present kind of more compact design (Fig. 7.1 b) was evolved. This saved space, reduced leakage flux and improved the efficiency in spite of the power bypassed for excitation purposes, so the merits of permanent magnets in this application were virtually forgotten until recent decades. They were revived owing to the tenfold improvement in coercivity made possible by the introduction of the cast alnico series of alloys, which could match the performance of electromagnets in equivalent space.

Though the possible market for low-power electrical machines with better performance was great, there were many practical difficulties and unknown factors. These cast alloys were mechanically weak and inhomogeneous, difficult to shape for the traditional designs and costly in both materials and manufacture. Technically, the estimation of their working conditions was far more complicated for these dynamic applications than for the usual fixed-reluctance magnetic circuits with small demagnetising forces. The $(BH)_{max}$ figure of merit usually had little significance, and pronounced curvature of the demagnetising curve gave low recoil permeability, though otherwise desirable. The magnet makers published detailed curves with contours of useful recoil energy so that users could design to best advantage, but in view of the recent progress in high-coercivity material it is possible to see that the expensive alloy materials were being used somewhat wastefully for this kind of application. Nevertheless, its importance must be judged by the variety of new machines developed and the practical obstacles overcome, on a considerable production scale for such competitive products as cycle dynamos which can be taken to represent small power conditions. The great numbers of small motors for timing and measurement-control are excluded from this analysis, though most work on the same permanent magnet principles.

To use its incorrect popular name, the cycle dynamo is really a low-voltage rotating magnet alternator required to supply a lighting load that can probably be more simply and cheaply provided by an expendable battery. But in the long run it is preferable to have the dynamo as part of the machine so that it is always available for service without further cost or attention to the user, though the added component also has its advantages. These points illustrate the need for the good lighting performance at low cost, which made this a much more complex technical and manufacturing problem than would appear on the surface. While a d.c. machine with a small accumulator may be the best engineering solution, various designs of alternator were the ultimate answer and the kinds of magnet used are shown in Fig. 9.1.

The advantage of alternating current with frequency high enough to avoid flicker is that the a.c. resistance varies with the speed and gives a self-regulating effect. The voltage must be maintained between limits which give efficient light without risk of burning out the bulb. The generator has the simplest design and assembly, with fixed coils and no moving contacts or conductors, so it should also have adequate trouble-free working life. The first type operated from the wheel or tyre to give the advantage of high speed without gears and the speed averaged around 50 rev/sec, giving a corresponding frequency value with a two-pole machine. Since the specified voltage depends on the magnetic flux cut per second, a high speed machine uses correspondingly less magnet material of given quality than one

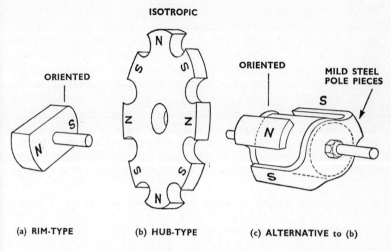

Fig. 9.1 Cycle Dynamo (Alternator) Metal Rotor Magnets.

running at slow speed, such as the hub-type in (*b*). This must have more poles to give the desired frequency because it can rotate at only a few revs/second. In practice this number must be 8 or more and the material has to be the lower energy isotropic grade. In order to use oriented material for this purpose it is necessary to fix the somewhat elaborate pole piece construction to each end of a cylindrical magnet, as in (*c*), which gives a more compact unit of different shape. It is difficult to assess these three designs because of differing manufacturing problems, such as the mounting on the shaft, and the contrast in working conditions; but all have found widespread use in various other fields of application. They give a good illustration of the rotating magnet principle which has much to recommend it from the design standpoint, although it creates mechanical problems owing to the generally unsatisfactory physical properties of earlier high energy magnet materials.

In the post-war period the development of oriented alnico materials of higher coercivity has enabled large alternators up to 100 kW output to be made with multi-pole rotors and machines with considerably greater power have been designed. So there is no doubt that permanent magnets can now be used in these relatively severe conditions for the whole of the medium-power range specified earlier; they need no longer be mainly confined to the light engineering field that has been their major sphere of application for so many years. In an example for hydroelectric generator excitation, the rotor had 24 poles each constructed from a row of magnet blocks with grooves at their ends for fixing and location in association with mild steel pole pieces at a radius of about 18 inches (45 cm). It was necessary to magnetise this rotor after assembly with a special cable wound round the poles in such directions as to give alternate polarity to adjacent magnet rows. This example shows the great operating merits of such an arrangement with permanent excitation, which avoids the cost and relative unreliability of a separate d.c. supply with sliprings and brush requirements. It reduces heating and increases the overall efficiency (which are of great significance in every design), together justifying the high cost of the magnet alloys with the special construction and methods that they require. Applications on this scale could well justify the use of ferrite magnets with their further threefold coercivity advantage and lower raw material cost.

9.2 Ferrite Magnet Excitation

One of the principal claims for the application of barium ferrite, when first produced commercially, was to provide the field in small electrical machines. The key property of coercivity for this purpose was double the value for the best alloy magnets and still more improvement was to become available with the later oriented grades of the ceramic material. Moreover, the unfamiliar insulator property was of special value under the alternating flux conditions of most commercial machines, as a means for eliminating or greatly reducing eddy current losses. While the effect might be greater in a.c. machines, the most urgent case was the improvement of d.c. motors needed for portable and mobile uses. But the problems of applying this novel material with its most unusual magnetic properties were even greater on a practical scale than those of the alloy magnets.

All existing d.c. motors use a rotating armature and fixed field system so this was an additional reason for giving this kind of electrical machine the main attention. The brittle ceramic could be more readily used under fixed conditions. But the remanence of the original isotropic grade was so much lower than the normal working flux density and little space was available for pole-pieces to concentrate the flux, apart from the mechanical difficulties in fixing them. Although there was a strong case for a complete design, it was economically desirable to fit the ferrite magnets into the range of standardised products which had given good service for many years. However, the cost of shaping a ceramic to meet conditions for soft metallic poles would be prohibitive and the reduced performance from low flux densities would outweigh the many expected advantages.

A simple solution was found in the form of an intermediate design based upon shallow ring-magnets assembled in the shape of a sleeve. These can be automatically ground on their outer periphery to fit closely into a thin mild steel shell which serves as a strong mechanical housing for the ferrite and the whole motor, while providing a high permeability return magnetic path and effective magnetic screen. This ironclad ferrite sleeve was magnetised in the factory by use of a special jig which provided two poles with each spread over a 140° arc; this gave maximum utilisation of magnet material as well as a considerable reduction in the mean length of magnetic path, in comparison with the original wound field version. Further, the ferrite sleeve length could be extended to fill the coil overhang space in order to compensate for the low flux density (B_d of 0.1 Wb/m²) of this ferrite. But the high coercivity brought corresponding advantages: the airgap could be increased in length three times or more without significant reduction of performance and efficiency of the motor. This was of great practical importance because the accurate grinding of the internal bore of such hard material is difficult and costly, so these wide mechanical tolerances made such processes unnecessary. Such large airgaps are technically feasible owing to the high intrinsic coercivity and almost linear demagnetising curve of the ferrite, giving recoil permeability approaching the value for air.

Tests on small motors made in this manner revealed an impressive list of advantages over the conventional design. The following were published soon after the material became available by the Company which pioneered it (Philips, Holland) and have been confirmed in the subsequent great volume of production motors based on this kind of design:

1. Commutation troubles due to armature reaction are eliminated.

2. Stator eddy-current and hysteresis losses are eliminated.

3. Unlike other permanent magnet-excited machines, the armature can be removed and replaced without affecting the motor performance, making inspection and maintenance a simple routine operation.

4. The coil ends of the armature cut magnetic flux, giving extra torque and efficiency.

5. The motor temperature rise is lower than that of machines with similar rating under continuous operation, using electro-magnetic excitation.

6. The motor becomes a simple two-terminal unit with easy reversing control without switching field windings.

7. Virtually sparkless commutation is achieved in either direction.

8. A high power/weight ratio is obtained.

9. Considerable cost savings can be made in quantity production.

While these improvements apply to small appliance motors, they are inherent to the design and to the new ferrite magnet materials, and could therefore apply on a larger scale to medium-power machines. It would appear to be only a question of time before the material can be made in much larger pieces, if the conventional armature-commutator system gives required results.

Oriented grades of barium ferrite which were introduced on a commercial scale some years later were found to be more difficult to apply in this manner, but success was recently attained by the use of 140° segments in place of the single sleeve. The greater area and length of ferrite in comparison with a typical wound field stator are shown in Fig. 9.2. In America a partially oriented grade of sintered ferrite is produced specially for this application and a simpler alter-native consists of flexible plastic-bonded powder sheet in an oriented grade which is cut to size and bent to the required shape; this latter material has about the same magnetic strength as the isotropic sintered ferrite but is claimed to be much less expensive to produce and fit for the large quantity production requirements of small d.c. motors. Automotive accessories, such as car heater motors, are typical of the great and continuous demand of small machine for which increased efficiency is of the utmost value, since they must be capable of operating for prolonged periods from what is often an overloaded battery.

Many advantages are claimed for these small motors in addition to the efficiency improvement from around 50% to the 65% region. The machines can be enclosed instead of ventilated, reducing noise and contamination risk; alternatively they can be uprated in a standard size. Their reliability is enhanced because there are no field

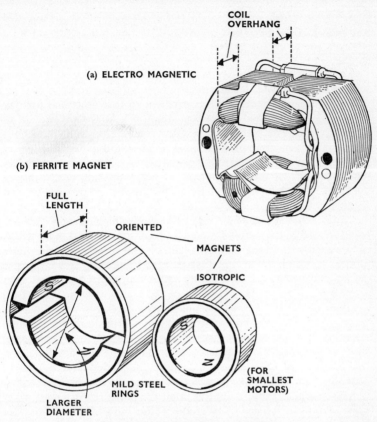

Fig. 9.2 Small D.C. Motor Excitation.

windings to burn out or to short circuit, as well as the performance improvements given above. Although ferrite magnets give reduced flux at higher temperatures, this effect is reversible and is about half of that due to the increased resistivity of copper-wire field windings, so this can also be regarded as an improvement.

The speed/torque curve of these ferrite-excited motors is almost linear, being between that of the drooping characteristic of the shunt-wound type (which it most resembles) and the reverse shape of the series-winding performance curve with its high starting torque. It is thus claimed that the speed can be kept more nearly constant with varying loads, which makes such motors suitable for a variety of applications. Their reduced weight is of great significance for portable uses and a recent power-drill incorporates such a d.c. motor with a small semi-conductor rectifier diode to operate from a.c. mains supply.

9.3 Ferrites for A.C. Motors

While no similar scale of improvement to that described for d.c. motors can be expected for a.c. machines, it is important enough to warrant detailed attention, and useful preliminary results have been reported. It is more limited in scope because, unlike the uniformity of design for all convention d.c. machines, there seem to be an infinite variety of a.c. alternatives to meet differing needs and to overcome the inherent cyclic effects which make speed variation and control so much more complicated.

All a.c. machines may be divided into those which run at a constant speed related to the supply frequency (synchronous) and those which do not (asynchronous). Electric clocks and timers are the most numerous examples of the first category and they generally use permanent magnets in their rotors and a simple electromagnet with multi-polar interleaved pole pieces of the kind shown in Fig. 9.1 (c) for the stator. Apart from the small force needed to overcome the friction of the associated gear-train, there is no load in the accepted electric motor sense and very small magnets of limited magnetic strength can perform this task adequately. In their simplest form this type is not self-starting and some added device is needed to start it.

Asynchronous motors depend upon the induction or transformer principle in which a changing or alternating current induces another such current in adjacent conductors by means of the moving magnetic field so created. This corresponds to all that has been stated earlier about the relative movement of conductor and magnetic flux but with alternating current this movement does not have to be physical (as in the case of direct current) because the current itself is always moving. In practice the currents induced into a conducting disc near the poles of an a.c. electromagnet will create magnetic fields which react with the main field to produce repulsion forces that can either drive it round on an axle as an *induction* motor, or can support it against the force of gravity; the latter effect is described more fully in the next chapter. It will be clear that the induction principle acts like two electromagnets, since power is absorbed in both the coil that generates the flux and in the conductor giving the secondary flux, so that there appears to be little scope for permanent magnets with this principle alone.

Synchronous motors, however, have electromagnetic excitation similar to that of the a.c. generators already considered and differing from the basic d.c. machines only in their use of rotating fields, since there is no need for the rotating armature essential to the commutator operation. So there is scope for permanent excitation in the rotors of synchronous machines and this would give the benefits of higher efficiency and less heating, with the resulting improvements already described. Such a machine is essentially for fixed speeds, unless used in a generator-motor drive unit of the kind mentioned in section 8.8 which operates on varying frequency, or for stepped speeds which operate on fixed ratios of the drive speed, but these are too complex for smaller sizes and are rather limited in application.

For these reasons the induction motor has become almost universal for large-scale production and widespread application in fixed installations that can be connected to the power network. Where a three-phase supply is available a relatively simple stator winding produces an invisible rotating magnetic field, moving at the synchronous speed of the a.c. supply for equivalent polar arrangement. In a squirrel-cage motor, the rotor consists of a laminated steel magnetic core with small airgaps to give the optimum magnetic circuit, and the winding is merely a set of axial conductors round the periphery fixed into slots, the conductors being short-circuited at each end of the core. This cylindrical cage of conductors carries the heavy circulating currents induced by the rotating field, which create powerful magnetic forces for reacting with the stator flux, to produce torque for doing useful work. This is technically the same as the circulating currents in the conducting disc of Fig. 8.1 (b) but here the movement comes from the pulsating flux of an a.c. electromagnet which transfers energy to the rotor by induction to promote rotation.

Self-starting and simplicity are the chief merits of induction motors. When they run up to speed, the current induced in the rotor becomes progressively less as synchronous speed is approached, so there must be a slight lag in its ultimate no-load speed compared with this limit in order to supply the power needed to overcome the motor losses; this lag increases as load is applied and there is little scope for speed variation unless the machine is coupled to some additional device used for this purpose. When such motors run unloaded they reduce the power factor of the supply, and this is usually penalised in the tariff on which a.c. power is generally charged (based on power factor), so there are various ways in which a.c. motors can be improved. When they are to be used where three-phase supply is generally not available, as in the home, there are a number of methods for producing rotating fields from single-phase supplies, and the induction principle can be widely used in other ways too numerous to describe here.

Synchronous motors have the advantage of operating at a good power factor and on a large scale can even be employed as "synchronous condensers" to correct a bad power factor, as well as their normal function. It is therefore clear that the ideal electric motor would be one which would start and run up to speed as an induction motor and then operate as a synchronous machine for constant speed applications. This would give good power factor at all loads and, with permanent magnet excitation, higher efficiency than could be obtained in conventional designs. The first of these improvements has been applied electro-magnetically on large machines for which the design complication and cost of the required d.c. supply can be justified; the use of permanent magnets was hitherto restricted by low coercivity and by the a.c. losses when metal magnets were required to operate within the magnetic circuit of such machines. Ferrite magnets are most suitable in both respects.

During the past ten years work has been carried out in America with best grades of alnico magnets fixed around the shaft of an induction motor, with the usual laminated rotor surrounding them, providing permanent excitation from inside as well as the usual stator rotating field. This gave the expected improvement in performance but at the cost of design complication and rotor size, largely owing to the need for isolating the metal magnets from the operating flux path. More recent work in Germany has been based upon the use of large ferrite disc-magnets housed inside the stator end-plates, providing the excitation flux through the ends of the main magnetic circuit and radially across the airgap. With axial magnetisation the ferrite discs provide a large amount of flux which can be concentrated at the main airgap, and the high coercivity provides adequate m.m.f. for overcoming the reluctance of the additional side gaps. At the same time the design is not greatly altered or enlarged and the cost increase could be proportionally small. Additionally, novel braking facilities can be provided by switching from the supply to short-circuiting links, or to rheostats which can be used to control the retardation rate.

In a small experimental machine the ferrite magnets were in the form of four right-angle segments with alternate polarity, fixed at each end of the rotor by mild steel plates which also served as the return magnetic circuit. This was claimed to raise the efficiency from 60 % to 77% and the power factor from 0.5 to 0.8, while raising the output by 12%. There was little increase in size because the magnets occupied space under the stator winding overhang; it was necessary to provide an interpolar spacing in the rotor, of sufficient reluctance to avoid bypassing an appreciable part of the flux.

9.4 Acyclic Machines

To this brief review of progress in small d.c. and a.c. motors by the use of permanent excitation with modern high-coercivity materials, must be added some very recent information on large d.c. homopolar machines with electromagnetic fields. This is valuable in the assessment of the practical possibilities of the simplest kinds of electrical machine described in the previous chapter, which depend upon the advantages of both ferrite magnets and the homopolar principle; for though the advantages of ferrites in the improvement of conventional designs are considerable, they cannot be expected alone to achieve the suggested tenfold reduction of size and cost that medium-power needs are considered to demand.

The great post-war progress in such large-scale research as nuclear energy has created a requirement for very great direct currents of up to a million amperes at low voltage, because they can be generated close to the place where they are used. Many types of homopolar machine have been investigated for this kind of use and it has been suggested that they should in future be described as *acyclic* machines, a term which will be adopted here. It was explained earlier that all present d.c. machines have limited claim to their name because their function is, in the case of generators, to generate alternating current in the armature coils and to rectify it by the commutator so that the external current is approximately uni-directional. In practice it always has some ripple in its waveform and this can cause various troubles according to its magnitude as a kind of superimposed alternating current. Acyclic machines, on the other hand, generate pure direct current like the output of a battery and this is one of many advantages.

For the reasons given in section 8.3 acyclic machines are inherently of low voltage type because they are confined to one-turn units, but this voltage can now be raised nearly to mains supply level in very large machines operating at the highest possible speeds. In the past, various attempts to raise the voltage to well beyond the low level to which existing techniques confined them brought troubles which gave dynamos of this class a bad reputation, obscuring their inherent merits. With no fluctuations in either current or flux, there are no hysteresis or eddy-current losses while the d.c. resistance of the rotor is usually negligible owing to the massive size of this single conductor; consequently the only significant loss is that due to brushgear or current collection. The magnetic circuit requires no lamination, so it can be made of mild steel or mechanically strong alloys with high magnetic saturation to simplify construction and to increase operating speed.

During the last century it was found that the conductor could be best made of iron instead of copper and used in a double-drum construction instead of the double-disc (Fig. 8.1 (c)), giving a very low magnetic reluctance and very efficient electromagnetic excitation. This is shown in Fig. 9.3, the arrangement allowing considerable space for the field windings but little for leakage. The design can be far more robust than that of conventional electrical machines because the rotor consists solely of a steel cylinder.

Within the period covered by electrical engineering there have been a succession of novel designs of this kind and a few will be

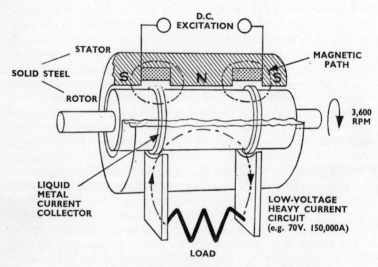

Fig. 9.3 Double Drum Design: Large Acyclic Machine.

mentioned. The first successful machine appears to have been made by Siemens in 1878 for electro-metallurgy processes and various patents followed to increase the voltage for power distribution purposes by complex brush arrangements. In 1905 General Electric of America published details of a 300kW machine for 500V driven by a turbine and giving 90% efficiency, followed by Westinghouse with a 2000kW machine giving 7700A at 260V and 20 rev/sec with 92% efficiency; in 1934 they made a further generator for welding large pipes, giving 150,000A at 7.5 V and 88% efficiency. This ran successfully for 18 years, mostly at 50% overload, and illustrates that good performance and high efficiency can be obtained at low voltages as well as at high.

In all these acyclic machines the ultimate limitation appears to have been the use of conventional brushgear developed for a.c. slipring and commutator machines, which imposed limits upon the operating speed, efficiency and output. Recent work has therefore concentrated upon the use of liquid metal current collectors with remarkable success, by the use of the traditional electrical contact element, mercury, and later a sodium-potassium alloy developed in America. At first a small 10 kW generator of 2 ft (60 cm) dimensions was made, giving 20,000 A at only 0.5 V with 60% efficiency; this proved to be so promising that a 6000 kW machine to give 80,000 A at 75 V was constructed. In about twice the dimensions, or 8 times the volume, the output was increased 600 times to give a greater output per unit weight than any conventional equivalent, while the efficiency of over 98% was the highest ever reached in electrical machines.

During 1962 General Electric of America introduced the first standardised acyclic machine for commercial use in plants requiring very heavy direct currents, such as electrochemical processes. Each machine is of 10,000kW output at 67V to give 150,000A and a large plant uses six such machines in series to give the specified voltage of 400V, driven on one shaft from a 60,000 kW steam turbine; for this purpose all parts of the generators are electrically insulated, with insulated flexible couplings between generators on the shaft. The excitation is as low as 0.1% of the output rating (less than one-fifth that of large commutator machines) so that little auxiliary plant is needed for the above typical large-scale installation, and shunt field control provides the full voltage range at the rated speed. From the operational standpoint there is no internal frictional wear, so these machines can run for several years without the need for maintenance shutdown. Their unprecedented robustness makes them suitable for the provision of current pulses exceeding a million amperes, the current rating being dependent solely upon the resistivity of the rotor steel and the ability to remove the heat produced (Fig. 9.3).

This information is given to show that the great merits of acyclic machines, which have been known for so many years, are at last being achieved on a commercial scale. It proves that the size can be smaller and the efficiency much higher than those of conventional alternatives, using a very simple rotor with an upper speed limit decided only by the tensile strength of the metal from which it is made, which can be a strong steel. Early development versions of this same machine were limited in speed and output by the use of conventional brushgear, so that the efficiency was comparable only to that of a commutator type. The great improvements are thus directly the result of better current collection methods.

9.5 Current Collection

Mercury, the classic contact metal of the pioneers, has many disadvantages—high cost, high density and relatively poor conductivity. Nevertheless, it is being successfully used in some modern acyclic generators, indicating the great advantages of liquid metals for this purpose. But recent developments in America have produced a much improved material of this kind, an eutectic alloy of sodium and potassium (known as *NaK* from its symbols). This is a light liquid at ordinary temperatures, with only 6% the density of mercury but having three times better conductivity, a sevenfold improvement in heat capacity with one-third the viscosity. To prevent the strong reaction of this liquid alloy with air and water, it must be circulated in an atmosphere of nitrogen, but these conditions are similar to those for cooling modern power-station machines with hydrogen and appropriate equipment is available.

With its low viscosity and lower density than water, this alloy can be used for current collection at the highest peripheral velocities decided by the bursting strength of the rotor, and it wets the contact surfaces in a manner that almost eliminates their electrical resistance. The limited heat generated by this and by small frictional drag is constantly removed by the circulating system and the operating temperature fixed at the optimum value. The wear is said to be negligible and the machine can thus operate for years without major overhaul. These details are given to show that, after nearly a century, the outstanding obstacle to the commercial application of acyclic machines has been solved to an extent that would have been regarded as unattainable only a few years ago.

There seems little chance, however, that such liquid current collection methods can be applied to machines in the medium-power sphere, more especially for mobile uses, on economic grounds. But the scale of the problem is quite different: instead of an efficiency increase of from around 94% to over 98% for the largest d.c. machines, the main mobile demand requires an increase of from the 60% region to, say, 90% for machines of only some kilowatts capacity. The ratio of loss reduction may be similar in both these cases, but there is plenty of scope for the use of better solid contacts in the smaller machines because the major part of this loss gap will be closed by the use of ferrite magnet excitation (which would be neither feasible nor justifiable economically for the large generators with their very low proportion of excitation power).

In the previous chapter (8.3) it was stated that a simple double-disc acyclic machine based on the largest ferrite ring magnets now available would give an output around 1 volt at typical maximum working speeds of present prime-movers (e.g. 100 rev/sec). Using the copper-carbon brush material with highest conductivity now on the market, the voltage drop for a pair is about 0.2 volt and an equal loss from frictional drag would give a level of efficiency similar to that of the conventional alternative in this size. But experiment shows that solid metal contacts based upon suitable alloys such as beryllium-copper with the graphite applied in the form of a lubricant could give a considerable improvement in this loss proportion. This results from simple conditions of current collection in acyclic machines operating at such very low voltages with unidirectional current. Though such a simple arrangement may never reach the performance of the above liquid metals, it could still meet all practical requirements to be discussed in the final chapter, and at the lowest cost possible.

Present commercial brushes for power-handling machines are mainly required for arduous service at mains voltages, for which a voltage drop of one or two volts is economically justified to give adequate life in spite of the arcing and wear that normally apply in commutator and slipring conditions. Many hundreds of different kinds are produced by the manufacturers, using a variety of grades of natural and artificial graphite; some have high proportions of copper powder incorporated to reduce the resistivity, which varies over the vast range of 100,000 down to around 10 microhm. cm. units. Natural graphite provides the best lubricating properties but most commercial brushes use processed grades and lowest voltage drop at present is obtained with copper-carbon grades containing up to 90% copper powder bonded with graphite. The resistivity of these grades thus varies from ten times to many thousands of times the value for solid copper, while the coefficient of friction usually lies between 0.1 and 0.2 with working pressures of around 2 lb/inch² (140 g/cm²) or higher for mobile uses. Operating speeds are generally in the range 50 to 200 ft/sec (15 to 60 m/sec) but the materials are tested to run at twice these speeds, which amount to 240 miles/hour (400 km/hr) or within the aircraft speed range referred to in the next chapter.

Specified values of working current density for brush materials vary from 0.2 to 1.5 A/mm², increasing with the proportion of copper powder, and the voltage drop is reduced if the contact area is increased and the current density lowered. This will increase the frictional drag and there is thus a limit to the extent to which this can be applied in practice, but in the double-disc design there is ample scope for this kind of variation to obtain optimum working conditions. The most important improvement that this has over all conventional practice, however, is the low operating voltage well below the minimum arcing potential of the kind of materials to be used; unless the circuit is actually broken there will be virtually no arcing and negligible wear of the kind that present brushes are designed to combat. A solid copper or copper-alloy contact would give the lowest voltage drop and highest current density but it would need lubrication by a suitable conducting lubricant, of which graphite is the most appropriate material.

It therefore seems probable that a simple type of solid current-collector system, rather than conventional brushgear, can provide the low voltage-drop contacts for the proposed double-disc units, in multiple groups for generators and in wheel-hubs for propulsion-braking purposes. It will be desirable to use springy copper-alloy contacts with means for adjusting the pressure to the optimum value for current density, to give minimum frictional-plus-resistive losses under the operating conditions. These must include the external electrical circuit which will have to use heavy-gauge conductors of shortest possible length. The overall efficiency can then be decided by the performance of the current-collectors, which could be better described as the sliding electrical contacts of the whole system.

A large acyclic generator of the liquid metal current-collector kind has recently been successfully operated with solid brushes (see reference 7).

9.6 Experimental Low-Voltage D.C. Machines

In order to reach a level above one volt with drives running at speeds in the 100 rev/sec region with the early isotropic grade of ferrite, it was necessary to make experimental machines nearly 1 foot (30 cm) in diameter. The design was based upon Fig. 8.2 with one double-disc unit containing a pair of massive 10-section ferrite rings comprising the stator excitation magnets; the rotor was about half the outside diameter and was first made of mild steel to minimise reluctance, as in the case of the large double-drum machines (Fig. 9.3). The powerful attraction force of the magnets made assembly difficult and later rotors used brass or aluminium which are satisfactory for wide airgap conditions using high-coercivity materials.

Sliding contacts of thin phosphor-bronze, and later of beryllium-copper, were arranged to operate around the periphery of each disc through the radial slots in the poleplates, which also minimise the magnetic distortion by the heavy rotor currents in a concentric direction. The machine was driven as a generator for most runs of any duration by a mains-operated a.c. motor, and as a motor from a large capacity 2-volt traction cell intermittently. It was found difficult and complicated to insulate the rotor from the shaft with the precision and stability necessary for high speed operation, although the voltage was so low, and the stator insulation also required more attention than expected. But the most important obstacle was the inaccessibility of the brushgear which necessitated partial dismantling of the poleplates. It soon became evident that this vital part of the machine must be on the outer periphery and this could be done only by the transfer of the magnets to the rotor and the heavy current circuit mainly to the stator. There is of course no way of avoiding the use of sliding electrical contacts for the whole of the current to be taken to and from the rotor, for this is fundamental to the interlinking of its flux with that of the excitation.

At this time the first large oriented ferrite ring-magnets for loud-speakers (Table 7.1) were becoming available commercially in Gr. II material (though Gr. III would be ultimately needed for this kind of application). It was found that the largest size would meet these requirements magnetically and that their tensile strength and uniformity of density were considerably better than those of the strongest alloy magnet materials, with over 30% lower density; consequently their bursting strength was higher than the forces exerted at maximum operating speed by an appropriate margin. In this rotating magnet design the poleplates projected outwards instead of inwards,

16

with radial airgaps for the multi-unit generator application corresponding to Fig. 8.2 and axial airgaps for the single unit motor shown in Fig. 9.4 incorporating controls. The brushes of the multiple leaf-spring kind project inwards through the airgaps to make electrical contact on sliprings, bolted together through radial slots cut into the outer part of the poleplates to complete the circuit. The equivalent of the original bobbin-shaped rotor conductor is the system of electrical contact springs and their insulated mounting, supported upon the circumferential holding bolts for the generator, and upon massive copper terminal rings (with sideways movement) mounted upon the endplates for the motor.

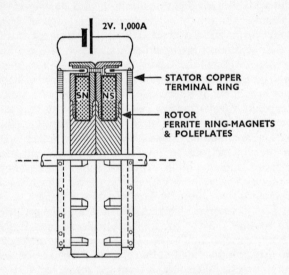

Fig. 9.4 Experimental Acyclic D.C. Motor.

Although this rotating magnet design appears to be original and unorthodox, it conforms with the conventional explanation for the operation of electromagnetic machines. In Fig. 9.4 the current passing through the gaps cuts the flux and produces torque in the same direction on both sides. To explain it in the terms used earlier, by the interaction of the fluxes produced by an electromagnet and a permanent magnet, the flux from the magnet pair passes outwards through the mild steel comprising the outer part of the rotor, where it reacts with peripheral magnetic flux from the applied direct current.

The equivalent of the single turn armature is clearly seen, but in this case it comprises the stator (apart from the sliprings).

This major change in design, intended to make the brushgear accessible, succeeded well in that respect but in addition overcame the other difficulties with the fixed magnet system. It also introduced the advantages of rotating excitation to which reference has been made on various occasions. The overall size and weight for equivalent rating were greatly reduced, with the threefold improvement in magnetic performance given by oriented material added to the better flux utilisation of a shorter, rotating magnetic circuit. The insulation problems were overcome by the use of tough insulating paper between the aluminium support discs on the rotor and the poleplates, which augmented the high resistance of the ferrite rings, so that each poleplate was insulated from the others and from the shaft as well as from the sliprings and their connecting bolts. The ferrite ring-magnets are supplied with their pole faces ground flat and parallel so the rotor assembly is simple and inexpensive; they are almost enclosed around their sides and periphery by thick mild steel which gives good mechanical protection, and this could be augmented if necessary by non-magnetic bands of high tensile metal such as stainless steel fixed around their circumference. The design thus seems to be appropriate for the roughest practical conditions, such as usage in wheel-hubs, and for the high speed operation which will provide the best power/weight ratio in this kind of application, with the use of suitable incorporated step-down gearing.

The arrangement shown in Fig. 9.4 has heavy copper braid connections at the top for providing highly flexible electrical connections to a vehicle chassis; it will be noted that the length of the electrical circuit is very short inside the machine to meet the condition of negligible resistance. A single strip screwed round the massive copper terminal rings has been found to give the robustness and freedom from vibration effects, even with thin beryllium-copper material, when assembled in this tubular form. This can be adapted to switching and control by mounting the copper terminal rings so that they can be moved inwards and outwards.

Experimental work on separate switching and control units for these heavy currents showed that they absorbed too much power in volt-drop and added contacts, so that controls within each motor by brushgear movement was almost essential as well as functionally desirable. It is necessary to use an arrangement to avoid arcing, which even at these low voltages can cause rapid wear if heavy currents are interrupted. This also promotes smooth operation when associated with the flywheel effect of the relatively heavy rotor which comprises most of the motor's weight. This brush movement with the current supply switched off is also intended to provide the frictional braking for the slow-and-stop conditions when its dynamic braking becomes ineffective or inoperative, but this is relatively simple with the considerable step-down ratio used in the hub application and the small retarding force needed for this light duty. Before the expected performance of this kind of machine can be assessed it is necessary to consider the requirements for its external circuit.

9.7 Low-Voltage Power

Recent extensive developments in direct methods for the conversion of fuel energy into electricity, such as fuel cells and thermoelectric generators, produce direct current at roughly a volt but could generate large currents to transmit appreciable power if the circuit resistance is low enough. This applies also to conventional traction batteries in the form of the single cell with 2 volts potential which could give thousands of amperes if the plate area is adequate for storage of this considerable amount of power; in practice the more complex arrangement of several cells in series is used to build up the voltage to what is considered essential for traction purposes. Such minimum values as 36 or 48V meet the conditions laid down by motor and equipment makers, for vehicles as well as for fixed installations.

While the merits of mains voltages for fixed electrical uses are most apparent in the considerable power that can be fed for some distance through a cable of tiny section, the benefits of very low voltages for vehicle power systems, in which transmission distances are inevitably short, are at last emerging in the possibilities of direct generation and acyclic machines, and this could be extended to most mobile power applications. To this must be added the great advantages and economies of direct current storage in cells or batteries which overcome the main drawback of fixed a.c. power supply, especially in competitive conditions with non-electric alternatives. It is thus surprising that low-voltage d.c. power seems to be a relatively unexplored subject.

A proposal is outlined in Fig. 9.5 for the propulsion-braking system of a road vehicle, though the arrangement could apply to other mobile uses. It is proposed that the front and back pair of wheels fitted with hub motors be each powered by a six-volt traction

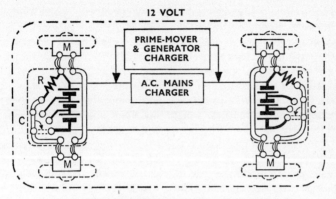

M: HUB-MOTORS & MOTOR CONTROLS

R: BRAKING RESISTORS

C: POWER CONTROLS

Fig. 9.5 Proposed Low-Voltage D.C. Propulsion-Braking of Typical Vehicle.

battery of suitable size and shape to fit between the wheels so that the heavy braid leads can be clamped directly to its terminals. The battery unit contains a simple controller with cell tappings and a resistor R for dynamic braking, all mounted in a metallic box or frame which can be insulated from the chassis and also serve as a low resistance return circuit (represented by a strap connection between the inner terminals). The hub-motors are connected in series and their brushgear control will apply the light or heavy pressure for slow or fast acceleration, or for deceleration with the power switched off in the controller position shown.

The tapped battery will give the coarse speed adjustment and this alone would tend to discharge the cells unevenly; but some measure of compensation for this by regenerative braking can be obtained by the slow return of the controller, when travelling at speed, to the "off" position. This will progressively charge the cells, but mainly that at the first tapping, before the point where the energy must be absorbed in the resistor for the braking to continue. The conditions for greatest braking are the same as those for greatest accelerating torque: the motor brushgear will be applied at maximum pressure to give the lowest contact resistance, which also gives the highest frictional drag to stop the vehicle when the motion is greatly reduced and little current is generated. Very low circuit resistance by the use of massive conductors of short length will result in more efficient regenerative braking as well as the best use of the stored power in the battery; in this arrangement virtually all the circuit resistance can be concentrated in the motor sliding contacts, which provide the means for current control in addition to the battery tappings.

Fig. 9.5 also shows this arrangement duplicated for the other pair of wheels to give the best weight distribution and vehicle control, with two-wheel or four-wheel drive and associated braking according to requirements. The added cost of this arrangement over the concentration of the drive into a single motor for economic reasons, necessary with present types of electric motor, is relatively small with the proposed motors. These are effectively subdivisions of a multi-unit generator that could be used with a prime-mover to provide the power unit for charging the batteries. They are shown connected in series to give the conventional 12 volt supply for lighting and the usual auxiliaries, and they can alternatively be charged at night with the vehicle in the garage, to obtain the economies of off-peak tariffs, by a built-in static rectifier unit. In both cases the charging current will be of much lower value, operating continuously, so that more conventional conductors and controls can be used for the longer interconnecting leads than for the short motor-battery connections which must carry up to 1000A or more without appreciable voltage drop.

Present mechanically propelled vehicles must have a prime-mover large enough to give the greatest power peak encountered during the life of any one of them, for the power unit is an inseparable part of the vehicle. With electric drive and intermediate battery, the power unit can be detachable and housed in any convenient position; moreover, power peaks can be met with the combined generated and stored energy so that the size and output of the prime-mover can be much less than in the mechanical drive alternative. Also the electric power can be generated under optimum conditions of constant speed of rotation at which prime-movers give their highest efficiency. Further, in place of the present rigidity of one vehicle giving one performance, there can be a great variety of combinations of prime-mover and battery sizes from something like a present car with electric drive and limited storage, to an electric vehicle mainly run from cheap rectified a.c. mains supply with a prime-mover charger unit added only for occasional long journeys; in the latter case the batteries will be large enough to take the vehicle around the routine local journeys with added charging at garages and (possibly in future) at parking meters.

The control of such vehicles would be better and safer than anything possible with non-electric systems, with dynamic braking to eliminate slipping under ice and mud conditions, in conjunction with four-wheel drive. While normally the front and back pairs of wheels will be operated together by two pedals—a *power* control and a *wheel* control—it is relatively simple to add variants such as individual wheel control for parking manoeuvres and possibly for steering. These and other relevant points can be settled only by practical tests and investigations carried out by vehicle designers and experts, and are mentioned here to show the kind of possibilities opened up by the development of low voltage d.c. power for vehicle and similar applications. This depends primarily upon the development of small and efficient acyclic machines for propulsion-braking and generating service, which in turn is mainly dependent upon the latest grades of high-coercivity ferrite ring-magnets.

9.8 Practical D.C. Tests

The above proposals are based upon some years of development work on the low-voltage d.c. motor and the circuit conditions for operating it. The ultimate solution from the performance and economic aspects appeared with the rotating magnet machine based upon oriented ferrites with highest coercivity, which have recently become available on a commercial scale and could be made into simple and cheap machines in any required quantity. But in the short time since this situation has arisen it has been possible to do little more than to prove that the design works in principle and gives every indication that it will meet all the targets set earlier, and with a useful margin. There remains to be done much more development and prolonged testing of machines with appropriate brushgear in order to arrive at the efficiency levels and useful life that can be achieved on a commercial scale.

A hand-made rotating magnet machine of about the required size and similar to Fig. 9.4 in design, but with radial airgaps and circumferential brushgear of the kind proposed for the multi-unit generator, first ran as a motor from a battery in mid-1963. It started and ran up to speeds of some revs/sec with currents of from 300 to 700 A and up to 1 volt across the terminals. The brushes were of multiple leafsprings cut from thin beryllium-copper sheet which showed no arcing or visible wear when allowed to run smoothly on the sliprings, but without precision construction and balance this would only apply at slower speeds without vibration. A better-made rotor started with as little as 100 watts of power to accelerate a mass of about 20 lb (9 Kg) indicating the expected low level of no-load losses and ultimate high efficiency, for it was designed to operate at over the 1000A level.

These experiments showed that the performance was rather unpredictable because the brush pressure could not be adequately adjusted through the narrow airgap, but measurement of the frictional drag torque at the pulley by added weights gave an accurate indication of the required current. For uses as a motor it became clear that full pressure control was necessary, from the "off" position to the full pressure needed to give the lowest contact resistance at maximum current; otherwise there would be excessive frictional drag at low loads and too much voltage drop at high loads; control of pressure would tend to level the efficiency curve. With the need for some frictional braking for slow-and-stop conditions and for some resistance variation to control the current between the 2-volt steps imposed by the typical traction battery, the inherent loss properties of solid current-collectors or brushgear could be used to advantage.

This was the prime reason for the use of axial airgaps in the motor application and Fig. 9.4 shows that this can also provide an efficient magnetic circuit with adequate contact area for sliprings under these sliding control conditions. Practical tests also showed the advantage that the tubular brush arrangement would give for the difficult mechanical circumstances in which such machines may be generally used, and this arrangement gives the smallest overall diameter, which is the limiting dimension for hub applications. While this design is limited to single units of the basic double-disc construction, the greater power needed for larger wheels can be obtained with correspondingly larger ferrite ring-magnets, in which the flux will increase roughly as the square of the diameter; the ring thickness must also be increased to provide more m.m.f. to meet the demands from the longer magnetic circuit or its higher reluctance. In general it appears that the optimum size of motor will come within the scope of the wheels which are in widespread use for road vehicles.

It is difficult to forecast a power rating for this very unorthodox kind of machine but it should be very high in terms of temperature rise limits because the natural cooling is so good, all the losses being dissipated at the periphery and the whole rotating magnetic circuit acting as a massive heat sink. Such points can be decided only by prolonged testing and are also related to the ultimate efficiency of the brushgear contacts and their best current density values.

A comparable experimental machine was a 2V 200A d.c. motor for operation from a single cell, with a rotating magnetic circuit excited electromagnetically by a spiral strip winding; this terminated on a brush bearing on to a bobbin-shaped mild steel rotor. The winding acted as a Faraday Disc in providing mechanical reaction with the magnetic circuit which was free to revolve independently of it. This work was done in Germany during the last war and the model with its records were destroyed, so only limited information was published there later, but this was followed up in this country and America. The relevant publications appeared before barium ferrite magnets had been developed, otherwise the considerable advantages that this new material could provide might have led to a commercial version, whereas this appears to have been impracticable. It shows a demand, however, with other isolated suggestions for a low-voltage heavy current machine. (Ref. 3.)

Experimental investigation into the feasibility of such low-voltage d.c. circuits, machines and equipment yielded unexpectedly favourable results once the prime condition of a very short circuit length with low resistance is met. This was a similar experience to that of the essential conditions for the use of high-coercivity magnets, which yielded important benefits in reduced magnetic leakage and greatly improved natural cooling. In the electrical circuit the main advantage was the simplicity of insulation methods, tough insulating paper fixed by impact adhesive being used with stock sizes of aluminium, brass and copper in sheet, strip and bar. In addition to the strength, simplicity and precision that this imparted to the machine, it was used in flexible strip form in place of cables for go-and-return circuit connections of much greater convenience and low cost. In terms of safety, reliability and simplicity such low voltage power circuits seem to meet the often severe conditions in vehicles and similar mobile uses in the best possible manner if electrical transmission of some kind is to be used. They are proof against electric shocks and sustained arcing.

To sum up the present overall situation on low-voltage d.c. power, all technical and economic factors examined from both theoretical and experimental standpoints are very favourable. The ultimate success depends mainly on one subject, the multiple sliding contacts; these show every sign of giving the required results in the suggested simple forms operated at voltages well below the arcing potential. These conditions appear to be novel and far less arduous than those of conventional machines, for the main cause of the failure of most acyclic generators in the past has been the need to produce power at relatively high voltages. But it is desirable also to compare progress in the a.c. alternatives which have no such contact problem.

9.9 High Frequency Power

The promising results obtained with a small model inductor alternator of the kind illustrated in Fig. 8.5 led to the development and construction of an experimental machine for generating high frequency power up to ultrasonic frequencies, originally intended for fluorescent lighting improvement. This machine was made in both the 40P and 120P designs in order to reach frequencies of up to 20 kc/s with drives at speeds below 200 rev/sec. It was tested in both the single-phase and three-phase versions, the latter overcoming the severe "cogging" effect of the single magnet-ring machine.

It was necessary to use the same massive 10-sector ferrite ring magnets as those in the first d.c. acyclic machine, in the isotropic grade because the design was produced before the oriented grades were available; hence the machine was much larger and less efficient than one with a rotating field of Gr. III magnet rings, to an extent already described for the low-voltage d.c. motor. This fixed-magnet inductor alternator must therefore be regarded as a means for proving that kilocycle power of appropriate voltage and waveform can be generated on a practical scale at reasonable cost with the simple machine design that ferrite magnets make possible.

Apart from the ferrite, the magnetic circuit was made from epoxy-cemented silicon steel strip stampings 0.007 inch (0.18 mm) thick. The poleplates had inwardly-projecting teeth with a contour, in association with the rounded rectangular section of the rotor inductors, to produce a sine waveform, one cycle for each tooth per revolution of the rotor. The inductors were shaped like commutator segments so that they could be firmly clamped to aluminium bosses keyed to the shaft, with considerable air space between adjacent projecting inductors in order to minimise eddy currents in the aluminium and to assist cooling.

Each coil was made from aluminium strip edge-wound on a special jig to form a robust, self-supporting winding. This was subsequently anodised and clamped between the poleplate teeth inside the ferrite ring to give a high metal space factor and good heat transfer. In the 120P version a 6-turn coil gave 115V power at 16 kc/s at a speed of about 130 rev/sec, with a maximum of 2kW per phase; this was about one-third of the calculated figure based upon efficient use of the available permanent flux, owing to the small dimensions of the tooth-inductor contour in the 120P version. This led to a low reluctance change when the rotor moved from the position with the inductors opposite the teeth to that midway between them, consequently most of the outer part of the magnet ring was unused; this performance could have been obtained with a machine of only half the diameter and greatly reduced weight.

The 40P version gave much better flux utilisation but produced frequencies in the most penetrating part of the audible range. It would give better use of the magnet rings to run it at three times the stated speed, for example directly from the rotor of a small gas turbine, and the rotor construction could be made to withstand the mechanical forces involved. However, the 120P machine gave valuable service in reaching the required frequency level with a margin and gave information on the kind of losses to be obtained under these power conditions; with a coil resistance (d.c.) of only 0.007 ohm, the main losses were due to eddy-currents in the teeth and inductors. The excellent natural cooling limited expansion and similar heat problems, though small airgaps are needed to give satisfactory flux utilisation in this general design.

With the rotating Gr. III magnet design, using similar cemented poleplates with from 12 (Fig. 9.6) to 20 projecting teeth, according to the speed, the inductors and coils could be fixed to the stator to provide a machine of about 10kW output. The stator inductors would best be made from U-shaped pressings of iron powder-core material to give low eddy current loss at small cost and adequate saturation flux-density; silicon-iron strip can now be obtained in thicknesses down to 0.002 inch (0.05 mm) at considerable cost in both material and assembly, with reduced saturation as cores owing to the greater space used for the cement. The higher losses in the rotor material of greater thickness tend to be concentrated at the outer part in the teeth where the cooling is best. Though there is considerable promise in this development, much more work and expenditure in a variety of tooling are needed before it can be regarded as a possible alternative to low-voltage d.c. for power transmission purposes of the kind considered.

But the development of cheap kilocycle power can be justified on the new or improved kind of service it could provide. Much of

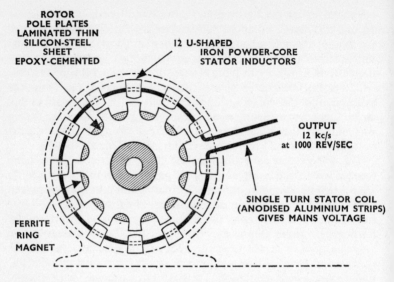

Fig. 9.6 High Frequency Inductor Alternator with Rotating Ferrite Ring-Magnet.

this is known from laboratory-scale experience using low power of this kind generated by thermionic valve or transistor oscillators at high capital and running costs in terms of the output. Such methods are at present being used to provide fluorescent lighting in railway coaches; at frequencies in the 15 to 20 kc/s region these give great improvements over 50 c/s performance in three respects: the light-producing efficiency is increased by 20%, the size and cost of the essential ballast-condenser control units are greatly reduced so that they can be installed with the lamp, and low-frequency flicker is eliminated.

These advantages could be obtained in buildings or other large fluorescent lighting installations if they merited the cost of the frequency conversion and distribution equipment on a many-kilowatt scale, and this does not appear to apply to conventional high frequency alternators. Moreover, new lighting developments, such as electroluminescence in which illumination can be supplied by large area panels in place of present concentrated sources, can be best operated at these frequencies and the economic factors will ultimately turn to a large extent on the cost of such kilocycle power, as in the case of fluorescent lighting.

Similarly, high frequency power can extend workshop machining methods of glass, ceramics including ferrites, and other such hard and brittle substances, and it can be used to augment present welding and fabricating processes. In the chemical industry it can perform or assist in emulsification and dispersion, precipitation and polymerisation, and for many industries it can provide new forms of heating by eddy current methods. It is already used for cleaning processes in the instrument industries and this could be extended to a large scale if the costs can be reduced to the right level, with the ultimate possibilities of the domestic market.

It has been necessary to mention this considerable diversity because the economic barrier may well be surmounted by the use of a separate high frequency ring main to serve both lighting and power needs. Fixed conversion units could best be directly coupled to an a.c. motor as a flywheel-shaped with 100 or more inductors to restrict the turning speed to present values. For the smallest mobile unit, however, it is desirable to operate at the highest practicable speed, such as that of small gas turbines which now approach the 1000 rev/sec level, since rotating inductors can run at this speed even if it is beyond the possibilities of ferrite rotor magnets.

9.10 Summary

The general conclusion in this chapter on possible applications of ferrite magnets to rotating machines is that there are good prospects of meeting the stringent conditions (expressed in the previous chapter) in the near future with the oriented grades now becoming available on a considerable commercial scale. These are already having an impact on conventional electrical machines but this cannot approach the scale needed for electricity to take a leading part in the vast field of mobile power outlined earlier; it is necessary to use the ferrite magnets in novel designs, in which their full merits can be utilised.

The most promising of these is the acyclic machine, which is appropriate for medium-power applications as well as for the large-scale uses which have recently been publicised abroad. But ferrite magnets would have little application in the latter case though they can provide the other factor, permanent excitation, for the great majority of mobile prime-mover power units. Machines smaller than the 1kW size which operate on direct current can be best made in a modification of the present commutator design with fixed ferrite excitation of the kind now being widely manufactured.

With the ferrite-excited acyclic machines it is possible only to use low voltages and the necessary power is obtained by heavy currents of some thousands of amperes. Thus, power at the present vehicle battery voltage of 12V will need about 1000A to give 12 hp with the kind of efficiency thought to be attainable in the near future, though appreciably better values are considered to be possible later. This power by the very conservative rating of electrical machines compared with mechanical methods used for prime-movers, which represents at least a 5/1 difference, is the equivalent of that needed to propel a typical small road vehicle; larger vehicles will use two or three times this current and give proportionally greater power. The size of the electric motors, running at speeds in the 100 to 200 rev/sec region and using up to 10/1 incorporated step-down gearing, preferably of nylon for silence and resilience, will be small enough to fit inside the hub of the wheel to be driven, and will also replace the present friction brake. Although the unsprung weight will be increased in this way, it is thought that this will not be to the detriment of the performance in view of the many advantages to be gained.

Dynamic braking augmented by the frictional braking effect of the brushgear can provide the ideal system from both performance and maintenance standpoints, and with permanent magnet excitation it is absolutely safe. Unlike all present electric motors that could be used for this purpose, the flux is always present at maximum strength and cannot be switched off. The value of the new kind of motor as a brake is such that it should be incorporated in every wheel which, also unlike present motors, can be done economically because each motor is like one double-disc unit of the kind used in multiple assembly for the generator. The latter converts the power from the prime-mover into the necessary low-voltage heavy current for operating the hub-motors in propelling the vehicle.

Low-voltage power of this sort must have short low-resistance circuits, which are feasible in vehicles if the battery is housed between the wheels it drives, with the power control as an associated part. Another control to the hub-motor brushgear gives propulsion-braking control according to whether the power control is on or off, and this simple arrangement gives automatic dynamic, resistive and frictional braking when appropriate according to the speed. This has become possible only recently, solely by the use of high-coercivity permanent magnets. They may be expected to have a profound effect upon the future design and control of road vehicles and allied mobile uses of electric power.

Traction batteries used in conjunction with the 'electrical transmission' between prime-mover and wheels give many advantages and economies, but notable unprecedented flexibility. At one extreme they can be a component in a variant of the present kind of vehicle but with electric drive; at the other they approach the all-electric car with its limited range and performance but economic, silent and fumeless operation. With the proposals given in this chapter the customer can choose the merits of either or of both and these can be altered as requirements change. There is also for the first time a choice of fuels for vehicle propulsion, by the use of a.c. rectified power in the batteries for local journeys. When obtained at night on off-peak rates, this will use mainly local fuel without added capital expenditure.

For so many advantages the required development of efficient current collection methods or brushgear may appear to be of small significance and it has recently been proved that the use of conventional brushes is now a practical proposition in the larger sizes of machine. In contrast to the many unknowns in the a.c. machine development programme it will be clear why the d.c. project is so much more important for this application. It has been shown, however, that the prospects of cheap kilocycle power for lighting and process applications are promising enough to warrant the considerable development needed to complete this programme.

Whatever the details of this investigation into the electrical power alternatives, alternating or direct current, the overriding fundamental factors for the vehicle and similar mobile applications are the acyclic nature and storage capability of direct current, regardless of voltage levels. These must inherently provide the best means for speed control, from zero to full speed, for the constantly changing load which (in any medium) needs an accumulator to level the peaks. Finally, to return to magnetic materials, it will be seen in this chapter that the most complex and costly part of the a.c. machine is the non-ferrite magnetic circuit; in the d.c. acyclic machine it is the most common of engineering metals, mild steel, the general use of which has never before been practicable in any electric machine handling power.

9.11 References

1. Gould J. E. 'Permanent Magnets. Their Materials & Application', *Elec. Review* 6.12, pp. 680-684, 1963. (see also ref: 1.9.2).

2. Burnett J. R. & Koestle F. L. 'Acyclic Generator: A New Power Generating Tool for Industry', *Direct Current*, pp. 196-203, July 1963.

3. Böning P. 'A New Homopolar Motor', (2 volt 100 ampere) *E.T.Z.* Germany, p. 76, February 1, 1952. (See also *Wireless Engg.*, II, pp. 1-33, 1952 & *Jour. Franklin Inst.*, pp. 7-20, 1954.

4. Hender B. S. 'The Future of the Battery-Electric Car', *Journal I.E.E.*, 8, pp. 250-254, 1964.

5. Walker J. H. 'High Frequency Alternators', *Journal I.E.E.*, Vol. 93, pt. II, pp. 67-80, 1946.

6. Technical Publications of Ferrite Magnet Manufacturers:
   Mullard Ltd. London.
   Indiana General Corp., Valparaiso, Indiana, U.S.A.
   Leyman Corp., Cincinnati, U.S.A.
   Deutsche Edelstahlwerke, Krefeld, Germany.

7. Marshall R. 'Solid Brushes on the Canberra Homopolar generator', *Nature*, p. 1079, December 12, 1964.

The above references, giving special attention to homopolar designs, represent only a small recent selection of much literature on this general subject.

10

MAGNETIC SUSPENSION AND LINEAR PROPULSION

Though the ideas behind them go back to the beginning of this century, both magnetic suspension and linear propulsion are only now being developed on an engineering scale. While rotating electrical machines have steadily increased in importance to the point that they are known and used universally, these two subjects have been almost forgotten; it is therefore necessary to include considerably more introductory material in this chapter. Though there are numerous possible applications of each development on small and large scales, the most important is their combined use for track transportation systems for the reasons given at the end of chapter 8.

10.1 Introduction

The possibility of freely suspending a body by magnetic repulsion of similar poles has probably been considered by a high proportion of those who have experimented with permanent magnets during the many centuries of their existence. But only since the development of high-coercivity ferrites has it become a technical reality; and only since cheap high quality barium ferrite became commercially available has it become an engineering possibility important enough to have a profound effect on the future of transportation. Once it is possible to suspend heavy loads so that they can move freely with negligible frictional drag, it becomes desirable to move them sideways in the simplest possible way with the minimum of moving parts, and this can be done by linear versions of the rotating machines already discussed, known collectively as linear motors.

The phenomenal success of motorcars and aircraft throughout most of this century, with their ability for random and virtually trackless travel, stifled much of the progress in special-purpose track systems; but the congestion and hazards this has caused have recently focused intense attention to the possibilities of carrying passengers, light vehicles and priority freight along tracks between the main centres of population at speeds up to those of local aircraft.

17

Such a system could vary from moving platforms or roads travelling at walking pace to light overhead tracks with automatically propelled and spaced vehicles like a continuous air-ferry service.

Most approaches to this problem, however, relate it to the conventional railway. But this has to use heavy vehicles in order to stay on the track at speed, about two-thirds the weight of a typical coach being wheels, bogies and their associated structure which it was shown earlier are now unnecessary, except for the carriage of heavy goods and minerals. The design of vehicles for operating at aircraft speeds must surely be based upon aircraft practice and this would ensure that the overhead track, the major part of the cost, will be as light as possible. For the same reason the main propulsion equipment should be housed along the track, preferably at support points, which indicates the need for an appropriate kind of linear motor using power from the supply network.

This introductory example of a possible future track system illustrates the need for the reduction of frictional drag on the largest scale for transportation uses. On the smallest scale, friction has always been a main problem in measuring instruments, including watches and clocks, though this is being minimised in some cases by the use of reliable amplifiers. Of the many attempts to use magnetic suspension in these miniature applications, none proved to be practicable until ferrite magnets were available and so far these are limited to fixed installations such as electricity meters and clocks. The possibility of frictionless bearings using the magnetic suspension principle will be of much interest to many machine designers in a range of sizes if the volume and cost are suitable, and these points are discussed in this chapter. It will be understood that the principles are the same regardless of scale, and these smaller examples are based on magnetic suspension only. It gives almost frictionless support with the need for guidance to maintain the fixed and moving parts in exact position, and this also provides resilient mounting with shock-absorbing properties which can be additionally valuable for many, but not all, applications. The scope of this subject is thus so wide that it is not possible to touch on more than the simplest or most important uses.

Where an appreciable load is supported by magnetic suspension, the required magnetic field is strong enough to be potentially valuable in assisting in its movement also, when this is required, as in track systems. This is a strong reason for associating the subject with motor techniques. The problem is essentially one of concentrating the load to be carried in such a manner that the frictional drag when moving it is greatly reduced, or alternatively of applying an upward force to the load in order to neutralise the force of gravity and virtually eliminate its weight during the time the load is being moved; for this reason the latter method is often referred to as 'levitation'. The first method, usually involving the use of wheels and axles with the added constructional complications required, is at best a palliative for the elimination of frictional drag; the second method could be a cure, at least for speeds up to around the present top average for land travel of 60 mph or 100 km/hr at which air pressure becomes the dominant retarding factor.

Much work has been done recently on levitation methods by the downwards pressure of air, for vehicles with random travel over land or water or both (e.g. swamps) and for track vehicles; the latter application is similar in principle to electromagnetic levitation experiments early this century in that great quantities of power are continually expended merely to support the vehicle, so that low sideways forces to propel it are of little practical value. At very high speeds propulsive forces to overcome air pressure require even greater power than that essential for levitation, so that this alternative to wheels for load-bearing purposes becomes technically feasible.

Permanent magnets have the overriding advantage for levitation that they provide support without any expenditure of power. For practical uses, however, they must have high coercivity to withstand the severe demagnetising forces that this application entails, and they must be cheap and plentiful; recent barium ferrite magnets meet these requirements admirably and it is now possible for the first time to consider economic levitation on an engineering scale in what is described here as 'magnetic suspension'. Once the possibilities of this new technique, in terms of levitation without power dissipation (apart from the negligible amount needed to magnetise the barium ferrite in the first or manufacturing stage), are understood it is possible to extend the methods to propulsion by linear motor in a manner that could not generally be achieved with the latter development alone.

For this reason the recent developments in magnetic suspension will precede the better-known work on linear motors, although the two subjects can be regarded as technically associated as well as being electromagnetically similar. Relatively little space can be given to non-electrical methods of levitation for track applications because there is little prospect of their meeting essential requirements of safety and silence for the congested conditions which justify the use of a track system in the first place, but their immense possibilities for random travel under most other ground conditions are becoming widely known in large as well as small units.

10.2 Magnetic Suspension

The general principles of magnetic repulsion forces follow closely those of attraction in reverse; short magnetic paths give the best weight-supporting results but with limited clearance. This is the equivalent of the short range of attraction and the considerable load lifted by a typical shallow ferrite brick magnet with poleplates, having the inevitable short distance between the poles. There is an important practical difference, however; the advantages of flux concentration by poleplates can be used only to a limited extent under repulsion conditions because the flux in them is transitory; under certain conditions it is possible to change the force of repulsion between two opposed flux-carrying poleplates into partial attraction. So the opposite faces of two magnet surfaces of similar polarity to give repulsion force between them must in practice be the magnets themselves, and this tends to limit the pressure intensity because the highest coercivity materials have low remanence and correspondingly small operating flux density.

By the reverse of the tractive force formula (Fig. 7.7) the repulsion force becomes maximum when the surfaces are in physical contact and this for unit area is proportional to the square of the working flux-density under these conditions. In spite of this low value by most standards, this force for Gr. III ferrite was found to be (Section 8.9) as high as one ton per square metre, so that heavy loads can be supported by appropriately large areas of ferrite magnet. On the basis of strip magnetisation (Fig. 7.4) the load can be supported with adequate clearance for movement, and a 50% reduction was proposed for this purpose; these are the circumstances that apply to track systems, and it is necessary to have endless rows or strips of magnets, each with the same polarity uppermost, along the track, with the same pattern duplicated under every vehicle to be supported in this manner. In this way every vehicle will be supported by magnetic suspension with a clearance for free movement dependent upon its weight plus the load carried; when moving at any speed some extra clearance will be needed for the movement of the vehicle brought about by the 'springiness' of the magnetic field which is the equivalent of the mechanical springs of conventional vehicles.

The remarkable merit of such a system is that its magnetic field does far more than support the vehicle at the required height over the track, though this at no operating and maintenance cost is of great value; it also replaces the traditional mechanical springs and shock-absorbers and provides the medium for one form of linear propulsion. Since this medium is weightless, the weight-lifting ability of such vehicles in their simplest form, sheet steel rafts with magnets fixed underneath and load carried above, is several times better than that of any alternative.

Earnshaw's Theory of 1840 stated that an object could not be suspended in space by permanent magnets alone. It needs an added force or guidance member fixed to the ground, and this must have appeared self-evident to any who may have tried throughout the following century with the bar- or horseshoe-shaped magnets then available (though lodestone blocks may have given some hopes to the contrary). The first practical demonstration of what could be done with lightweight magnet ferrites of high coercivity was the plastic-bonded discs of Fig. 6.2 supported on the vertical glass rod; it required an appreciable force or weight relative to that of the disc to make them touch. With the poles spread over an appreciable area and short magnetic length (i.e. disc thickness), the opposed flux paths were mainly vertical and thus coincident with the force of gravity; hence only small guidance force was needed to maintain equilibrium whilst the upper disc was kept exactly over the lower disc. The equilibrium also depends upon the uniformity of the magnetic field and upon that of the physical density, which are somewhat related, and these factors are generally good in materials made by powder-metallurgy methods.

Whether it is possible with all modern facilities to upset this theory remains to be seen, but it will be an academic matter. In practice it is not possible to obtain the ideal balance of the various factors for free suspension, and the virtual neutralisation of 90% or more of the weight to be moved will be of great practical value. There are limits to the accuracy of dimensions in construction, to the uniformity of the magnets and to the exactness of load distribution in a transportation system, while firm protection against sideways wind force and shocks must be provided. There are thus three essential requirements for such a system (or its equivalent for other uses):

1. A fixed horizontal track containing endless rows of high-coercivity track magnets with unipolar flux in the vertical direction.

2. Vehicles consisting of horizontal rafts, preferably of steel plate, with an identical arrangement of magnets to the track, but with their flux pointing downwards.

3. Suitable fixed guidance members at the sides of the track to maintain the vehicles always exactly above the track.

It is desirable to build the track of steel girders and plate so that it provides the mechanical framework, as well as a return magnetic circuit, to use the magnetic field to best advantage and to avoid the troubles caused by leakage fields. The practical forms that this can take are shown in Fig. 10.1 for a vertical rotating shaft bearing, and for a horizontal track using both isotropic and oriented ferrite sintered bricks with horizontal nylon rollers for guidance.

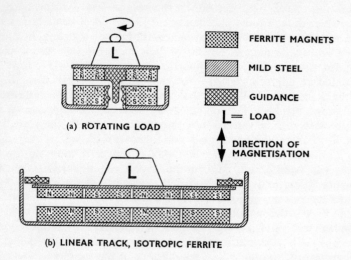

FERRITE MAGNETS

MILD STEEL

GUIDANCE

L = LOAD

DIRECTION OF MAGNETISATION

(a) ROTATING LOAD

(b) LINEAR TRACK, ISOTROPIC FERRITE

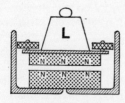

(c) LINEAR TRACK, ORIENTED FERRITE

Fig. 10.1 Magnetic Suspension Designs.

The system with four rows of isotropic ferrite fixed inside a mild steel trough represents the early design with the first kind of barium ferrite that was commercially available. It will be seen to correspond to the strip magnetisation method mentioned earlier for giving maximum load-carrying ability consistent with adequate clearance. The recent introduction of oriented grades enables the same load-carrying to be obtained with the much smaller, simpler and lighter arrangement of Fig. 10.1 (c), using thicker girders to carry the extra flux and to give better mechanical strength appropriate to the overhead construction; it is also more suitable for the combined propulsion-suspension design given later.

10.3 Operating Factors

In these magnetic suspension systems *all* the vehicle weight including the load is neutralised by the upward forces of repulsion and a high degree of stability is achieved because the space between the two repelling magnet surfaces varies with changes of load intensity upon the moving surface. The average vertical height between these surfaces, the clearance (usually about one centimetre or ⅜ inch), is a prime design factor; it is desirable that the surfaces should not touch under worst practical conditions, though the impact force will be normally very small owing to the steep increase in restoring torque when one side of the vehicle magnet system approaches the track and the other side moves away from it. Consequently the vehicles can carry a relatively light load considerably out of balance, or withstand appreciable sideways force such as might be experienced with a high wind, without loss of stability.

These practical points were proved in early experiments with a monorail design (Fig. 8.6), with central guidance only; this gave impressive demonstrations of stability, better than preliminary calculations indicated. This also applied to the ability to carry heavy loads, because the flux utilisation of ferrite magnets with appropriate return magnetic circuits in mild steel was appreciably higher than expected, based on general experience with conventional metal magnets. Nevertheless, it was soon found desirable to revert to the traditional methods of maintaining sideways stability, first the trough design of (b) and later the 'railway' design with two rails of the (c) construction separated by, and fixed to, the equivalent of sleepers. The chief reason was economic, to give the best load-carrying results with the smallest clearance, which amounted to the minimum volume of ferrite magnet bricks; the reason will be clear when this magnet arrangement is compared with the conditions for attracting a keeper over a relatively great distance, the larger volume of flux requiring a correspondingly greater amount of magnet material to maintain it.

Whichever of these alternative guidance methods is used, it must be strong and rigid enough to withstand the maximum sideways forces to be experienced in service. These are the sum of the horizontal forces normal to the axis of movement due to wind or changes of direction, effects of out-of-balance loading, and irregularities in the dimensions and in material uniformity. The last of these can be mainly overcome by an arranged balance of the magnet performance on each side of the track, and giving special attention to the uniformity of vehicle construction, so that the total sideways force is a small percentage of the total suspended weight. The guidance members for ordinary speeds can thus be light nylon rollers which are non-magnetic insulators with low frictional drag and good shock-absorbing qualities, and can operate near or in the magnetic fields supporting the vehicles, as shown in Fig. 10.1 for the linear motion uses.

A typical curve for the change of clearance with applied load is shown in Fig. 10.2 for early isotropic ferrite bricks and one recent grade of oriented ferrite with nearly linear demagnetising curve. (Gr. II material was found to lose some of its power under these conditions, which is in accordance with other experience under strong demagnetising influences). The weight of the vehicle with its magnets is shown below the zero line to indicate the load carried above it, and the clearance has been put at 1 cm to give 100% overload before it is reduced to zero; this gives the kind of values indicated in the experimental programme. The curve indicated the great advance in this application of ferrite magnets made possible by the new oriented grades, giving a threefold improvement in load-carrying ability when Gr. III material is used. Since this is the same raw material as Gr. I with added manufacturing processes, there is no reason why it should not be regarded as equally available for ultimate use on the largest scale at little increase in price per ton; with the great reduction of total weight for a given project, this material has greatly improved the economic possibilities of magnetic suspension on a large scale. The figure from this curve, 500 kg/m^2 or about 100 lb^2/sq. ft. will be used in later calculations on the above basis but can be considerably improved by increasing the ferrite thickness.

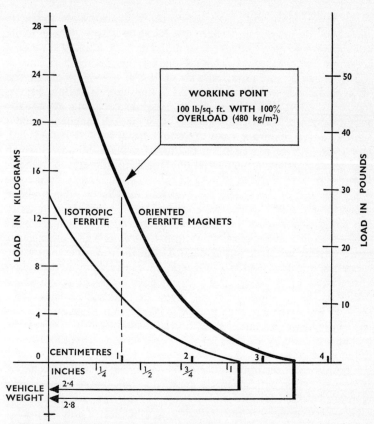

Fig. 10.2 Load/Clearance Curves for Magnetic Suspension Systems.

It will be understood that these figures could be varied considerably by the use of wider magnet rows to give greater suspension height, since these two dimensions are roughly similar at zero load, but this would entail increase of brick thickness for maintaining the loaded performance owing to the increase in length of magnetic path. This is another way of saying that the volume of magnet material must be increased in order to provide the extra flux needed to fill the space added by the greater clearance. When the load is applied, this flux is compressed and exerts a higher pressure to support it, in the manner described in section 7.4 for high intensity electromagnets; this also tends to confirm the fluid analogies used earlier in this book and a comparison can be made for the magnetic suspension design of Fig. 10.1 (*b*) to a barge on a canal. These points are mentioned here because it is difficult to explain these novel conditions by traditional electrical engineering methods.

The use of simple rafts, each consisting of a steel plate covered on its under-side with ferrite magnets in the shape of shallow bricks, for the support and movement of large loads along an equally simple design of track, indicates the basic merit of magnetic suspension. It is far shallower than the above canal and its barges and, moreover, it uses a weightless medium (in place of water) which opposes negligible inertial or frictional forces to sideways movement. In order to economise in the use of this medium, and to reduce the overall weight of the system for overhead installation, the modified design of Fig. 10.1 (*c*) may be compared with hydroplane floats or skis when used in pairs; but, to revert to land conditions, it is closely similar to the traditional railway without the wheels and other heavy space-wasting construction associated with them. In this final form, therefore, it is described as a magnetic railway or, in more distinctive abbreviated form, 'Magnarail'. From eight years of accumulated experience in its development it gives the full-scale prospect of a ten-fold improvement over present conventional railways and aircraft in load/weight ratio, based on the assumption that its vehicles will be propelled by a simple form of linear motor with electric power fed along the track.

This indicates the importance of the second subject of this chapter in its association with magnetic suspension but, before the details of combined suspension-propulsion projects are given, it is desirable to give a brief review of the underlying principles of linear motors, which have in recent years been investigated for conventional applications. This is preceded by a summary of power-consuming methods of levitation and of other proposals for the development of high-speed railways.

10.4 Levitation by Induction Methods

In the historical survey the development of a.c. machines appeared late in the last century when the vital importance of transmission capability became apparent. During the 1880s in America the famous inventor Elihu Thomson made important discoveries which led to the induction motor, but which also showed that a piece of metal could be supported in space above an electromagnet carrying alternating current. This can be well demonstrated in the form illustrated

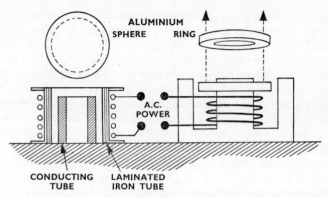

Fig. 10.3 Levitation by Alternating Current Power.

in Fig. 10.3, with an aluminium ball suspended without any contact with the ground; it does not follow Earnshaw's Theory because power has to be continuously expended for this electromagnetic levitation, whereas permanent magnets provide static magnetic fields. The free suspension method is generally explained as the result of induced eddy-currents, and its effectiveness is increased by raising the frequency of the a.c. power and by the use of metals with the highest ratio of electrical conductivity to physical density, aluminium being typical. The levitation method has been employed to melt metals by use of high-frequency power without need for any crucible or support, in free space, in order to eliminate contamination.

The aluminium ball can be replaced by a ring of the same metal on the centre limb of a transformer with the top part of the magnetic circuit removed and considerable force can be imparted to it which will shoot it into the air. In this form it is possible to explain the eddy-current formation more readily by traditional means, but in each case there are magnetic fields created in the aluminium by the heavy induced current which repel the main field set up by the alternating current flowing through the electromagnet. Losses are inevitably dissipated in fixed and moving members, the equivalent of two electromagnets with their polarity changing cyclically with the frequency of supply. This is the principle of operation of the induction motor and in linear form it can be one way of directly propelling a track vehicle without the use of moving parts, the same advantages of self-starting and transfer of power without physical contact being applicable.

Both levitation and linear propulsion methods were given considerable publicity at the beginning of this century when railway speeds had reached a plateau and before the first aircraft had flown. It was thus to be expected that proposals and patents should appear to turn these considerable electro-magnetic forces to practical use. At this time various monorail projects were being investigated and widespread effort was devoted to any way in which the speed could be increased. Linear motors were considered as an improved use of electric power for propulsion, and electro-magnetic levitation as a proposed advance on the monorail principle.

Space does not permit the description of the many such proposals of over half a century ago, but one of the latest in this series which reached the practical demonstration stage is of considerable interest as a combination of the two principles. This was the work of a French engineer, Emile Bachelet, who demonstrated a working model in America and this country with the object of developing a full-sized 'railway' system; it was to be levitated (his word) by a.c. power from the 50 c/s supply, possibly stepped up in frequency, and propelled by magnetic attraction from large solenoids. He first carried out a series of experiments of the kind illustrated in Fig. 10.3, but in order to show the considerable load-bearing ability of aluminium rings or discs suspended in the a.c. field; with a load of iron on the aluminium in the right proportions, there would be repulsion instead of attraction by the levitating coils. Hence a modified arrangement that would permit sideways movement could use the magnetic attraction of iron by a separate horizontal field for propulsion.

A model railway system several metres long was constructed on this principle and described as a 'Foucault Railway' after the French pioneer who first investigated eddy-currents (and whose name is used in French to describe them). The vehicles were long horizontal cylinders with pointed ends, an early version of streamlining to minimise air resistance, because it was planned to operate the system ultimately at speeds up to 500 km/hr or 300 mph. A simplified section of the arrangement is shown in Fig. 10.4 (a) in the form demonstrated in 1912-14; the vehicles were iron tube fixed above a thick aluminium rectangular bar into which eddy-currents were induced by a continuous row of coils fixed under the track along its full length. With the free movement of a levitated vehicle it was possible to propel it with solenoids fixed at intervals greater than the length of the iron tube with what amounted to a pulse of power.

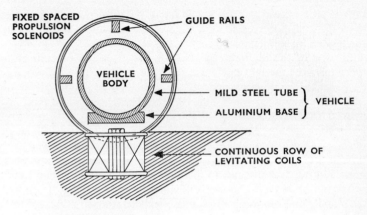

(a) AS EXHIBITED 1912/14

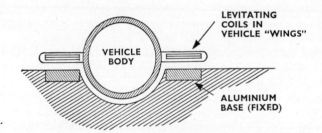

(b) PROPOSED FULL-SCALE DESIGN

Fig. 10.4 Bachelet's 'Foucault Railway'.

This and the much greater energy needed for levitation were switched on and off by contacts on the vehicle, operating circuits along the track by its movement.

The vehicle of this model was said to weigh 35 kg and to require about 15kW of power to support it at a height of one centimetre, which was considered to be adequate clearance for practical purposes. It required three guidance rails above the track, which caused a critic to comment that it used more rails than usual, not less; but these were mainly for safety and carried only a small part of the vehicle weight, so were of light construction. The levitation coils had cores made from 'faggots' of iron wire, which indicated that higher frequency operation was contemplated for the more effective use of the induction principle; this would have made the economic situation more difficult, however, in view of the great amount of power needed for levitation.

In view of the high capital cost for the provision of coils along the track—the model vehicle used eight to support it—an alternative design with the coils carried on the vehicles was proposed for the full-scale system, shown in Fig. 10.3 (b). These were to be built into 'wings' projecting on each side for inducing eddy-currents into fixed horizontal rectangular bars of aluminium running the full length of the track along each side. Plans were considered for the construction of a length of full-scale track on railway land near London in mid-1914 but it is difficult to discover if they were cancelled by the onset of the war or by the difficulty in proving that they were technically and economically sound. Bachelet himself appeared to be in favour of a mail-carrying track using unmanned $\frac{1}{2}$-ton vehicles, but extravagant claims for passenger-carrying railways operating at what are now aircraft speeds (published in the non-technical press) seem to have prejudiced his case. The value of it can be shown by the facts that those working in this field 50 years later are using his terms, speed range limits and clearance values, while linear motors of the induction kind are being developed along similar lines to those he proposed for levitation.

The chief criticism of these proposals is the use of power-consuming methods for obtaining levitation, which represents a very great cost to maintain the vehicles at rest or at ordinary speeds. If this has to be transferred to the vehicles by sliding contacts it would have presented a formidable problem, whereas the amount needed for propulsion only would be well within present practice. However, the latest air-levitation developments are facing this same problem in their track applications.

10.5 Recent High-Speed Railway Projects

During the past decade the rapid increase in the number of road vehicles in industrialised countries and large cities has presented such problems that much effort and attention have been given to appropriate new forms of track transportation. These proposals are generally either for passengers or for light road vehicles but a brief review of them indicates the importance of aiming at a system capable of dealing with both forms of traffic together. The most prominent is what is popularly called the 'monorail' though this may have little reference to the number of rails used; but it is a compact and expressive word now generally taken to mean a relatively quiet wheel-operated transportation system for passengers for speeds up to the 100 mph or 150 km/hr region. This must be electrically operated, mainly on overhead track, at speeds for which air-pressure does not demand exceptional propulsive power by present vehicle standards, such as a few hundred kilowatts or horsepower per vehicle.

The technical possibilities of linear systems for higher speeds in the aircraft range became apparent in America and Germany during World War II by arrangements developed for the launching of aircraft in confined spaces. In the latter country proposals for high speed railways by similar methods, but with the use of a.c. power with ten times the present frequency, were published by Kemper in 1953, but the economic aspects were not adequately assessed.

In 1958 appeared the first news of novel developments by the Ford Company of America in the use of air-levitation methods for the support and propulsion of wheel-less cars using internal combustion engines. By the methods adopted it was possible to obtain clearance values of only a few thousandths of an inch or fractions of a millimetre, so these vehicles were unsuitable for roads and needed a special track. The use of a light overhead structure was proposed in order to give the necessary isolation and to avoid the sterilisation of valuable land. This method therefore came to be somewhat similar to the monorail projects but with individual prime-movers. The principle of air-levitation is shown in Fig. 10.5, with alternative shapes of rail in use for similar development projects in other countries.

This isolated track is made necessary by the proposed speeds of up to 300 mph (500 km/hr) or about five times the present best average by roads or conventional railway, which makes automatic propulsion and control essential. The prime-mover for generating air pressure in volume required for levitation at first had to produce 50 hp for every ton of vehicle weight but this figure has more recently been reduced to 20 hp by improvements achieved in the vehicle-track system. The propulsive power increases as the square of the speed so about 25 times the usual power per ton weight is needed for this purpose; hence a power of some thousands of horse-power is required to propel a vehicle equivalent to a railway coach (without wheels and their associated construction) at these aircraft speeds with an appreciable proportion of it, say one-third, expended continuously for levitation.

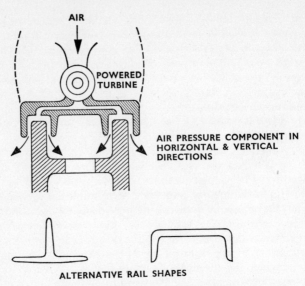

Fig. 10.5 Typical Air-Levitation Systems.

Another version of air-levitation is the Tracked Hovercraft which was described in 1961 and is being developed in this country. It uses the full track width for support and consequently works with a larger clearance than the Ford Levacar referred to above, and generally relies on the extensive experience gained with the well-known amphibian versions of this principle. For this analysis, however, the differences are small and these projects with others relying upon air pressure provided by prime-movers carried on the vehicle will be grouped as 'air-levitation systems'. There are three inherent objections to their proposed applications for track transportation in or between centres of high population density;

1. The high cost in power expenditure and complex machinery for levitation can be justified only at the highest speeds in the above range.

2. No satisfactory answer has yet been found to the hazards that would immediately arise in the event of power failure.

3. The noise and fumes emitted by prime movers in built-up areas on raised tracks, especially under accelerating conditions with full power, would be unacceptable.

To these should be added the need for fully automatic control which would almost certainly be electrical, and this would be a complex addition. In the proposed all-electric alternatives with magnetic suspension, the control will be a part of the propulsion system, the method can be used at any speed and there are no significant hazards, noise or fumes.

These two air-levitation projects have been primarily intended for the carriage of passengers, which have a relatively light weight when compared with that of machines and fuel that must also be carried to propel them at aircraft speeds by these methods. If light road vehicles are also to be carried, and this is of equal importance to solve future traffic problems, much lighter and more spacious track vehicles are required and the present need for this specialised form of transportation is shown by recent developments in Germany and America.

Investigations are being made for a special 'car-railway' to run from the Ruhr to Stuttgart at a speed of up to 250 km/hr (150 mph) by a leading railway authority, Professor Baeseler. This is planned to carry 10 000 cars a day over this 400 km (250 mile) route, although there is an excellent autobahn that has been in existence for 30 years. It is thought that such a scheme would be justifiable on account of the 50% reduction in time required for the journey and the saving in wear-and-tear of drivers as well as their vehicles. In America Westinghouse are developing another kind of car-railway using lightweight metal containers propelled by an endless row of fixed induction motors installed at regular intervals along the track. These motors drive rubber-covered wheels which are rotated in a timed sequence so that they propel the containers carrying the cars in a smooth manner along the track; though the track vehicles in this instance are of simplest kind without moving parts, the cost of the track and its control will be so high that it would appear to be desirable to use it for passengers and light freight also to cover the heavy capital expenditure involved.

Although these examples are subject to criticism, they all indicate the urgent need of high speed track transportation for passengers, light vehicles and priority freight for congested areas with a high traffic density, leaving heavy goods and materials to the present road and rail networks. If the weight of track and vehicles can be made low enough and yet capable of operating at aircraft speeds silently, a relatively high overhead structure would have outstanding practical and economic advantages for this purpose, augmented by lower

18

level systems for slower speeds and moving platforms on the ground itself. With an endless series of track vehicles like aircraft fusilages moving at speeds up to five times the present best average on present track or road systems, and accurate controlled spacing between them, a very great volume of this priority traffic could be carried on a single slender go-and-return overhead track. It could be installed with little interference with the generally congested area below it and without the need for the sterilisation of appreciable amounts of valuable land.

It is claimed here that such a system is now feasible by the use of permanent magnet suspension operated by oriented ferrite magnets, with associated electrical propulsion by linear motors. Hence details of this kind of transportation system will occupy most of the remainder of this chapter.

10.6 Linear Motors

It is possible to envisage a linear version of the various kinds of electric motor outlined in the previous chapter, with the general assumption that their characteristics will approximately correspond. Thus an a.c. linear induction motor will have self-starting properties that would not apply to a synchronous design of machine, but the latter could give more economical performance if permanent excitation by ferrite magnets could be provided. Moreover, the synchronous capability of the latter could be used to good effect for the exact timing and spacing of an endless series of track vehicles in the above proposals, like a gigantic electric clock in linear form. It would be technically desirable to combine these two a.c. alternative designs into a single system, rather like the development described in section 9.3, if it could be made simple enough, a vital matter for a construction which may extend for hundreds of miles or kilometres.

A d.c. linear motor could be expected to give, in principle, the most favourable traction characteristics but the linear version of a commutator motor would seem to be too complex for consideration. The proposed homopolar motor version of Fig. 9.4, however, looks most promising in linear form, with a single endless pole of ferrite magnet straddled by a thin-sheet conductor carrying a heavy direct current, but in this case it is obviously desirable that the magnets should be the fixed member so that the relatively light conductor can comprise the mobile element. It was pointed out earlier that the most difficult feature of linear motors compared with their rotary counterparts is the lack of the restraining force of the axle/bearing system which ensures uniformity of airgap length in conventional generators and motors, in spite of powerful forces of attraction between the rotor and stator iron cores. It is therefore desirable to avoid the use of iron cores in the moving element of a linear motor, which tends to favour the use of the d.c. homopolar design or the induction a.c. principle. From Fig. 10.4 it will be apparent that the use of an aluminium strip conductor arrangement along the track means that power must be fed to coils in each vehicle, so that high speed sliding contacts are required for the a.c. linear motor and there is no advantage in this case over the d.c. alternative which has to use such contacts in all circumstances.

There is thus a preference for d.c. linear motors for this purpose which is greatly strengthened by the availability of a homopolar suspension system of the kind shown in Fig. 10.1 (c), if a low-voltage heavy current supply can be made available economically along the track. This could be done by the installation of step-down transformers and semi-conductor static rectifiers at frequent intervals. Alternatively unidirectional condenser discharges on the lines of the simple circuit in Fig. 7.3 would have the merit of storage, allowing almost continuous a.c. supply to be converted to high intensity d.c. pulses. The latter could be associated with the automatic control and incorporate a timing or spacing feature from the a.c. supply frequency.

It will be seen from this brief analysis of linear motor possibilities that electric power can be made available along the track in a variety of ways, but the best appears to be the counterpart of latest railway electrification methods; a.c. transmission and d.c. utilisation in the propulsion-braking form of the low-voltage acyclic motor described in Chapter 9. But in the track linear version there is the added advantage that the converting equipment can be housed in the vertical track supports without the need for added weight in the vehicles or to the track between the supports. Though the best arrangement will doubtless require years of research work, there is enough information, with experience and materials to back it, for the development of a relatively simple and efficient method of propulsion incorporating automatic control. With the low frictional drag of a magnetic suspension system, this would require little power for speeds within the present road and rail range, but it could be extended to provide many megawatts for the propulsion of streamlined vehicles at aircraft speeds, for the first time in a silent and predictable manner.

Some of the linear motor references (refs. 1 and 3) cover the best-known application to high-speed railway traction, though others deal with varied uses such as oscillatory motions in the textile and machine tool industries. The railway application is of the induction type used with conventional wheeled vehicles carrying the coils powered by the a.c. mains supply; these coils straddle a vertical aluminium strip fixed along the track so that horizontal magnetisation is applied symmetrically on each side. It is important to note that the wheels provide the usual guidance and load-bearing service for free movement but do not come into the propulsion or braking operations; consequently the acceleration and deceleration are greatly improved in effectiveness and reliability, which have been proved by impressive demonstrations.

The use of mains frequency supply gives optimum performance well above the upper speed limit of present railway track and its wheeled vehicles, so that a somewhat similar set of circumstances arises as in the best use of air-levitation methods. A cheap source of high frequency power, possibly with variable frequency up to the 500 c/s region, would extend the usefulness down to speeds more appropriate for present railway conditions and this subject is an extension of section 9.9 on cheap high-frequency power but on a much greater scale. If this kind of linear motor were to be used with the proposed magnetic suspension methods, by allowing for appropriate up-and-down motion since the guidance will restrict the sideways movement, it could better justify the economics of frequency change and be used on a more suitable scale for the practical conditions of operation. However, it would involve additional equipment and construction and would thus be less attractive than a system, such as the d.c. proposal, which can use the magnetic field of the track suspension magnets; but this has still to be proved on a practical scale.

This again amounts to the sliding contact problem but with low-voltage d.c. power this should be equally capable of practical solution in linear as in rotary form, being the only significant source of loss in a system using permanent magnet excitation. When this was discussed in section 9.5 it was mentioned that conventional brushes are tested at velocities up to 240 mph or 400 km/hr, or near to the suggested upper limit of a high-speed railway. So linear motor propulsion of this kind should be feasible on an engineering scale up to aircraft speeds.

10.7 Magnetic Bearings

Because it was never possible to forecast the arrival of strong and plentiful permanent magnets suitable for power applications, there have been no known attempts to use them previously on any but the instrumentation scale and the practical applications are correspondingly restricted. Much development work has appeared in patent literature on this subject, especially in the days before reliable amplifiers could be used for this purpose, since the ultimate sensitivity of a reasonably robust instrument depended upon the ability to neutralise the effects of friction. Electromagnets were never popular for this kind of service owing to the need for a power supply and the complication of maintaining a constant magnetic field by this means, even though all early permanent magnets were poor in stability by modern standards.

Commercial instruments and electricity meters, as well as good quality watches and similar mechanisms, depended for low frictional drag upon the use of hard steel pivots of exacting metallurgical standard fitting into sapphire bearings. This arrangement generally provided the limiting factor to life and performance, so an entirely different method of eliminating friction was constantly sought. Since this kind of manufacture entailed much experience of permanent magnets, it is natural that most ideas on their use for the reduction of frictional effects should come from this source, and the first commercial application of magnetic suspension was for the frictionless support of the vertical shafts of electricity meters. This gave the essential conditions for the neutralisation of the force of gravity by the repulsion of concentric alnico cylinder magnets in the highest coercivity grade of two decades ago, and this innovation had been accelerated by wartime shortages of Swiss sapphire bearings. The first use of magnetic suspension for production of electricity meters at that time appears to have been a technical success but was not adopted widely until the arrival of the cheaper, more uniform barium ferrite during the present decade; but the deciding factor can well be the threefold increase of coercivity which permitted a shallower bearing assembly and gave far greater resistance to demagnetising effects from outside as well as from within. Temperature effects are fully compensated over the widest working range, and it is claimed that bearing wear and maintenance are now eliminated.

The simplicity of the magnetic suspension system for a shaft that always operates in the vertical position is shown in Fig. 10.6 (*a*) but it will be clearly limited to certain kinds of application such as fixed clocks or meters. To use the great benefits of this new way for overcoming the effects of friction in the case of horizontal shafts or for portable instuments, a more complex arrangement is required,

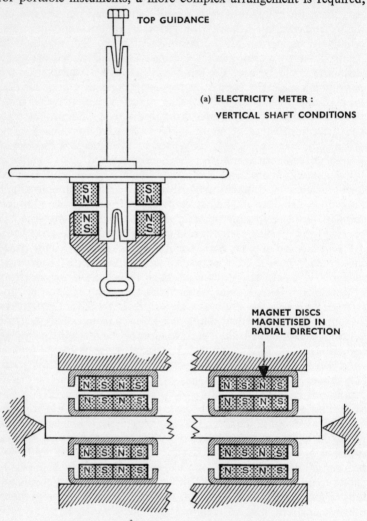

(a) ELECTRICITY METER :

VERTICAL SHAFT CONDITIONS

TOP GUIDANCE

MAGNET DISCS MAGNETISED IN RADIAL DIRECTION

(b) MAGNETIC BEARING FOR HORIZONTAL OR PORTABLE USES

Fig. 10.6 Magnetic Bearings.

shown at (*b*). Bearings are built up from numbers of ferrite magnet discs with radial magnetisation, one pole being at the outer periphery and the other at the inner, and large discs are assembled inside a mild steel sleeve with alternate polarities adjacent to form the fixed part of the bearing. The moving part is constructed similarly, but with the poles pointing outwards with similar polarities opposite to the fixed magnet system poles, giving continuous repulsion at every point whether the shaft is moving or stopped. It will be seen that the outer mild steel sleeves for the fixed part, and the inner for the moving part, act as return magnetic paths as well as mechanical housings, to keep the magnetic circuit as short as possible and to eliminate leakage flux.

This arrangement is the rotary version of Fig. 10.1 (*b*) with a number of magnetic paths to carry a large load, but it requires a precise guidance construction at the ends with some vertical play to allow for limited movement of the rotor system. As in the linear motion version, the friction is not eliminated but can be so much reduced that it represents a great advance on any alternative. It has been suggested that the friction could be virtually zero if electromagnets connected to a servo-mechanism were fixed at the shaft ends to provide free suspension (by automatic supply of external energy to neutralize the end forces due to the out-of-balance rotor weight), and this is certainly possible from a technical standpoint. In practice it has the disadvantage, however, of adding greatly to the cost and complication for a marginal improvement; it tends to spoil the inherent merit of modern permanent magnets in cutting out maintenance and the use of unnecessary power.

As in other magnet systems there is much scope for design improvements to meet various practical requirements. The use of fewer but thicker magnet discs will reduce the load-bearing ability of the rotor but simplify the guidance and construction, and an increase in the airgap length will tend to have a similar effect. If space and weight are not restricted, the best results will be obtained by the use of large magnetic bearings of this type and the relative low cost of the ferrite material will avoid appreciable cost increase by designing generously, unlike earlier conditions. The disc is the simplest shape to manufacture by automatic powder-metallurgy methods and the product has the greatest uniformity in strength and magnetic properties, while a considerable variety of stock sizes is now available on the market. It is therefore possible to produce such magnetic bearings as specialist components, sealed in their steel housings and ready to be fitted to standard shaft diameters. Some protection against the ingress of magnetic dirt at the ends is desirable but a steel thickness appropriate to the magnetic circuit conditions for each such bearing could ensure negligible external leakage flux. This is important to avoid eddy current losses which would tend to re-introduce the frictional effects which the bearing was intended to eliminate [Fig. 10.6 (b).]

Such magnetic bearings provide more than the reduction of frictional drag: they also act as a spring mounting and shock absorber, advantages already mentioned in the linear applications for track transportation. Whether they can be applied to the severe conditions that road vehicles must be able to withstand remains to be seen after testing in fixed machines. Though the use of vertical magnetic bearings of a small size has now been proved successful for some years in large quantities of electricity meters, this represents very light mechanical loading conditions. Much development work must be done before this degree of success can be extended to power engineering conditions, though there is now no technical or economic reason why this cannot be achieved in the near future with the use of commercial barium ferrite magnet material. Special precautions and assembly methods must be evolved to overcome the effect of the powerful forces of attraction when opposite poles become temporarily adjacent while the rotor shaft is being fitted into its bearings, but this is part of the general experience that has to be learned in the handling of novel materials and techniques.

10.8 Experimental Work

While linear motors have received considerable attention in the technical press during recent years, magnetic suspension has been limited to a few general remarks on work being done abroad. Consequently the necessary information on the great practical possibilities of the latter has been obtained by extensive experimental work carried out by the author from first principles and this is briefly reported here for the first time, apart from patent specifications which summarise eight years of practical development. It has already been stated that the possibilities of magnetic suspension became apparent as soon as ferrite magnets appeared; it was merely a case of placing one magnetised ferrite disc or brick upon a table and holding a similar magnet above it with similar poles adjacent. The normal method of magnetising high-coercivity material is through its minimum dimension, so that the poles are spread uniformly over an appreciable area. This provides the essential conditions for the first time in the history of industrial permanent magnets.

The means for extending this area by fixing rows of ferrite shallow bricks to a steel sheet by their own force of attraction, and separating them by narrow non-magnetic strips of hardboard or aluminium, multiplied the force of repulsion of each brick to any desired extent and this effect added another great advantage to the list already given of the merits of this new material over the traditional steels and cast alloys. It was necessary to use rows of alternate polarity with limited width in order to keep the length of magnetic circuit short, and this was discovered some time before bonded ferrite powder sheet was developed, and strip magnetisation was needed to give the best holding effects (Fig. 7.4). By duplicating this simple construction with one sheet fixed horizontally on the ground and the other suspended above it with appropriate guidance members to restrict any sideways movement, design data such as the great load-bearing properties in relation to clearance distance were readily obtained for a variety of materials and dimensional layouts. The curves of Fig. 10.2 are summarised from a great mass of information obtained in this way, which indicated the influence of the main variables described earlier. It was noted that this simple magnet/steel arrangement could give negligible leakage and provide the highest flux-utilisation ever obtained, which explained the unexpectedly high load-carrying ability of this form of magnetic suspension, in spite of the unusually low working value of flux density from ferrites.

It was a logical step to extend the magnet rows to form a track and to provide a movable platform to travel along it carrying a heavy load; by 1959 a track about 12 ft (4 m) long in the form of a shallow trough 18 inches (46 cm) wide was made to carry the weight of a man on a platform 28 inches (70 cm) long, using a construction of the kind shown in Fig. 10.1(b) with the early isotropic grade of barium ferrite. Low-friction guidance was provided by PTFE plastic buffers bearing upon the reinforced sides of the sheet-steel trough.

As a parallel line of development to this mainly static test programme, work was also carried out on a series of small table-type working models 3 inches (76 mm) wide in order to test the dynamic stability of magnetically suspended vehicles. This was also an unexplored subject and the impressive results obtained with relatively crude models led to the construction of a miniature railway track, about 3% scale of conventional size, at first in straight lengths of 6 ft (1.8 m). It was mentioned earlier that the first model had a single rail central guidance construction with propulsion by a small electric motor driving a single rubber-tyred wheel bearing on the top of the rail, direct current being fed along insulated brass strips cemented to the vertical sides of the rail. This gave excellent running stability even when unevenly loaded and gave clear proof of the great possibilities of this kind of vehicle suspension; but (as in the case of traditional railways) it was better to use two guidance rails instead of one in order to provide the best form of lateral stability, though it made the cornering problems more complex. Ultimately an elementary method of varying the magnetic repulsion force along curves, increasing it on the outside and decreasing it inside, gave the required results without banking, though this present method could also be used effectively.

A loop track 30 ft (10 m) long was then made for prolonged running tests at high scale speeds, and it was found that the equivalent of 100 mph (160 km/hr) could be maintained around this curved course, much higher than that possible with a corresponding model of a conventional railway. This confirmed the considerable experience that had by then been accumulated on the general merits of magnetic suspension for this kind of application, the vehicle magnet system providing a uniformly loaded raft with low centre of gravity which had had the ideal weightless form of springing and shock absorbing capabilities.

Tests with gradients of different values showed that this magnetic suspension method is at least as good as present railways, the slope never being steep enough to reduce appreciably the vertical component of the force of repulsion which decides the working clearance. Any form of applied vibration was quickly damped out and the riding was smooth in all adverse circumstances which could be reproduced to scale. Points or switches for changing the track can be provided by arranging for a suitable length of it to be hinged appropriately; though this is more complicated than the present methods, it can be equally effective and similarly controlled.

Although the original plans were to propel the vehicles by a simple linear motor arrangement, preferably by the use of the track magnetic field, the above experiments showed the effectiveness of traditional kinds of d.c. drive using a geared electric motor driving a wheel for both propulsion and braking purposes. Here only a single rubber-tyred wheel running on a uniform surface along the centre of the track met all requirements; by adjustment of the wheel axle position above the track it was possible to vary the average pressure upon it from zero up to a high proportion of the total vehicle weight, or in other words to transfer any desired proportion of the vehicle weight from the track magnetic field to the wheel, the remainder providing the springing and shock absorbing requirements. This could be varied to increase the ability to accelerate or decelerate, or to reduce the retarding effect of the drive—a freewheel effect with the wheel stationary, if required. All these novel advantages are possible when wheels are no longer needed for their age-old load-bearing service, and can be used only as a convenient gearing link in an electric drive. It illustrates a significant disadvantage of the linear motor, which lacks the speed flexibility of gear trains.

At this stage in the development the first commercial grades of oriented ferrite became available, and these gave good prospects of solving the remaining problems, first the great tonnage and high cost of the ferrite needed for a full-sized system of this kind, and secondly the relatively high track weight for overhead installation, which appeared to be essential for the higher speed versions, though less significant for the moving platform application.

10.9 Magnetic Railway (Magnarail)

The Gr. III sintered barium ferrite bricks were found to give about three times the suspension force of the early material and, although the intrinsic coercivity was somewhat lower, it gave every indication that it would stand up to the demagnetising forces equally well. The higher working flux density of this ferrite required a thicker return path in the mild steel, and the desire for some kind of d.c. linear propulsion, in order to utilise the track magnets for excitation as well as suspension, led to a unipolar system. The practical version was based upon two or more 'rails' of the kind shown in Fig. 10.2 (c) with the same polarity upwards in the rows of ferrite bricks, and a strong inexpensive construction was now possible with the use of standard steel channels and angles, with aluminium for the track guidance members. So this design is described as a 'magnetic railway' ('Magnarail') in contrast to the earlier version which was more like a magnetic canal.

Years of small-scale experimental work had now proved that this novel kind of track transportation had outstanding possibilities when compared with either conventional or proposed alternatives. It was now desirable to test a larger model and at the same time examine the probable performance of a full-scale system for the carriage of passengers and road vehicles at slow, medium and

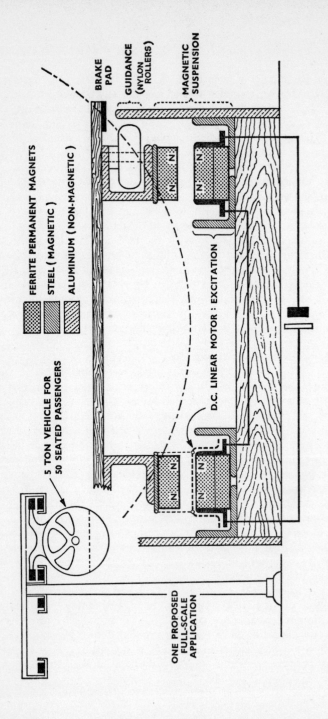

FERRITE PERMANENT MAGNETS

STEEL (MAGNETIC)

ALUMINIUM (NON-MAGNETIC)

BRAKE PAD

GUIDANCE (NYLON ROLLERS)

MAGNETIC SUSPENSION

5 TON VEHICLE FOR 50 SEATED PASSENGERS

D.C. LINEAR MOTOR : EXCITATION

ONE PROPOSED FULL-SCALE APPLICATION

Fig. 10.7 Magnetic Railway: One-Sixth Scale Model and Proposed Ultimate Application.

aircraft speeds. This would require, respectively, a moving platform arrangement at ground level, a covered vehicle hanging downwards from a low overhead structure, and a high-level version of the latter. All these could be based upon the simple magnetic suspension structure shown in Fig. 10.7. In the overhead installations it would be reversed, meeting the important need for the open parts of the magnetic circuit to be covered and isolated in order to prevent contamination. This protection is also important in connection with the sliding electric contacts for low-voltage power.

The proposed full-scale magnetic railway track is 9 ft (2.7 m) wide with the angle-iron 'rails' separated and spaced by the equivalent of railway sleepers at full width to give best sideways stability, and therefore the best degree of clearance uniformity. The guidance rollers on the vehicles bear intermittently on shallow walls of aluminium along each side of the track.

Extra rows of magnets with their associated angle-girders can be added between those at the ends of the sleepers, if required, to carry heavier loads with economical use of ferrite bricks, the dominating economic factor. If the dimensions of each 'rail' magnetic circuit are increased proportionally, the load-carrying ability will tend to improve as the square of this increase while the weight of ferrite will grow as its cube. This will of course increase the clearance, which may be desirable for a combined suspension-propulsion system, but at the expense of track weight and ferrite cost. These variables will require detailed investigation coupled with practical tests before the optimum can be approached.

For a track which must contain curves equivalent to present road or rail routes, it is necessary to use articulated vehicles and experiment has shown that these can be built up from square platform units to fit the track width. Five such units with rounded ends would, with suitable lightweight envelope, comprise a vehicle about 50 ft (15 m) long to carry a 5 ton load with an equivalent weight for structure and support magnets, making a loaded total of around 10 tons. This could be fitted with seats to carry an average of 50 passengers, or alternatively carry three or four road vehicles on the basis of an air-ferry or the same weight of priority freight. Larger vehicles can be made if wanted but there is no incentive for this with fully automatic propulsion and spacing, which can provide the equivalent of a continuous service; also the full benefit of a lightweight track, which this magnetic system makes possible, can be attained only when the added loading of two passing vehicles travelling in opposite directions is relatively small. In this case it is only 20 tons on a single track support, acting through a magnetic field that can absorb shock and vibration, but these will be exceptionally small in a vehicle without moving parts.

All these factors are of great importance in assessing the merits of this system with proposed alternatives. Those relying upon the continuous expenditure of power to provide levitation, such as the old electro-magnetic induction methods or the new air-levitation systems, can be justified only for aircraft speeds at which there are a host of unsolved hazards and problems. In addition to the safety difficulties and high suspension costs, mentioned earlier, great reaction forces between track and vehicle must be absorbed whenever there is a change of direction, sideways and vertically, unless done very gradually. An aircraft has no track but absorbs these forces in its large wing areas and by freedom of movement in any direction. Magnetic suspension can do this to a far smaller degree so that it is much better to make the track almost straight and level throughout its high speed sections. This makes it necessary to operate such sections at appreciable height in order to become reasonably independent of ground contour and obstacles, so that the weight of the track and its vehicles must be reduced to a minimum. It would not be possible to carry rotating machinery and fuel economically under these conditions, so that linear motors of the simplest kind with power fed from the fixed vertical supports of the track would appear to be essential. The recent progress in high tubular towers with no external supporting structure and the spanning of great distances by steel-rope suspension bridges point to methods for the construction of such high-level tracks without temporary or permanent dislocation of the ground below.

From the economic policy standpoint, however, it will be best to prove these magnetic suspension and linear propulsion proposals at conventional track speeds, for which there can be an equally important demand if the system can be made as cheaply in capital and operating cost as present information indicates. The lightweight vehicles operating over existing roads could give rapid suburban communication independent of the traffic jams below, and there would be no objection to a silent fumeless system being installed in any closed or open situation. If at the start it carried passengers only, there is a considerable demand for such service in most new towns now being planned, so that the moving streets and ultra-high speed versions can be evolved from the experience gained in the simplest kind of application. This approach would avoid the difficulty of high expenditure for many years for a project which takes an unpredictable time to become a practical proposition.

An experimental track of one-sixth scale relative to this proposed system is being made for installation along the ground to prove the running properties of this magnetic railway on a man-carrying basis. This will run at speeds within the present track range to test the efficiency and stability under outside conditions, which could not be done on a smaller scale. This has been designed on the basis of the section shown in Fig. 10.7 to be made in transportable lengths using ferrite bricks on iron angle-girders fixed to wooden sleepers. It is planned to make the track in the form of a closed loop about 300 ft long (nearly 100 m) with appropriate gradients so that the table-model tests can be repeated on a six-times greater scale, a similar ratio to the further increase needed later to make the ultimate full-sized system. This should not only demonstrate the superb riding properties but also provide data for the full-scale project.

10.10 Performance

Of the two main features described in this chapter, magnetic suspension is relatively straightforward in assessment but the best form of linear motor requires considerable development in view of the novel operating conditions. It has been made clear that the success of the whole project is dependent upon a simple, lightweight propulsion-braking arrangement and such a proposal is shown in Fig. 10.7. This is an inverted channel-shaped copper-alloy sheet fixed under each vehicle in such a manner that it can be raised or lowered independently of the main magnet-carrying structure, so that it straddles the row of track magnets. Between the latter and the inner vertical sides of the angle-irons are fixed endless insulated brass strips the full length of the track, to which electrical contact can be made by a number of leaf-springs. There is thus appreciable contact area for passing heavy direct current across the top of the track magnets for propulsion of the vehicle, or for braking by various methods. This arrangement is the linear motor version of the low-voltage motor shown in Fig. 9.4, but the magnet row is fixed and the conductor moves with the vehicle it drives. These two designs were evolved quite independently from the requirements of the project and confirmed by calculation from first principles, and it was discovered much later that they were basically the same technical problem.

While the final full-scale arrangements for an automatic operating system have still to be worked out, this kind of propulsion appears to be suitable for the man-carrying model to be controlled from the vehicle, by the vertical movement of this propulsion conductor. With a separate switch for power control this same action can give friction-braking in the same manner as that described for the rotary machine in the previous chapter, with dynamic braking if the circuit is closed with the power off. In this case the power supply position is simplified by the ease with which large direct currents at any required voltage could be made available from the a.c. mains supply with static rectifiers or capacitance discharge circuits; this tends to overcome the limitation that linear motors cannot use the advantage of gearing, which in any case would entail the introduction of moving parts.

The most important point to be proved experimentally with this linear version, as with the low-voltage rotary d.c. machine, is the power absorbed by the moving electrical contacts which carry the heavy direct current. For both this is the only significant source of loss at ordinary speeds and could be quite high before the project became impracticable on account of low efficiency or high temperature. On the other hand there are good prospects that the efficiency could become better than that of any alternative when the best kind of contact has been developed for these unusual requirements. If this can be satisfactorily solved, the main outstanding problem will be the provision of vast tonnages of ferrite bricks at low cost.

For the reasons already given it is difficult to state what clearance of vehicles over the track will be needed in practice but it will probably increase with the operating speed. The suggested one centimetre appears to be a good average and to agree with the work on other levitation systems. With the use of Gr. III ferrite bricks in the Fig. 10.7 design this would need an estimated 350 tons per mile of double track, being roughly one-third of the total track weight (without vertical fixed supports) which mainly consists of stock angle-iron. When made in the largest scale by continuous automatic methods the barium ferrite could reach the price of a special steel, which it resembles from the constituents aspect, and it is therefore priced at £100/ton for this estimate. (If made from large unusable by-products, as suggested at the end of Chapter 6, it could be even lower). This price is roughly one-fifth the present estimated cost with the use of higher grade materials and production on the several-ton basis, for a variety of uses.

A comparison of the Magnarail with present and proposed alternatives is given in Table 10.1. It is based upon a city-centre to city-centre run of 100 miles or somewhat greater, for which road, rail and aircraft generally give similar performance around 60 mph. These are expensive and use considerable land and, in the case of aircraft and railways, have a vehicle/load weight ratio ten times greater than that estimated for the Magnarail; they also need a large skilled staff to operate them. While aircraft do not use a track, they require an airport and airterminal with a constant special-purpose road transport service between them, and the high capital and maintenance charges make it unlikely that they can compete in this field of transportation unless it is over long stretches of sea.

The proposed alternatives are the high-speed wheel-operated track vehicle, generally described as a 'monorail', to run at speeds up to the 100 mph average level by electric propulsion, and air-levitation systems to run at up to three times that speed. It is considered that the magnetic railway can compete with either of these categories in all respects, but all have certain common advantages over the present three categories in regard to the use of overhead tracks. With spaced single-car vehicles this makes it possible to build a track at much lower cost without the use of valuable land, which is the greatest present obstacle in time and cost in congested industrial countries.

It appears that the cost of the ferrite magnets will not unduly inflate the track price nor will their weight place the magnetic method of suspension-propulsion at a disadvantage, owing to the general lightness of the system. Hence the figures for track weight and costs are given as the same for all the overhead systems. The Magnarail shows the greatest merit in the low cost of the vehicles and the lower power required to propel them in each category, and this is especially apparent in the highest speed version because no power is needed for levitation; this will also make an immense difference to the maintenance charges (which are not included in the Table). It will be understood that all the figures vary considerably according to conditions and locality of installation and must be taken as a means for indicating approximate proportions only.

The above conclusions on the feasibility of magnetic suspension with linear propulsion for an overhead track transportation system have been generally confirmed by independent information recently published by the Westinghouse Electric Corporation of America (February 1965).

19

TABLE 10.1. TRACK TRANSPORTATION COMPARISON

City-Centre to City-Centre Basis: Typical 100 mile run.

GROUP		SPEED RANGE	DOUBLE-TRACK per Mile		VEHICLE FOR 50-PASSENGERS or EQUIVALENT			REMARKS
			WEIGHT 1000s Tons	COST £Millions	FULL WEIGHT Tons	HORSE-POWER	COST £1000s	
PRESENT	RAILWAY	60 mph av.	5	0·5—1	50	200	20	10% of 10-coach train
	MOTORWAY		—	0·5—1	15	200	10	Motorcoach or 10 cars
	AIRCRAFT (Local)		NO TRACK but airport, air-terminal, motor-coaches etc.		50	10 000	500	High running costs
FUTURE (overhead track)	WHEEL-OPERATED "MONORAIL"	to 100mph	1	0·25	20	250	40	Averaged from numerous claims in Press
	AIR-LEVITATED VEHICLES	100—300 mph			25	3000 (up to 1000 for lift)	100	
	MAGNETIC RAILWAY (MAGNARAIL)	to 100mph 100—300 mph	1*	0·25*	10 (half load)	125 1200	5	with d.c. linear motor and fixed electrical equipment

(All figures very approximate for comparison purposes only)

* Horizontal parts of track only.

Though much remains to be confirmed on a practical scale regarding the economics of magnetic suspension for track transportation, especially in relation to propulsion methods, this also applies to air-levitation proposals which have a more restricted application. They need at present about one-third of the corresponding aircraft power for combined levitation-propulsion but magnetic suspension requires no energy to support the vehicles and provides most of the linear motor bulk in the track; hence the unloaded vehicle can be reduced in weight to that of the load carried, which is the minimum that could be considered on stability grounds. This advantage becomes greater at lower speed and thus the Magnarail system could be applied for all new track requirements, from lowest to highest speeds.

10.11 References

1. Barwell F. T. 'Speculations on the Future of Railway Mechanical Engineering', *Inst. Mech. Engineers*, Oct. 1961.

2. Laithwaite E. R. 'Linear Induction Motors', *Proc. I.E.E.*, Vol. 104A, pp. 461-70, 1957.

3. Laithwaite E. R. & Barwell F. T. 'Linear Induction Motors for High-Speed Railways, *J.I.E.E.* Vol. 10, pp. 100-103, April 1964.

4. Baeckers F. T. 'A Magnetic Journal Bearing', *Philips Tech. Rev.*, Vol. 22, No. 7, pp. 232-238, April 1961.

5. McCaig M. 'Permanent Magnets for Repulsion Systems', *Elec. Review*, 15 September 1961.

6. Kerr C. & Lynn C. 'The Roller Road', *Westinghouse Engineer*, March 1961 (*also* Jan. 1963 pp. 2-7).

7. British Patent Specification No. 867045 gives details of early work in relation to section 10.8.

8. Polgreen G. R. 'Transport Possibilities with Magnetic Suspension', *Electrical Times*, V. 148, pp. 298-303, 26 August 1965.

11

FUTURE PROSPECTS

The properties and widespread possible applications of modern magnets have been examined individually from both theoretical and practical aspects. They will now be considered collectively in order to arrive at general conclusions and to outline a pattern of future development. This will need to be on a large and extensive scale: while most of the applications come into the present scope of mechanical engineering, the ferrite materials will ultimately be required on a brick-making or steel-producing scale in place of the present high-quality component basis. The task of extending knowledge of this new technology accordingly is facilitated by the fact that these new magnets are much simpler in every way than traditional magnetic materials and so can be treated in isolation as a separate subject by those whose chief technical interest lies elsewhere. The main incentive for this work should come from its great importance to modern communities, especially in the field of mobile power and transportation. Hence the final pages of the book contain general observations on the ultimate impact of these proposals.

11.1 General Conclusions

The most significant factor in this whole study of modern magnets, from which most of the remainder is derived, is that it is no longer necessary to tolerate waste of costly electric power for the excitation of machines and equipment, particularly in the important medium-power range; similarly, in track systems, the unnecessary dead weight of multiple-wheel support and propulsion can be eliminated by permanent fields which use no power for suspension and can provide the simplest kind of linear propulsion. These two general functions can now be provided on any desired scale by use of the latest grades of high-coercivity ferrite material, respectively in the simplest ring and brick shapes. Permanent magnets in this form can be made automatically at low cost from abundant non-strategic raw materials, principally iron oxide.

Theoretically this is in accordance with the first principle that a magnetic field is created almost instantaneously at full strength by the passage of an electric current through the winding of an electromagnet, and all subsequent power consumed by the flow of the current to maintain it is dissipated as generally harmful heat. If the electromagnet had high-coercivity magnet material of suitable size and shape included in its magnetic circuit, the required magnetic field could have been created merely by the passage of a short high-intensity pulse of direct current. This could serve for an indefinite time for such valuable purposes as the excitation of machines under power-handling conditions. The magnetic field so created thus acts as a permanent static store of the electrical energy used to magnetise it and can be employed thereafter as the essential agent or catalyst required for the inter-conversion of mechanical and electrical energy, a weightless invisible medium analogous in function to a hydraulic fluid. In such an electromagnetic system the electric current is the power-transfer medium confined to the conductor circuit, and generates unavoidable losses proportional to its resistance. Consequently, electromagnets used to maintain uni-directional magnetic fields, such as excitation, must inevitably create continuous losses of considerable magnitude which could be entirely avoided if permanent magnets were substituted.

Until the past decade no suitable permanent magnet material was commercially available for the severe mechanical, as well as magnetic, conditions that apply in power-handling machines at prices competitive with the traditional electromagnet alternative. Hence the efficiency and performance of a wide range of electrical machines and equipment have been considerably worse than was technically necessary, owing to the continual drain of excitation power and the resulting inflation of heat loss above the essential minimum. It is true that the electromagnet also provided a valuable control service that is difficult to replace when permanent magnets are substituted, but the ideal magnet principle provides this also, with the minimum of extra power needed and thus far more efficiently than in any previous arrangement.

Degradation of performance due to electromagnetic excitation varies greatly with the physical size of the magnetic circuit, and hence of the machine and its power capacity. It is almost negligible in the largest acyclic machine, small in latest power station alternators, but becomes progressively more important as size becomes smaller, in terms of the *proportion* of power by-passed, both from first principles and leakage aspects. In very small sizes, for which the efficiency can be as low as the 50% level, much of the high loss is due to this cause and it can be greatly reduced by the substitution of ferrite magnets for the field windings (although this uses them inefficiently) in small d.c. motors. But poor efficiency is no bar to the phenomenal success of the smallest electrical machines, because of their outstanding convenience and lack of non-electric competitors; this applies particularly to the simple and cheap a.c. induction motors which use power from the supply mains at low cost. While they are capable of appreciable improvement by the proposed methods of section 9.3, the effect on the market for them would be marginal, whereas it could be profound in the case of medium-power machines for mobile applications in which the cost of power is high. This is also the application sphere in which competition from mechanical and hydraulic alternatives is most severe and indeed has virtually ousted electrical transmission systems from all but a few special uses.

Though useful improvements to d.c. machines of the usual commutator kind could be achieved also in this all-important medium power range by the use of permanent magnet excitation, this alone cannot close the wide gap in size, cost and efficiency between them and non-electric alternatives. The machines should be redesigned from first principles in order to obtain the full magnetic efficiency of the new ferrite materials. This results in a simple acyclic design based on the Faraday Disc which shows every sign of meeting all requirements in this medium-power range where it is most urgently needed as both motor and generator and, in combination, as an electric drive or transmission system. Consisting essentially of one pole and one armature-winding turn, and being made primarily of mild steel and iron oxide, it is among all electric machines the ultimate in simplicity, and gives prospects of being developed to give a level of efficiency approaching that of large machines which have long been used for these purposes.

While the support and propulsion of road vehicles by the complex and heavy construction associated with a number of wheels appears to be inevitable in the foreseeable future, they present undesirable obstacles in track transportation systems when alternative methods can be employed. Power-consuming levitation methods, whether by electromagnetic induction or air pressure, use so much energy to support a vehicle that they are suitable only for future track systems operating at aircraft speeds, which need comparable propulsion power. In sharp contrast, vehicle suspension by the mutual repulsion of ferrite magnet bricks can be applied for track transportation at *any* speed range because no power is consumed for this purpose; for the whole range of present land speeds, at which air resistance effects are small or moderate, propulsion power should be much less than for any conventional alternative. If the track magnets are also used to excite the linear equivalent of the proposed acyclic motor, the vehicle 'armature' would consist of light channel-shaped conductor plates fitted at the sides with suitable sets of sliding contacts for current collection. Such vehicles would have the unique merit of no moving parts and could be made with the lowest possible weight consistent with dynamic stability. If the vehicle length is extended to cover the whole track and is articulated, it becomes a moving platform or roadway for slow speed operation.

Both rotary and linear propulsion methods of this kind depend for their operation upon the unfamiliar conditions imposed by peak direct currents of some thousands of amperes. Investigations have shown that the predominant loss occurs at the sliding contacts if the circuit is very short and has large section, with limited voltage drop for appropriate metallic contacts to carry the unidirectional current. On a full-scale system the track could be supplied at frequent intervals with static rectifier units, possibly with condensers (capacitances) to level the electrical load, and fully automatic propulsion could be incorporated with little additional equipment. The use of brush movement for control and braking, both dynamic electrical and frictional for slow and stop conditions, is equally applicable to linear and rotary forms.

The initial stages of development for both linear and rotary propulsion projects are thus so closely related that they should be fully coordinated, in order to evolve the best kind of sliding contacts for these novel conditions. This is being done by the use of a simple acyclic machine of the kind indicated by Fig. 9.6 as a generator, driven by a commercial a.c. motor from the power mains. In this way prolonged testing by the use of varying electrical loads at the heavy current output can be readily carried out.

11.2 Elementary Electrical Machines

The above conclusions may be briefly summarised by a statement that the new high-coercivity magnets permit for the first time the most elementary kind of electrical machines for the conversion of energy. This will be converted into two relatively unknown electrical forms, either low-voltage direct current or high frequency alternating current; the conversion may be from chemical or mechanical energy and the latter may be from the electricity supply network by means of an a.c. motor, in fixed applications, and from a prime-mover for most mobile uses.

Though track and control applications are generally described in other ways, all these methods of energy conversion are being grouped together here as elementary electrical machines for five reasons:

1. Their principle stems from the earliest electrical machines ever made.

2. In design each element has the simplest form with one pole and one turn.

3. Each element has the shape of a disc, permitting a number to be assembled on a single shaft in the rotary versions.

4. With modern units the force and voltage relationship with other factors is of the simplest kind.

5. Magnetic shapes of the most appropriate and elementary kind are used, flat rings for rotary machines and shallow blocks for linear uses.

All these points are given in Table 11.1 which presents a compact summary of the main applications described in this book. The designs are directly derived from the ideal magnet concept of Chapter 7, in which the basic flux is provided by high-coercivity magnets and a closely coupled winding comprises the channel for energy flow, the essential electromagnet function. In this way the highest efficiency level can be ultimately achieved by eliminating all unnecessary losses in excitation and leakage, regardless of physical size.

Groups 1 and 2 are classed together as acyclic with unidirectional flux and current, the current being varied for operational purposes. In contrast, groups 3 and 4 are cyclic with pulsating flux. The latter (actuator) uses only single pulses for control purposes, sharing the advantage with 1 and 2 that ordinary mild steel can be used for its magnetic circuit. The need for highly subdivided magnetic and electric circuits in group 3 is a severe disadvantage for the use of high frequency power in variable frequency form as an alternative to group 1 for electric drives, so the main applications are expected to lie in other directions. It may appear from the second column that the high frequency alternating current is the end product but the third column shows that it is in fact heat, light and mechanical

TABLE 11.1. ENERGY CONVERSION IN ELEMENTARY ELECTRICAL MACHINES

GROUP	ENERGY CONVERSION ORDER	MAJOR APPLICATIONS	RELATIONSHIP IN MODERN UNITS (MKSA)
1. ELECTRIC DRIVE (rotary)	MECH → LVDC → MECH CHEM ↗	AUTOMATIC TRANSMISSIONS & PROPULSION/BRAKING by HUB-MOTORS for Road Vehicles, and many fixed uses	VOLTS = FLUX × REVS/SEC (webers)
2. TRACK SYSTEM (linear)	AC → LVDC → MECH	TRANSPORTATION BY PERMANENT MAGNETIC SUSPENSION & LINEAR PROPULSION AT LOW, MEDIUM & HIGH SPEEDS for Passengers, Light Vehicles & Priority Freight	FORCE = FLUX DENSITY × CURRENT × L (newtons) (webers/m^2) (amps) L is length of conductor in metres
3. KILOCYCLE POWER (rotary)	MECH → HFAC (mobile) AC → HFAC (fixed) (MECH → HFAC → MECH)	CHEAP HIGH FREQUENCY ELECTRIC POWER for New Lighting, H.F. Heating & Processing, Special Machining & Cleaning .....Possible alternative to Group 1)	VOLTS = FLUX CHANGE × P × REVS/SEC (webers) P is number of flux pulsations per rev (i.e. no. of inductors)
4. CONTROL	LVDC (pulse) → MECH & others	ROTARY & LINEAR ACTUATORS, FRICTIONLESS CLUTCHES etc.	FORCE = 1/2 (FLUX DENSITY)^2 × POLE AREA (metre)^2 (newtons)
ENERGY KEY	Mechanical: MECH .. Prime-Mover Chemical: CHEM .. Traction Battery (2V/cell approx) Fuel Cell (Future, 1V/cell approx)	Electrical: AC .. Fixed A. C. Network e.g. 240 V 50 c/s LVDC .. Low-Voltage Direct Current e.g. 1 to 12V 1000A HFAC .. High Frequency A.C. e.g. 10-20 kc/s (ultrasonic)	

FOR MEDIUM POWER RANGE: 1 to 100 kW (approx) for Road Vehicles; 100 to 1000 kW or more for Track Vehicles.

BASIC MACHINE DESIGN: Rotating Permanent Magnet Field (one pole) & Fixed Single-Turn Armature Winding. Rotors run up to highest prime-mover speeds. Disc shape permits multiple assembly for voltage increase etc.

energy of special kinds which are so far available only experimentally or on a small power scale. With cheap and efficient conversion machinery of the suggested kind, this kind of power could in due course justify its own ring main in view of this great diversity of service.

Table 11.1 confirms the earlier definition of electricity as a method or medium for the transmission or transfer of energy. The essential operating condition is that there should be relative movement of a magnetic field and an electrical conductor when mechanical energy is involved in either the first or last step in the energy conversion chain, and this creates the need for these elementary machines of the various groups. They must be very simple, small and efficient to compete with purely mechanical or fluid alternatives; but, by matching the latest prime-movers in operating speed, this can now be achieved by the use of permanent magnetic excitation on the proposed scale.

In this connection the most important development of the past few years is the introduction of oriented grades of sintered barium ferrite in a variety of ring-shapes (Table 7.1). These have a greater tensile strength than that of the strongest metal alloy magnets with appreciably lower physical density, so they have a considerably higher bursting speed when built into high-speed rotors. This speed can be raised to any required level by surrounding the ring-magnet periphery with non-magnetic metal bands in a suitable manner added to the natural reinforcement afforded by the poleplate construction already described. This factor is of the utmost value for both Groups 1 and 3 in raising the power/weight ratio and in reducing the cost; in Group 1 it is important for reducing the minimum size of machine that will comply with the minimum voltage under acyclic conditions. It represents the most efficient way of utilising magnetic flux, comparable with power station practice without the need for feeding power to the rotor for excitation purposes.

The final column of the Table shows the merits of these elementary electrical machines from the design and calculation standpoints when the modern MKSA units are used. This applies especially to Group 1 which gives the voltage when used as a generator and the back-e.m.f. as a motor; it explains why the value is inevitably low for smaller machines since there is no multiplier effect with the number of turns, as in the case of conventional machines. On the other hand, the value of P in Group 3 is under the designer's control and can give a considerable multiplication of voltage for a single turn winding at a given speed, but it is not difficult in this case to increase the number of turns for this purpose. The main object of increasing P is to give the highest frequency at practical speeds and there is a limit imposed by the reduction of flux utilization if the physical size of the inductor/tooth arrangement (Ch. 9) is too small relative to the allowable airgap length.

Both Groups 2 and 4 are primarily concerned with the motor function, conversion of electrical energy into movement, so the design relationship is in terms of force in newtons. This is approximately 0.1 kilograms for 1 newton in more familiar units; the actual value being obtained from the acceleration due to gravity (g) in metres/sec^2 necessary to convert force to weight. It is important to note that the relationships depend upon flux *density* in weber/m^2 units in contrast to flux in webers for Groups 1 and 3, and the control applications with limited movement depend upon (flux density)^2. This may give the impression that flux concentration is less important in the other groups but voltage is only one factor in power relationship and must be multiplied by current, which depends on the circuit resistance inside and outside the machine.

The Grouping in Fig 11.1 also serves as a basis for the study of the development programme necessary to follow up this general investigation. It is convenient to take the subjects in the order given and with the headings employed, grouping 3 and 4 together; this does not denote their limited importance so much as the magnitude of the scope of the first two. It will be clear that all depend ultimately upon the quality and performance of the magnet materials used.

11.3 Electric Drives

The conclusions so far reached have explained the reasons for the relatively poor performance and uncompetitive position of smaller d.c. machines for power applications. The elementary acyclic design with permanent excitation gives every prospect of meeting all requirements, but one vitally important question remains to be answered: *What will be the working efficiency level?*

Theoretically, by the use of liquid current collectors with low drag and negligible resistance, this could be extremely high. At the other end of the scale, the use of conventional brushes gives prospects of reaching at least to present efficiency levels for conventional machines in the medium-power range, with the advantages of much lower size and cost. But the development of the most appropriate kind of solid electrical sliding contact system for these novel conditions could well raise the efficiency to the 90% region in a simple and cheap manner without the cost and complication of liquid metals. The latter would in any circumstances be difficult and probably impracticable for mobile uses for which this development is primarily intended. This can be settled only by the development programme already mentioned, since working life is probably the key factor. Calculations based upon the performance figures of known materials give favourable results for the larger sizes of ferrite ring-magnets now on the market and considerably larger rings are becoming available.

The merits of present d.c. motors for traction purposes are so great that the efficiency level of around 60% for smaller sizes of battery operated vehicles is accepted as a practical proposition. Any higher figure would be of importance commercially, especially if reduced cost and size resulted, because these factors are far more significant for mobile uses when more payload and greater range per charge are gained. But the prospect of the suggested ultimate gain in efficiency would have a profound and far-reaching effect upon the whole of automotive engineering because it would bring the electric drive back into commercial prominence. To show how far away such a system with conventional commutator machines has receded, a recent symposium on present and proposed automatic transmissions for motorcars did not even include the electric drive on the agenda.

In order to compete with present gear-trains and their associated shafting on the one hand, and the best hydraulic transmission on the other hand, the losses would have to be reduced to at least one quarter of the present figures for electric machines, assuming that the size and cost limits are achieved. At no time has this been regarded as remotely possible with present designs in this size, using wound fields; this is the situation today regardless of the growing interest in electric vehicles from many directions on account of their incomparable advantages in simplicity, reliability, low operating costs, long life and the well-known amenity factors. But even if a much higher efficiency in smaller and cheaper motors were attained, the present traction battery shows no sign of giving comparable improvements and the fuel cell is still an uncertain development. So the all-electric car for general use is unlikely to oust the prime-mover propelled alternative in the foreseeable future.

However, the development of a cheap and very efficient electric drive could well give all the many benefits of electric propulsion

within a short time if introduced as an optional extra in competition
with the present mechanical and hydraulic systems. Again using the
analogy that the permanent magnet excitation of the elementary
electric machines is a superior weightless fluid, the fourwheel electric
drive serving as a dynamic brake as well as a propulsion system can
be regarded as an advance on the Ferguson hydraulic design which
has given outstanding performance demonstrations in this country
for several years. The electric alternative can be readily fitted with
an auxiliary traction battery to level load peaks, to provide a measure
of regenerative braking and for fumeless propulsion in congested
areas, while relying on the conventional prime-mover coupled to an
appropriate generator for providing the main power as at present.

The need for such a high conversion efficiency in an electric drive
is brought about by the use of two machines—the motor and the
generator—in every link of the electric drive. With present machines
this would be prohibitive because four small machines cost far more
than one machine of the same total power, and the weight increase
is similarly much too high for practical purposes. This penalty is
nearly negligible with the elementary design, and one multiple unit
generator can feed four divided, but similar, motors. It can therefore
be concluded that the electric drive based on the use of low-voltage
direct current with acyclic elementary machines is the most important development of the whole programme, if it can be shown
that the combined efficiency of a motor unit coupled to a similar
kind of generator by short and heavy conductors will be in the 80
to 90% region. For this to apply, each machine must have an
efficiency in excess of 90%.

All the work associated with this programme shows that this
could be reached with appropriate solid sliding contacts, in a precision mechanical design of simple construction, at the proposed
speed range to match the latest prime-movers; but it remains to be
proved conclusively. The prospects are such that the alternative of
using high frequency alternating current power (which has been the
subject of extensive work in America and France for military vehicle
propulsion-braking systems) for electric drives has been regarded
as uncompetitive and impractical by comparison. This is in spite of
the possibility of the elimination of the sliding contact problem by
this means; but it substitutes the performance degradation of a.c.
propulsion which seems to be inevitable with cyclic currents of any
frequency, as well as the need for the development of magnetic
circuits of high saturation and very low losses on an engineering

scale. It has been pointed out that this latter development is well within the technology of chapter 5 and would seem to be inevitable if the many other benefits of kilocycle power are to be achieved; but in all respects it would appear to be far more expensive than the direct current alternative of mild steel constructon, with solid sliding contacts to conduct the heavy current to and from the rotor with low voltage drop.

It will thus be concluded that the next stage in the development programme priority will be the design of a d.c. electric drive consisting of two of the proposed hub motors of the kind outlined in Fig. 9.6 coupled together with heavy but flexible electrical connections as a generator-motor unit. This can then be tested as another kind of mechanical link to the traditional two pulleys and belt tramsmission, the cardan shaft and gearbox-differential transmission, and the latest hydraulic alternatives; their relative overall efficiencies could be readily measured and compared. Their final assessment must, of course, include many other factors.

The present wide gap between these mechanical and hydraulic drives on the one hand, and possible future electric drives on the other, can be substantially reduced even if it is not actually closed in all important respects. With the great variety of valuable advantages that such a system used in conjunction with a traction battery could give, electric drives could well become universal even at somewhat lower efficiency or with a limited disadvantage in weight or cost. But present information points to the ultimate closing of this gap.

If this can be proved on a suitable scale, electricity can be expected to dominate in due course all short mobile transmission links in the same way that it has virtually eliminated the forests of belts and shafting in factories and workshops. In vehicles and similar mechanical systems the intermediate gears, shafts and friction-operated devices would make way for silent, clean, unobtrusive electrical conductors. The effect upon mechanical engineering would be profound. Future prime-movers throughout the vast medium-power range could well be made with built-in electric generators as a single unit in both design and manufacture. If the output was then measured in kilowatts by internationally agreed units and scientific methods, in place of local and traditional units, it would be of greatest value to all automotive engineering as well as to the general public who have become accustomed to such advances in the home.

In America during recent years such steps have been taken to integrate a small gas-turbine with a high-frequency alternator, by assembling a single cast turbine wheel and a disc-shaped electrical machine on one shaft with only two bearings and without step-down gearing (Ref. 1). Apart from the extreme simplicity and potential cheapness of such an arrangement, unprecedented power/weight and power/volume values can be achieved. Such a power unit used in conjunction with the proposed electric drive would appear to have better prospects for propelling road vehicles of the future than the direct generation methods outlined in Chapter 2 and indicated in the chart (Fig. 2.1). Such a step would, of course, help to introduce the fuel cell at a later stage, which has been forecast by some on account of the remarkably high efficiency (around 80%) theoretically attainable in this non-rotating equipment.

11.4 Track Systems

The main difficulty in developing a system for track transportation, the principal future use of permanent magnetic suspension, is the magnitude and long period of development entailed. The suggested analogy to an air-ferry rather than a conventional railway indicates the great importance of lightweight vehicles and track, vital in what must generally be an overhead system with automatic propulsion of single carrier units rather than a train of them. Electrical power from the a.c. supply network is essential for the reasons given earlier but this still gives a choice of methods for propulsion; the linear motor version of the homopolar motor for the d.c. drive already described is the simplest vehicle arrangement but it entails the use of frequent rectifier or condenser installations to give the necessary low-voltage heavy direct current all along the track. However, it is the most suitable way of reaching a combined suspension-propulsion arrangement by the use of ferrite magnet bricks.

From the development standpoint, therefore, the most important step would appear to be the construction of the one-sixth scale model on the lines of Fig. 10.7, primarily as a way of testing the propulsion possibilities at present track speeds with the use of horizontal nylon roller guidance. This is expected to give considerably better performance than any alternative that has to use the conventional heavy steel wheel construction for support and guidance, because the sideways force and the structure to absorb it in the magnetic suspension design are very light in comparison. Tests on such an intermediate scale should provide the essential design data for the full-scale applications whether for moving platforms, suburban passenger traffic, or the high speed transportation of light vehicles as well as passengers; if successful they could justify the considerable further expenditure for the full-scale developments.

With the limited experimental work that has been possible in the short time that suitable oriented ferrite magnet bricks have been commercially available, the new magnetic suspension-propulsion methods show promise of providing a major advance in the passenger-carrying 'monorail' system at present speeds, indicated as a separate category in Table 10.1. This alone is a major feature in many recent town-planning projects and could well justify the preliminary development without extending the work into the uncertainties of moving roads or aircraft speeds; it would also be a suitable way of testing the proposed d.c. linear drive for either driver-control or automatic propulsion. Both a.c. linear motors and air-levitation schemes in their present forms are quite unsuitable for this important field of application.

From the demand standpoint, however, the development of the track to carry passengers and light vehicles at aircraft speeds is of greatest importance and urgency, since it seems to be the only ultimate answer to the worst traffic problems. If light road vehicles can be carried at up to five times their best average speed at low cost, which seems to be most probable economically if the volume of traffic is consistent with the capacity of the system, there will be no need to operate them under their own power more than is necessary in making random journeys from door-to-door by way of the nearest high-speed track terminals. The advantages of personal transport for families and their belongings are so great that it is doubtful if a public passenger service with hire cars at the terminals could ever replace it. Ultimately the safety aspect of a high speed track should be enough to recommend it to a majority of the population instead of the risks of motorways at the kind of speeds that present cars can maintain for long journeys.

Investigations have shown that there are many unsolved problems in the use of a track at aircraft speeds, but none appear to be incapable of solution though they are magnified roughly as the square of the speed increase. The most important are the guidance reaction and the magnitude of propulsion power per vehicle. This power will almost certainly have to be transferred from the track electrically, an additional reason why none of it should be used unnecessarily for suspension purposes. For propulsion alone the minimum power for a ten-ton vehicle is of the order of 1000 kW or ten times that of the 'monorail' conditions, and roughly one-tenth of the corresponding aircraft power. It must be remembered that an aeroplane, in making a journey across a few hundred miles or kilometres of flat country has to cross the equivalent of a phantom range of Alps or Andes to no avail, as far as its power consumption is concerned; this high cost is added to that of the aircraft crew, the ground staff and maintenance services. All these are fully justified from every standpoint for much longer journeys, generally of inter-continental magnitude. As the traffic density in thickly populated industrial areas increases, so does the need for a track network operating at aircraft speeds become more urgent to handle it.

It would appear that the ultimate answer is a magnetic suspension system with a combined guidance-brushgear arrangement to carry the heavy current of the linear version of the d.c. homopolar motor proposed for the road vehicle electric drive. It has already been stated that the sliding contact speeds are not greatly different from those already in widespread use in power station rotating machinery for slip-rings, and the use of graphite can give lubrication as well as low resistance when in a thin enough layer between metallic sliding surfaces. In this case there is less restriction on working voltage than in the rotating machine for road vehicles because power used on this large scale would be much less expensive, but in both cases the ultimate operating efficiency will be mainly dependent upon the extent to which the frictional and electrical resistance of the sliding contacts can be minimised. This would warrant an extensive research programme to develop special methods and materials.

In Chapter 10 it was suggested that the overhead track of the high speed routes should be installed at considerable height in order to make it mainly straight and level regardless of the contour and obstacles on the ground. This would make use of long spans, like those of a suspension bridge but in this case carrying a far lighter and more predictable load. They would help to overcome the objections and delays common in power line installations which at present have to use relatively short spans. To aid this difficult situation it would be best to group these differing overhead services along the same rows of high supporting towers, since their routes will tend to coincide. This will also improve the overall economic situation and provide the considerable volume of power needed along the track.

If aircraft speeds can be maintained silently over long runs in densely populated countries by this track system, it will be possible to instal airports over shallow stretches of sea or in uninhabited

20

districts where their noise, especially with supersonic craft, would do little damage. It might become feasible to transfer at these airports the tubular vehicle body of the kind shown in Fig. 10.7 to the fusilage of a carrier aircraft to avoid the delays and considerable additional facilities needed for passenger transit conditions.

11.5 Other Applications

The widespread possibilities that the use of ferrite magnets on the largest scale can create in the all-important sphere of road and track transportation, described as mobile power, tend to dwarf the many other important uses mentioned earlier in this book. Of these, the prospects of cheap kilocycle power come next in order of importance but this requires a considerably wider range of development before it can be regarded as a commercial proposition, in the generating machinery as well as in the circuitry and apparatus which convey and use it.

The summary of Chapter 8 gave this as a possible alternative to low-voltage direct current for general uses such as mobile power, but the subsequent details tend to favour the simple designs of d.c. machine for most of such applications; the two main advantages of the a.c. alternative, ease of transmission and transfer of power without physical contact, being less significant in the usual conditions found in practice. The main interest in high frequency power is thus in new process applications outlined in Chapter 9, in the directions of lighting, cleaning and special treatments. One of the most important uses of frequencies which are lower multiples of the standardised fixed power values generated in power stations is in mobile installations for railways and aircraft, and the much smaller size and weight of the apparatus for equivalent power-handling ability are of great importance even though their cost is considerably higher.

Recent investigations have indicated that the simple type of inductor alternator of the kind shown in Fig. 8.4, when using the latest oriented ferrite magnet material in the stator, has a considerably higher weight/power ratio than modern inductor alternators used in aircraft, employing electromagnetic excitation, so in this form they are at a disadvantage for mobile uses. But the design appears to be much less costly and it could well be justified economically for fixed installations. However, there is considerable scope for further improvement by the use of rotating field magnets with the coils and inductors comprising the surrounding stator (Fig. 9.6);

in these conditions the flux density in the inductors could be much lower in the earlier design and moulded magnetic material could be used in place of the far more expensive thin silicon-steel laminations. This could be an appropriate grade of iron powder-core or possibly the highest permeability grade of low-loss ferrite, or even a combination of both to give the combined benefits of the high saturation of the first and the insulating properties of the second.

The limited experimental work reported earlier should thus be regarded as a beginning of new techniques in the generation of high frequency or ultrasonic power, either directly from a prime mover or as a motor-generator unit coupled to an a.c. mains motor. In the former case which would probably denote mobile use, a small high speed rotor of the suggested integrated unit with a small gas turbine appears to be the best type but the fixed installation powered from the a.c. supply will be restricted to present rotational speeds; the required high peripheral speed could best be obtained with a narrow flywheel design using a single stator conductor of many parallel strips of anodised aluminium foil. The main point is that a far simpler and less expensive machine than any conventional kind is well within the scope of present development, so that cheap ultrasonic power is within sight for both fixed and mobile installations. In the latter case it would seem to be a better proposition to provide than power at present low frequencies, but it will require much further development in transmitting methods and utilisation equipment before this can be attained on a considerable commercial basis.

In contrast, the use of ferrite magnets for pulse-operated control gear of the contactor kind is simple in principle and could be made commercially available in limited time with the use of standard components. The advantages go far beyond the economy of power which is the primary aim in the replacement of electromagnets with permanent magnets for the holding function, using the minimum of electrical energy solely for movement or control. With a good mechanical design this energy, a tiny proportion of that used in a conventional contactor, could be provided by a small rectifier-plus-battery unit giving the merits of emergency standby gear for all times and conditions. As the complexity of modern automatic plant increases, so does the penalty for the failure of control gear multiply, and ultimate reliability is increasingly far more significant than purchase price, bulk or operating cost. However, in this case there appear to be excellent prospects for all these factors to be improved also; as in the case of electrical machines, the removal of unnecessary power dissipation by the use of permanent magnet excitation has the cumulative effect (by eliminating heat) of greatly reducing size, and hence of saving cost when simple designs and cheap materials are involved, as in this case.

It will be understood that this control example can be the basis of a whole range of similar applications. Some are quite novel, as in the case of the recent demonstration in America of a man walking upside down along the *under* surface of a horizontal steel girder. His boots were fitted with ferrite magnet blocks and poleplates for concentrating the flux towards the girder face, and wound with a control coil for temporary neutralisation of the flux by current from a portable battery; it was necessary to pass a pulse of direct current through each boot magnet in turn when it became necessary to lift it, and the switch had to operate on only one of these magnets at a time. As this was done with relatively small, cheap and compact equipment it will be evident that considerable force can be remotely controlled for industrial uses by such methods. This principle can be applied in rotary form as a kind of clutch and in various ways as linear actuators by the use of known mechanisms of the toggle variety so that the new magnets may be expected to have a considerable effect in the extension of electrical methods of control for power-handling purposes.

Much has been heard in recent years of new kinds of electric control based upon power versions of the transistor, generally known as silicon-controlled rectifiers (often abbreviated to SCR), which can perform rapid switching operations without the traditional breaking of the circuit. Relatively small-sized components able to handle 100 amperes or more are coming on the market for the control of machines of appreciable power and widespread development is directed to the control of electrically propelled vehicles by their means. However, this appears to be inherently an expensive method, with present cost estimates in the region of the price of the equipment to be controlled, which is uneconomic for all but special applications. On these grounds it would seem to be preferable to develop the suggested pulse-operated improvements of the conventional contactor and switches for the low-cost large quantity demands, as well as for the widespread non-electrical uses.

11.6 Future Magnetic Materials

It will be evident from the contents of these chapters that all the proposed applications are primarily dependent upon the properties of the permanent magnet materials, especially coercivity. This has to reach a certain level, given as 100 AT/mm, before power applications are generally viable and the latest oriented ferrites on the market have over twice this value. Further improvements in barium ferrite up to 400 AT/mm are theoretically possible and these would correspondingly reduce the thickness of the bricks or rings made from them for equivalent service; but this would not embrace any further vast field of application equivalent to the result of the rise from 5 and 50 AT/mm, respectively, during the past half- and quarter-century.

The vital conclusion is that the materials have already reached the desired level to perform all these valuable services but their application is in its infancy. As a result of the great demand for barium ferrite rings in television receivers, which soon became obsolete, there arose the unusual circumstances of large tonnages of a novel kind of magnetic material looking for a market at a remarkably low price for such a high quality product. Indeed, much of the new developments described in earlier chapters was initiated as a result of this situation. Those responsible for the production of the materials developed the remarkable range of grades described in Chaper 6, such as flexible and rigid plastic-bonded sheet and strip, with properties and at price levels which would have been thought unattainable only a few years earlier. Yet all these novel materials come above or near to this 100AT/mm coercivity level, exceeding almost all the traditional alloy magnets in this regard. In retrospect it is surprising how quickly the severe handicaps of the original sintered barium ferrite, notably brittleness and very low remanence, were overcome or turned to good advantage. The need to concentrate the flux with mild steel sheet provided an excellent mechanical assembly with unusually low magnetic leakage, so that high coercivity could be regarded as a figure of merit for this new range of applications, as was suggested earlier.

With the latest available knowledge it is thus desirable to re-assess the position of remanence in terms of permanent magnet quality, remembering that it traditionally has equal status with coercivity in the $(BH)_{max}$ energy product for static applications. It is clearly desirable that the remanence of a magnet material shall be as high as possible; but in the range of new materials in which these two main properties are interdependent and controllable during the manufacturing stage, it is undesirable to gain remanence at the expense of coercivity after a reasonable level of working flux density has been reached. The recent practice of some manufacturers in providing a range of coercivities for different applications, especially for barium ferrite, is a good solution if some degree of standardisation (with limitation to number of grades) is adopted. The upper limit of remanence for dynamic applications is the point where the linearity of the demagnetizing curve in the second quadrant (of the hysteresis loop) starts to change into the pronounced curvature of the high remanence grades, developed for loudspeaker magnets or other such static uses (see Figs. 4.5, 6.3 and 6.5).

The main objection to low remanence is the extra bulk of the magnet material with its larger poleplates, the corresponding higher cost in this and other parts of the magnetic circuit and the additional inertia in the important new applications in the rotors of elementary electrical machines. For the latter it would pay to use a more expensive material with higher remanence if the coercivity were maintained. There is some scope for limited improvement of barium ferrite, possibly 30%, and this would be of great value in magnetic suspension where flux concentration is difficult and the ultimate loading is dependent upon the square of the working flux density.

Technically, the best prospects for further marked improvements of this kind appear to lie in a combination of ferrite and micropowder effects in the same material, and the most interesting example of this was given at the end of Chapter 5 (5.8) in the form of an oxidised ESD iron-cobalt micropowder. This has a coercivity of the required level with nearly double the remanence of oriented barium ferrite and could come into the price requirements of machine rotors though probably too costly for magnetic suspension. A cheap way of making iron micropowder and applying an oxide layer with the magnetic properties of barium ferrite would be required to match the outstanding economic advantages of the ceramic kind of the latter material These could well be the subject of extensive research which would give great economic and technical rewards.

But the outstanding feature of practically all the applications of modern magnets described in these chapters is that they can be followed up now on any required scale with a range of fully tested materials at low cost. While further progress in magnetic materials would improve their competitive position or reduce their bulk, their progress is mainly dependent upon the scale and quality of the engineering devoted to their development in the application sphere.

Coming much lower in priority, the development of high saturation low-loss magnetic material is needed for ultrasonic frequency electric power. This could be used in stators and transformer cores so that there is no prime requirement for the mechanical qualities of rotor magnet assemblies, for which present thin silicon-steel sheet with epoxy-resin cement is probably adequate. A compacted form of oriented needle-shaped particles in a high permeability iron alloy (e.g. with limited proportions of silicon and aluminium) would probably give low losses at fairly high flux density up to the desired frequency band of 15 to 20 kc/s. It was shown in Chapter 5 that there is much information available on the coarser iron and iron-alloy powders as well as on their micropowders, but it needs a demand and development facilities to make suitable core material available to those responsible for the variety of special-purpose machines and equipment needed.

11.7 The Future of Mobile Power

While the many applications of modern magnets described in Part II cover most kinds of human activity, the greatest in possible scale and incomparably the most important now and in the future can be summarised in two words—mobile power. This covers practically all land transportation of both road and rail (track) kind, using road in the sense of a means for almost universal random travel in contrast to the special-purpose track. It cannot be too strongly emphasised that they must be partners and not competitors because they each fulfil a task that cannot be done in another way.

With the use of cheap electric power from the nation-wide 'grid' network, the track can provide unlimited power to propel light container vehicles for passenger, road vehicles and priority freight at any desired speed which, by the proposed methods, could be developed to extend from walking pace to sub-sonic aircraft speeds. The high ratio of load carried to vehicle weight by the use of magnetic suspension, based upon cheap ferrite bricks which also provide excitation, can be several times better than any alternative and the cost of propulsion can be correspondingly lower. Moreover the high speed version could be made fully automatic and completely safe, which cannot be claimed for any other form of transportation. The ultimate criterion for such a system is the speed it can average between centres of population relative to the cost per passenger-mile (or ton-mile).

At five times the best average speed that can be maintained by present railways and motorways, there would be every incentive to use the track system whenever the journey route makes this feasible if the cost is not much greater, but there are prospects that it can eventually be appreciably less. The light overhead structure for the equivalent of a tracked air-ferry service could be provided at a lower cost than present alternatives along the ground, and the endless chain of automatically spaced carriers in the highest speed system could far exceed the traffic-handling ability of the equivalent two-way road or railway. The fivefold increase of speed provides the effect of five lanes each way, so the capital cost of the overhead structure can be related to an unprecedented capacity of traffic.

But the potential economy in power consumption and reduced wear in road vehicles is even more striking. In America where road transport by internal combustion engine has led the world, it was recently estimated that the total price of all the oil delivered to the filling stations for this purpose was as much as eight times that of all the fuel delivered to power stations, though in terms of energy value the two amounts were comparable. With the cost of electricity distribution approximately equalling its fuel cost, there is still a four-fold advantage for electric power for fixed installations. The track system would make this available for transportation on a massive scale.

It must inevitably be much more expensive to travel faster than the present maximum land speeds but present figures for this cost increase are excessive compared with those based upon future possibilities. In Chapter 10 the power to propel an aircraft carrying the same load as the Magnarail vehicle was given as ten times greater. But this does not account for such savings as regenerative braking that could readily be applied to all track vehicles, and the great savings in wear-and-tear on road vehicles and their drivers when road vehicles are transported in this manner.

However bright the prospects of track systems may be, they cannot act as substitutes for the door-to-door service and convenience of road vehicles. The solution of the principal traffic problem lies in the prospect of carrying them as well as their owners at low cost, on moving roadways in congested areas such as tunnels and bridges as well as at speeds they could never approach with their small and inefficient prime-movers. The use of electric propulsion could make great improvements, however, in their efficiency and running costs by enabling them to operate for their shorter journeys upon the cheapest kind of high-grade energy, electric power consumed at night at off-peak tariffs and carried in the auxiliary traction battery associated with the proposed electric drive applied to petrol-engine cars.

It has already been stated that the prospects of all-electric vehicles replacing the present mechanical kind appear to be remote, on account of the excessive weight of traction batteries in comparison with the energy they carry. The weight penalty is accentuated in the proposed track system, but a small and light prime-mover vehicle with electric drive could well be developed into a lighter version of the present car even with an auxiliary traction battery of useful capacity included. Such innovations could be introduced by the well-known method of optional extras at first and later by standardising them as soon as the new manufacturing plant has been installed and the improvements have been fully approved under practical operating conditions by he consumer. It would allow time to build up the great increase in the electrical requirements—batteries, ferrite magnets, special conducting and contact metals and other components.

One of the many advantages of this gradual change-over from all-mechanical to mechanical-electric propulsion is the unprecedented degree of flexibility introduced. The prime-mover would no longer be tethered for life to the vehicle; it could be removed for sawing down trees, operating a motor-boat or other mobile power services. The car designer could have much greater freedom in the arrangement of the essential components, with the motors being installed in or near the wheels (according to unsprung weight requirements) and the prime-mover/generator unit plus fuel tank being housed in any convenient place. Each car could be provided with the kind of motive power needed by the owner and could be modified for appropriate times, for example holidays or long journeys. A far better balance between the conflicting demands of economy and performance would thus be available.

On a much wider scale transportation could be freed from the undesirable dependence upon oil in limited grades and a considerable part of the energy could come from coal and nuclear energy by way of the fixed electric power link (Fig. 2.1). In energy units oil is rapidly gaining on coal which now provides less than half the world's requirements, in comparison with one-third for oil; but the reserves of coal are much greater and are more conveniently distributed in relation to the main demand centres.

From the national economy standpoint a greater use of electric power during nights and in the summer would be of the utmost value because the electric power generation and distribution network is absorbing such a high proportion of available capital resources. The present load factor is 48% which means that the costly plant is being used throughout the year for less than half the time. Some kind of storage, such as batteries, is essential to make the desired improvement because the load *must* be taken at times, principally during the night, when the power stations are under-loaded. There is enough available capacity to provide the energy for a high proportion of all the daily routine journeys to work or for shopping by family cars, without any further capital expenditure on fixed plant and by the consumption of low-grade coal in place of high-grade oil, with corresponding reductions in running costs.

Though the considerable additional electric load needed to operate track systems would have to be provided as part of the power station expansion system, they could operate continuously, the spacing of their vehicles being altered to meet the varying demands throughout the 24-hour periods. The electrical load could be spread by use of day and night tariffs with a considerable reduction in cost of transportation at off-peak periods.

11.9 The Importance of Permanent Magnets

It may have surprised the general reader to find such a wide range of important activities in the world, now and in the future, attributed to improvements in a little known corner of technology, magnetic materials; moreover, this is mainly confined to a hitherto obscure branch of that subject—permanent magnetism. In the historical chart summarising Chapter 3 (Fig. 3. 1) the first half of this century could perhaps be described as the 'Electromagnet Era' to denote the great and growing success of nation-wide electric power for fixed installations; if the proposed developments outlined here are achieved, the second half could become the 'Era of the Permanent Magnet' and electricity the main mobile power transmission medium.

Perhaps the most remarkable factor is the relatively small change in the ingredients needed for the best permanent magnets. At the turn of the century they were steels—mainly iron with a small percentage of alloying metal. The present best permanent magnets for the wide range of dynamic applications are still principally iron with a small metallic addition, but in oxide form. The vast improvement is mainly the results of theoretical and applied science, multiplying the coercivity fifty times and possibly more to follow. The remainder of the magnetic circuits of the machines and devices considered are also principally iron in the relatively pure form of mild steel or in powder with small amounts of common metals added to reduce the a.c. losses. In most examples the engineering use of mild steel is combined with its magnetic merits to give a highly favourable economic result. From the standpoint of cost and availability, these factors are of the utmost importance to the whole range of applications.

But the possibilities of great economies in the highest grade and most expensive form of energy are equally impressive. Electric power, like money, can be easily dissipated but can yield dividends indefinitely if wisely invested. One unit (kWh) will provide heat from the smallest domestic electric fire for an hour and light a small electric lamp for a day, but it can be stored indefinitely in magnetising a ton of barium ferrite. In this form it could be used to provide the best kind of propulsion-braking for dozens of small cars throughout their lifetime, or support and act as propelling agent for a much greater load in a track system. Alternatively it could be the principal agent in the introduction of cheap ultrasonic electric power for many new uses in lighting, heating or cleaning now in the laboratory or small-scale stage. Electrical power supply has always suffered from lack of storage facilities and here is a way of storing it statically in an extremely efficient manner and in what is probably the most durable form known.

This remarkable economy brings many secondary advantages in its train. Most of these arise from the elimination of the unnecessary heat generated in electromagnets when used to provide steady magnetic fields. In electrical machines, this leads to smaller size, greater reliability, better performance and reduced noise, owing to the reduction or elimination of ventilation. While these are apparent in the improvements already attained with large numbers of small d.c. motors of conventional design fitted with ferrite magnet excitation, they would apply in a far greater degree to the elementary machine designs with rotating permanent magnet fields in which the heat is dissipated around the periphery of a disc-shaped structure. These give the optimum conditions for natural cooling, in contrast to present designs in which the heat is most difficult to remove, being mainly generated in the centre of a barrel-shaped structure.

It has been stated earlier that these new designs have become more mechanical than electrical by present engineering standards, and the great progress in magnetic materials has led to another curious result. As their coercivity has increased, the design and performance of magnetic circuits associated with them have become progressively simpler and more easily understood. An example of this is to be found in magnet makers' catalogues. In the past these tended to become bound volumes in colour with many pages of curves and diagrams to assist in the explanation; but they usually ended with a plea to consult the experts. Latest ferrite magnets, however, can be covered by a monochrome leaflet with few curves and essentially only two shapes, blocks and rings; for most of the applications given here curves are not required; the performance of the highest coercivity grades is almost linear for the usual demagnetizing curve and this can therefore be approximately expressed solely in figures.

In these circumstances the development of new machines and equipment based on these ferrite materials does not necessarily require trained specialists in applied magnetism and electricity. Indeed, the heritage of past units and misconceptions gives an advantage to one who approaches the subject with only a general knowledge of engineering and technology. Moreover, in the testing of strong magnetic fields of the kind required for medium-power applications, the needs for special equipment are very limited. Most of these can be done with a spring balance calibrated in kilograms with a set of weights in metric units, and multirange electrical measuring instruments of the kind generally used for this kind of power. Magnetizing of initial ferrite magnet samples is done by request by the supplier and the production process for factory quantities can be carried out in simple jigs based upon the final application magnetic circuit using local power mains, with an appropriate rectifier if a d.c. source is not available.

For those who are deterred from working in this field by lack of understanding of the way in which electromagnetic devices and machines perform their varied tasks, it should be stated that this applies to many professionals also. The ideas put forward early last century by the pioneers, particularly Ampere and Faraday, are still in general use in spite of the great advances in all branches of pure and applied science since that time. Electrical engineers still argue whether magnetic flux has to be cut or linked with a conductor in order to generate an electromotive force, though in most respects the electric circuit is an exact science. But magnetism has always been difficult and obscure until very recently because its units were based upon false assumptions, especially the unit magnet pole considered in isolation from its inseparable partner as a point. It is a measure of the progress made, and the changes in thinking, that the magnetic suspension project specifies a single pole that covers a complete railway system track.

Yet the old and proved methods of dealing with these engineering problems cannot be discarded until there is a better explanation, and moreover this must be generally accepted and employed. The use of strong permanent magnet fields for magnetic suspension and power transmission on a large scale is sufficiently novel that the use of the better hydraulic fluid analogy was devised to explain it in practical terms. But the traditional notation of any kind of permanent magnet by writing the letters N and S in the right places (used in the drawings in this book) is of great practical value to indicate the position and direction of the magnetic field, even though massive rings and bricks of barium ferrite have little in common with compasses and north-seeking poles.

This point leads back to Bacon's famous remark about the mariner's compass given on the opening page, which has significance to the above situation. The compass needles contained an infinitesimal amount of magnetism in terms of energy value, and were certainly not understood by any who used them; yet they were good enough to discover America and most of the unexplored regions of the world.

11.10 References

1. Toesca R. 'An Integrated Turbo-Generator Unit', *Gas Turbine*, pp. 28-30, September-October, 1961.

2. Polgreen G. R. 'Powerful Permanent Magnets'. *New Scientist*, pp. 368-371, 6 May, 1965.

GLOSSARY OF TECHNICAL TERMS USED

Symbols used in the book are given in brackets and can be related to the units in Table A.1.

Acyclic. A category of electrical machines in which the current and magnetic flux are unidirectional at all times, based upon the Faraday Disc principle.

Alnico. A general term for the large group of cast permanent magnet alloys, based mainly upon aluminium, nickel and cobalt and other metals with iron; they have been the principal commercial metal magnets for about 30 years.

Anisotropy. Directional effects in the crystal structure of materials which can provide much improved magnetic performance along certain axes. Grades of magnetic material so treated are described as anisotropic or oriented (the latter mostly used here).

Coercivity (H_c). The value of reverse field required to reduce the flux density due to magnetic induction (B) to zero after a material has been magnetised to saturation. This is the most important property of a permanent magnet material, and indicates its degree of permanence of magnetic performance.

Coercivity, Intrinsic (H_{ci}). The reverse field needed to reduce the total flux density in a magnetic material, due to both induction (B) and magnetising force (H), to zero after magnetising to saturation. This is a measure of the ability of a material to withstand demagnetisation and can be much higher than H_c in modern ferrite magnets, though similar in earlier materials.

Curie Point. The temperature at which a magnetic material becomes non-magnetic, e.g. barium ferrite 450°C and typical alnico 850°C.

Domain. The smallest zone of a magnetic material which retains its magnetic identity. These are as tiny as 0.01 micron in sectional dimension in iron but about one micron in ferrite magnets. The Domain Theory assumes they are all spontaneously magnetised to saturation but can be moved and oriented by externally applied fields, thus explaining magnetic phenomena.

Demagnetising Curve (*or demagnetisation characteristic*). The portion of the hysteresis loop of a permanent magnet material in the second, and in high H_C magnets also the third, quadrant; These give the performance under reverse field conditions which represent practical operating circumstances.

Eddy (*or Foucault*) *Currents*. Circulating currents generated when electrically conducting materials (e.g. any metal) are placed in fluctuating magnetic fields. These are a main source of losses in the magnetic circuits of a.c. machines, especially at higher frequencies.

Energy Product. A figure of merit for permanent magnet materials (see Table A.1 for units) based upon optimum attainable values of flux density (B) times demagnetising force (H). For modern materials it should be related to conditions of use: static—$(BH)_{max}$, dynamic—$(B_pH)_{max}$. See Table 6.1.

Ferrite. The general name for a new category of magnetic materials, developed in the last 20 years, with ceramic (insulator) properties and made from mixed oxides of iron and of certain other metals sintered at high temperature. Now both high permeability (low-loss) and permanent magnet grades are in widespread commercial use, the latter as barium ferrite.

Ferromagnetism. Traditionally all materials with permeability much greater than that of air (most typically, iron with relative permeability of around 1000 but varying greatly with purity). But the category must also include latest high-coercivity materials with permeability approaching 1 (air) owing to their pronounced magnetic properties.

Field, Magnetic (H). The general name for the zone surrounding a magnet in which a compass needle will be deflected and all other well-known magnetic effects take place.

Flux Density (B). The additional magnetic effect (also called induction) when a ferromagnetic material is placed in a magnetic field on account of its higher permeability (B/H). For a uniform specimen of area A in m^2 placed with its axis in the direction of the field, the total flux is BA measured in webers.

Hysteresis. When a ferromagnetic material is placed in a changing magnetic field, the flux density B lags behind the magnetising force H that causes it, an effect known as hysteresis. A complete cycle of H in forward and reverse direction traces out, when the corresponding values of B are plotted, the distinctive shape of the hysteresis loop. Its area is the hysteresis loss per cycle, of maximum value for permanent magnets and minimum for high permeability low-loss magnetic materials.

Induction. Generally used to indicate the method by which current is generated (induced) in an electrical conductor by relative movement in a magnetic field: (see also flux density).

Intrinsic Coercivity (H_{ci}). See *Coercivity.*

Isotropic. A magnetic material with roughly uniform magnetic properties in all directions; also described as non-oriented. It is the opposite of anisotropic.

Leakage Flux. In a magnetic circuit much of the flux generated by a current-carrying coil or permanent magnet does not reach the airgap owing to leakage in the surrounding air. The percentage of useful to total flux is leakage flux, or the reverse ratio of the leakage factor.

Magneto-motive Force (M.M.F.). That which creates the flux, corresponding to E.M.F. in the electrical circuit creating current. It is measured in ampere-turns (AT).

Magnetising Force (H). The M.M.F. per unit length of magnetising coil, and general measure of field strength, however produced. Now measured in units of ampere-turns per metre (AT/m).

Magnetostriction. Small dimensional changes in ferromagnetic materials brought about by magnetisation.

Micropowder. A very fine powder of ferromagnetic material with particle size approaching domain dimensions, thus giving high coercivity and permanent magnet properties when compacted.

Orientation. Method applied during manufacture of magnetic materials to give highest permeability in a direction which corresponds to the flux path in the final application (see anisotropy).

21

Permeability (μ). The ratio of flux density to magnetising force producing it (B/H). For air the relative permeability (μ_r) is 1 and is (B/μ_oH) for a ferromagnetic material, the absolute permeability of free space (μ_o) being $4\pi \times 10^{-7}$. All ferromagnetic materials vary widely in μ according to purity, treatment, magnetising force, etc.

Pole, Magnetic. Now used to describe the areas of a magnet where the flux emanates into space, North and South (N & S) indicating its direction. Formerly regarded as points, as in compass needle, (north-seeking pole).

Recoil (Permeability, Loop). Applicable to permanent magnet circuits operating with variable airgaps or other dynamic conditions. The recoil is the minor hysteresis loop, whose slope tends to merge with the demagnetising curve as the latter approaches linearity.

Remanence (B_r). The flux density value of a ferromagnetic specimen with magnetising force removed, after being magnetised to saturation. Used with coercivity value to express performance of permanent magnet material, usually followed by energy product figure(s).

Reluctance. The magnetic equivalent of resistance in an electrical circuit, it equals m.m.f./flux (corresponding to e.m.f./current). For a uniform magnetic circuit of area A and length L with material permeability μ, reluctance $= \dfrac{L}{A \mu_o \mu_r}$.

Resistivity (ρ). or Specific Resistance. The electrical resistance of a centimetre cube of a material, usually expressed for metals in microhm. cm units. Its reciprocal is conductivity, which is the equivalent of magnetic permeability, and the relationship which corresponds to the reluctance formula is thus $R = \dfrac{\rho L}{A}$.

Saturation. All ferromagnetic materials have an upper limit to their capability for carrying flux, called magnetic saturation. It is much higher for metals than for ferrites, but the latter have the compensating advantage of far higher resistivity.

1 Tesla = 10^4 gauss

APPENDIX

TABLE A.1. COMPARISON OF UNITS
NEW: M.K.S.A. (Metre, Kilogram, Second, Ampere).
OLD: C.G.S. (Centimetre, Gram, Second).

TERM	M.K.S.A.	C.G.S. equivalent
Length	1 metre (m)	100 cm
Mass	1 kilogram (kg)	100 gram
Time	1 second (sec)	1 sec
Force	1 newton	10^5 dynes
Work	1 joule (J)	10^7 ergs
Power	1 watt (W)	10^7 erg/sec
Current	1 ampere (A)	—
Charge	1 coulomb	—
Electromotive Force (E.M.F.)	1 volt (V)	—
Resistance	1 ohm	—
Inductance	1 henry (H)	—
Capacitance	1 farad (F)	—
Magnetomotive Force (M.M.F.)	1 ampere-turn (AT)	$0 \cdot 4\pi$ gilberts
Magnetising Force (H)	1 amp-turn/metre (AT/m)	$4\pi \times 10^{-3}$ oersted
Magnetic Flux	1 weber (Wb)	10^8 maxwells or lines
Magnetic Flux Density (B)	1 weber/metre^2 (Wb/m^2)	10^4 gauss
Magnetic Energy Product (BH)$_{max}$ etc.	1 joule/metre^3 (J/m^3)	$4\pi \times 10$ gauss-oersted
Permeability of Free Space	$4\pi \times 10^{-7}$ unit	1 unit

Notes: The above list is confined to those used in this book, including the abbreviations (in brackets).

Multiples (M: mega-10^6, k: kilo-10^3) and sub-multiples (m: milli-10^{-3} μ, micro-10^{-6}) are used where appropriate. e.g. AT/mm, kJ/m^3, kW, MW. The abbreviation Mgo for megagauss-oersted is commonly used to express permanent magnet strength in old (c.g.s.) units.

TABLE A.2. PHYSICAL PROPERTIES OF RELEVANT MATERIALS

GROUP	MATERIAL	RESISTIVITY	DENSITY
A. INSULATORS			
Good Insulators	Porcelain	10^6–10^9 megohm.cm.	2·4
	Glass	10^8 ,,	2·9
Ferrite Magnet	Plastic-bonded	10 000 ,,	3—3·7
	Sintered	100 ,,	4·8
Poor Insulators	Fibre	5000 ,,	1·3
	Slate	50 ,,	2·8
Low-loss Ferrite	Low permeability	0·01 ,,	3·7
	High permeability	0·0001 ,,	4·7
B. CONDUCTORS			
Good Conductors	Silver	1·5 microhm.cm.	10·5
	Copper	1·7 ,,	8·8
	Aluminium	2·6 ,,	2·6
Construction Metals	Duralumin	4·7 ,,	2·8
	Brass	8·0 ,,	8·1
	Iron	10–20 ,,	7·7
Magnetic Metals	4½% Silicon Steel	60 ,,	7·8
(typical)	Permalloy	60–90 ,,	8·6
	Alnico Magnets	70–90 ,,	7·3
Contact Materials	Beryllium-copper	5–8 ,,	8·2
	NaK (see ch. 9.5)	30 ,,	1
	Mercury	95 ,,	13·6
	Copper-carbon Brush	15–500 ,,	—
	Carbon (Graphite)	1000–100 000 ,,	—

INDEX

Authors' names in italics

A.C. power 36
Acicular crystals 93, 132
Actuators 216–9
Acyclic machines 199, 235, 319
  double-disc 200–06, 238–45
  double-drum 235–8
Aerial rods, ferrite 142
Aircraft comparison 290, 304–6
Airgap flux densities 190
  percentage 125
  reluctance 62, 182–3
Alni magnets 91
Alnico group magnets 56, 61, 91, 185, 319
Alternator, inductor 27, 37, 212–6, 250–3
Aluminium 267–8
  anodised, 175, 209, 250, 307
Aluminium strip coils 172–5, 209, 250, 307
Ammonium sulphate 116
Ampere 77, 79, 195, 316
  (unit) 38, 45
Ampere-turn (unit) 45–7, 321, 323
Andrade E. N. da C. 94
Anisotropy 319
  crystal 100, 154, 156
  shape 104, 154
  strain 102
Annealing process 120
Armature 41–2, 191, 198, 201
  Gramme ring 84
  shuttle 84
Asynchronous machines 232
Atomic structure 98–100
Automotive accessories 155, 230
Axial airgap machine 242

Bachelet E. 268–9
Bacon, Francis 13, 72, 317
Baeckers F. T. 291
Baermann M. 154

Baeseler Prof. 273
Barber I. G. 137
Bardell P. R. 32
Barium carbonate 148–9, 160
Barium ferrite 19, 146–53 etc.
Barkhausen effect 103
Barlow's Wheel 81–2, 94, 199
Barwell F. T. 291
Battery, traction 244–5 etc.
Bearings, magnetic 277–80
Benedickts 115
Beryllium-copper 241, 243, 247
Bitter F. 103, 193
Boening F. 256
Bonded alnico powder 154–5
  ferrite powder 152, 154, 180
Boyle R. 75
Bozorth R. 110
Braking, electric 27, 199–206
  dynamic, regenerative 27, 254
Bricks, ferrite 30, 64, 161, 168, 180 2, 263, 283, 286
Brinkmann K. 162
Brushes, copper-carbon 203, 239–40
  graphite 239
  liquid 238
Burnett J. R. 256
By-product iron oxide 161

C.g.s. units (conversion) 21, 52, 59, 323
Capacitance (condenser) magnetising process 178–9, 295
Car, electric 28, 88, 203, 245, 301
Carbon steel magnets 91
Carbonyl iron powder 118–9
'Caslox' 146, 152
Cast iron 50
Catalogue, magnet 316
Ceramic magnets 19, 146–53 etc.
Ceramics 31, 68, 138–
Christie magnet 75

Chrome steel 91
Clarke (dynamo) 83
Cleaning, ultrasonic 253
Clutch, friction 206
  magnetic 27, 206–12
Coal fuel 33–4, 313
Cobalt crystal 101
  –iron alloys 130, 136, 190
  –ferrite 145–6, 152
  steel magnets 91
Coercivity 17, 22, 52–61, 158, 319 etc.
  intrinsic 52–3, 152, 156–7, 319
Cogging (in alternators) 215, 250
Columbus 70
Commutator 27, 94, 191, 198, 238, 250
Compass, magnetic 43, 70
  mariner's 13, 69–72, 317
Condenser (see capacitance)
Controller, electric 245
Co-precipitation process 121
Copper 140
  –carbon brush 203, 239–40
Core, magnetic pot 141
  toroid 113, 141
Coulomb 76, (unit) 323
Crosstalk, telephone 121
Crowther J. G. 94
Crystal anisotropy 100
Crystallography 100
Cunife ductile magnet 91–2
Curie point 24, 143, 154, 157, 180, 319
Current density 29, 61–2, 172
  collection 238–40
Cycle dynamos 226–8

D.C. power 36, 244
Dalancé 74
Dal Negro 82
Davison 86
Demagnetising curves 49, 53, 56
  conditions 55–8, 179
Diamagnetic material 96
Dimensional tolerances
  ferrite magnets 149–50
  micropowder magnets 131
Dip compass 72
Domain rotation 103
  size 104–6
  theory 54, 102–4

Dunsheath P. 94
Dynamic braking 27, 200, 203, 254
  electricity 71, 76–80
  energy product 152–3
  permanent magnetism 71, 314
Dynamo, cycle 226–8
  Faraday 80
  others 83
  self-excited 84

E.S.D. (elongated single domain)
  micropowders 132–6
Earnshaw's therorem 261
Earth as magnet 73, 81
Eddy current loss 20, 51, 60, 86, 112–3,
  120, 211, 320
Edison T. A. 86, 171
Edwards A. 94
Efficiency, flux-utilisation 186–8, 191,
  263
Efficiency, machine 65, 196, 239, 299–
  303
Electric cars 24, 88, 162, 203, 245
  drives 299–303
  motors 81–89 etc.
Electrical instrument magnets 64,
  131–2, 196
Electrical power 33–37 etc.
Electricity, dynamic 71, 76–80
Electricity meter magnets 28, 64, 131–2
  bearings 278–9
Electrolytic plant 116–7, 132–3
Electromagnet 16, 18, 41–6, 172–5 etc.
Electromagnetism 33, 44, 66, 71
Electromotive force (e.m.f.) 44, 316,
  323
Electron 37–8, 49, 175
  spin 98–9. 138
Electroplating 83
Electrostatics 71–3
Elementary machines 295–8
Elmen G. W. 97, 137
Energy conversion 31, 197, 200, 297
Energy product, dynamic 58, 152–3
  static 21, 52, 58–60, 152
Epoxy resin cement 171, 250–2
Evershed S. 90
Ewing A. 102
Excitation, machine 27, 175, 191–7,
  223, 225–33

Extruded ferrites 140, 142, 192

Falk R. B. 137
Faraday M. 77–81, 195, 316
  disc machine 80, 94
  Double-disc m, 27, 199–203
Ferguson car 301
Ferri-magnetism 96, 138
Ferric oxide, gamma 144
Ferrite, barium 19, 146–53 etc.
  cobalt 145–6, 152
  ferrous 143
  manganese-zinc 40, 143
  nickel-zinc 40, 143
Ferromagnetism 95–7
Ferrous chloride 116
Field, magnetic 320
Flake magnetic cores 20, 127
Fluorescent lighting 252
Flux density, magnetic 45–55 etc.
Focus unit (television) 147
Ford, Henry 88
Formates, iron 128
Foucault railway 268–9
Franklin, Benjamin 76
Friction braking 28, 203–5, 259
Fritts 112
Froment 82
Fuel cells 31, 34–5, 68, 223, 300, 303

Galileo 73
Galvani 76
Galvanometer 78
Gamma ferric oxide 114
Gas turbine 69, 303
Gasket, magnetic 153, 155
Gauss (unit) 46, 323
Gilbert 72–75
Glossary of technical terms 319–322
Gorter E. W. 162
Gould J. E. 255
Gowin Knight 74–5
Gramme ring armature 84
Graphite 239
Grey 76
Grove cell 86
Guericke von 76
Guillaud 106

Hadfield D. (Ed.) 32

Hadfield silicon steel 89
Hametag eddy mill 118
Heaviside O. 112
Hender B. S. 256
Henry, Joseph 71, 77, 79, 200
Heusler alloys 91, 100
High-energy magnetic material 22
High-frequency power 41, 214, 250–3, 306
High-intensity electromagnets 175–7
H.f. iron powder cores 40, 118, 121
Historical survey 67–94
Homopolar machines 199, 201–3, 305
Hooper G. B. 137
Hopkinson 84, 171, 177
Horsepower 39
Horseshoe magnet 63, 168–70, 182–3
Hotop W. 162
Hub-dynamo, cycle 226–7
  –motors, car 244–7
Hughes E. 66
Hydraulic analogy 25–6, 37–8, 207 etc.
Hydro-electric generator 277–8
Hydrogen-reduced iron powders 121–3
Hysteresis, magnetic 52–3, 97, 321
  loss 86, 89, 112–3 etc.

Ideal magnet 18, 165, 191–3
Inductance coils 141
Induction, electromagnetic 79–80
  magnetic 321
Induction levitation 266–7
  motor 232–5
Inductor alternator 27, 37, 213–6, 252
Insulators 40, 98, 139, 324
Insulated powder 120–1
Integrated prime-mover/generator 303, 317
Intrinsic coercivity 52–3, 177, 319
  magnetising curve 48
  demagnetising curves 56–7
Iron, commercial 48, 59 etc.
  alloys 17, 123
  powder reduced 211–3
  carbonyl 118–9
  electrolytic 116–7
  wire cores 92, 114
Isotropic material 101, 321
  ferrite magnets 150–2

metal magnets 59
micropowder magnets 131

Janin 75
Joule J. P. 79
Joule (unit) 21, 45, 52, 58, 323

Kato's Oxide 145, 152
Kemper H. 271
Kerr C. & Lynn C. 291
Kilocycle frequency power 16, 27, 36, 297
Kilowatt kW 39, 323
Koestle F.L. 256
Kronenburg K. J. 162

Laithwaite E. R. 291
Lead ferrite 148
  filler 132
Leakage flux 23, 46, 62–3, 169–70, 181–7, 321 etc.
Lee E. W. 32
Levacar (Ford U.S.) 271
Levitation 28, 259, 266–73
Lifting magnets 74–80, 191
Lighthouse generator 84
Linear demagnetising curves 64, 108–9, 150, 160, 178, 183, 212
Linear motor 219–21, 257–91
Liquid current collectors 238–40
Load factor (electric) 314
Loading coils (telephone cable) 113
Lodestone 13, 61, 67, 69–74, 143, 152
'Lodex' 132, 136
Loudspeaker magnets 64, 184–7
Low-energy magnetic material 22
Low-voltage d.c. power 27, 41, 201, 222, 244–7
Luborsky F. E. 111

M.K.S.A. units 39, 45, 58, 62, 167, 297, 323 etc.
McCaig M. 111, 291
Machines, rotating 225–55
'Magnarail' 266, 283–91
Magnesium (ferrite) 140
Magnets, ferrite 59, 152, 185 etc.
  metal 59, 91 etc.
  micropowder 127–37

Magnetic bearings 277–80
  circuit 42–4, 168, 181–4
  field 43
  gaskets 153, 155
  material 40, 59 etc.
  orientation 92, 321
  powder cores 116
  railways 29, 283–90
  repulsion 260
  sandwich 180
  saturation 17–8, 22, 48–54, 322
  suspension 28, 257–60
  tape 144–5
Magnetising force H 46, 49, 321 etc.
  curves 48–50, 53
  methods 177–81
Magnetite 13, 69–71, 143–5, 152
Magneto 13, 17, 64
Magnetomotive force (m.m.f.) 44, 168
Magnetoplumbite 147
Magnetostriction 101
Manganese 100
  –bismuth 106
  –zinc ferrite 143
Mariner's compress 13, 69–72, 317
Marshall R. 256
Maxwell (unit) 323
Megawatt MW 39, 324
Megohm 39–40, 324
Mercury 132–3, 238
Metal properties 324
Meyer R. 137
Microhm 39–40, 324
Micropowder 22, 104, 127
  iron 130
  iron-cobalt 130
  isotropic 130–2
  oriented 132–7
Mild steel 50, 51 etc.
Military vehicles 301
Mobile power 33–7, 197–9, 311–4
Modern magnets 20–25, 135, 165–93
Molloy & Say (Ed.), Morley E. 66
Monorail 221, 270, 290, 305
Moulded magnetic materials 135–7
Multiple-strip magnetising 180

NaK liquid metal brush 238
Néel L. 128
Newton (unit) 45, 299, 323

Nickel crystal 101
  –iron (permalloy), 21, 97, 119
  –iron 50/50 121
  –zinc ferrite 143
Niobium-tin alloy 176
Nylon rollers 264

Oersted H. C. 71, 77
Oersted (unit) 46, 167, 323
Off-peak tariff 255, 314
Ohm (unit) 38, 323
Oil fuel 33–4, 312–3
Oliver D. A. 94
Oosterhout, van 162
Orientation, magnetic 60, 93, 321
Oriented alnicos 56, 91
  ferrites 147, 150–2
  micropowders 134
Oxalates, iron 128
Oxide, bonded 74
  iron 143–6, 161 etc
  iron-cobalt 136
  nickel-iron 121

Pacinotti 86
Packing factor 108–9, 133–4
Paramagnetism 96
Parker R. J. 32
Peregrinus 70
Permanence of magnets 19 etc.
Permalloy 21, 97, 119
Permeability 125, 170, 181–3, 322
  relative 40, 46, 96, etc.
Petrol-electric drive 31, 207
Plastic-bonded powders 153
Platinum-iron magnets 91–2
Poisson 76
Polarised relay 26, 218
Pole, magnetic 180, 317 etc.
  notation 181, 317
  –pieces 17–21, 74, 124
  –plates 26–7, 143, 157, 165–72
Polgreen G. R. 137, 291, 317
Potassium alloy brush 237–8
Powder insulation 127–9
Powder, magnetic iron 112–7
  iron alloy 123
  carbonyl iron 118–9
  nickel-iron 119–23

Powder metallurgy 18, 54, 68, 116, 149, 153, 261, 279
Power drill 232
Power, mobile 30, 311–4 etc.
Power transmission chart 34
Priestley 76
Printed circuit motor 191
Propulsion, electric 203, 244–7, 299–303
Pulse-operated controls 217–9
Pyrophoric powders 54, 128

Rabinow J 207, 209
Radio cores 118–21
Rado & Suhl (Eds.) 32
Railways, electric 86–9
  magnetic 283–91
Rathenau G. W 162
Recoil loop, magnetic 56–7, 153, 226, 322
Record, speed 88
Reduced magnetic powders 114–23
Refrigerator gaskets 155
Regenerative braking 28, 88, 203–6, 301
Relay, polarised 218
Reluctance, magnetic 46–7, 322
Remalloy magnets 91–2
Remanence 52–3, 59–60, 157, 320, 322 etc.
Resistance 38–9
Resistivity 22, 39–40, 324
Rim cycle dynamo 226–8
Ring-magnet, ferrite 63–4, 168, 179–82, 201–3, 298–300 etc.
Rods, aerial (ferrite) 142
Rotary actuator 216–9
Rotary kiln 128
Rotating magnets (rotor) 64, 119, 298
Royal Society 75–6

Sapphire bearings 277
Saturation, magnetic 17–22, 48–50, 53–4, 59, 156, 190, 311
Schweigger 78
Science Museum (London) 94
Semi-conductors 37–8, 68, 223
Series and shunt wound machines 204–6, 231, etc.
Shackleton W. J. 137

Shells, atomic 99
Short magnetic paths 168–75, 192
Shuttle armature 84
Siemens 84, 237
Silicon-controlled rectifier 308
Silicon steels 20, 51, 89, 250–2
Silmanal 91–2, 100
Silver 92, 324
Sine waveform 214, 250
Sintering process 121, 138
Sixtus K. J., Smit J., Snoek J. L. 162
Sodium-potassium alloy brush 237–8
Solenoid 43, 77
Speed B. 76
Speed records 88
Speeds, rotating 65, 199, 201
Spin, electron 98–9, 138
Spinel structure 140
Spring balance 189, 316
Squirrel-cage motor 233
Stability, magnetic 24, 64–5, 130 etc.
Strontium (ferrite) 148
Strip-magnetising 180, 263
Studders R. J. 32, 137
Stuijts A. L. 162
Sturgeon 77, 82, 95, 200
Subdivision effects, magnetic 54, 125–7
Superconducting magnets 167, 176
Synchronous motors 232–4

Tape cores 124
    magnetic 144–5
Telegraph, electric 42, 78
Telephone cable loading 113
    receiver magnets 64, 92
Temperature coefficients 148, 158
Tenzer R. K. 162
Theoretical background 94–111

Thermo-electric generator 34, 68, 223'
    244
Thomson, Elihu 260
Toesca R. 317
Tonnage-oxygen steel by-product 30,
    161
Torque conversion 207
Track systems 219–22, 303–6
Tracked hovercraft 272
Traction battery, cell 87–8, 244–7 etc.
Traction, electric 85–9, 299–303 etc.
Tractive force, magnet 190–1
Tramway, electric 31, 87, 198, 203
Transducer 25
Transformer 80
Transportation 14, 31, 287–91
'Tromalit' 155
Tungsten steel 90–1

Ultrasonic freq. power 297
    machining 149, 253
Units 15, 45–7, 323

'Vectolite' 145, 152
Volt (unit) 76, 323
Voltage level 41
Voltaic Pile 68, 71, 76

Walker J. H. 256
Watt (unit), 39, 323
Weber G. H. 162
Weber (unit) 46, 320, 323 etc.
Weiss P. 102
Went J. 162
Wijn H. P. 162
Wire recording, magnetic 145
Wohlfarth E. P. 111
Woolrich 83